So you really want to learn

Junior History
Book 3

GALORE PARK

So you really want to learn

Junior History

Book 3

Fiona Macdonald

Series Editor: Niall Murphy

www.galorepark.co.uk

Published by Galore Park Publishing Ltd
19/21 Sayers Lane, Tenterden, Kent TN30 6BW
www.galorepark.co.uk

Design and typography Typetechnique, London
Illustrations by Gwyneth Williamson, Emmanuel Cerisier, Simon Tegg
and Ian Douglass

Printed by Lego SpA, Italy

ISBN-13: 978 1 902984 99 5

First published 2008

An answer book to accompany this course is available from
www.galorepark.co.uk

Details of other Galore Park publications are available at
www.galorepark.co.uk

ISEB Revision Guides, publications and examination papers may also be
obtained from Galore Park.

Acknowledgements

The author and publishers are grateful to Jenny Vaughan for preparing the manuscript for typesetting.

The publishers are grateful for permission to use the extracts and photographs as follows:

p9 © Dorset County Museum, p10 © Photolibrary Group, p13 © Bettmann/ Corbis UK Ltd, p18 © Adam Woolfitt/ Corbis UK Ltd, p19 © Museum of London/HIP/TopFoto, p21 © Loolee/Alamy, p22 © Museum of London/HIP/ TopFoto, p24 © Museum of London/HIP/TopFoto, p31t © Ashmolean Museum/Bridgeman Art Library, p31b © Roger Eritja/ Alamy, p33 © British Museum/Bridgeman Art Library, p36 © National Museums of Scotland, p46 © Christopher Wood Gallery, London, UK/Bridgeman Art Library, p49 © Martyn F. Chillmaid, p51 © National Museum of Iceland, Reykjavik/ Bridgeman Art Library, p61 © Bede's World, p62 © British Library/akg-images, p67 © Visual Arts Library (London)/ Alamy, p69t © Topham Picturepoint/ TopFoto, p69b © Mike Harrington/Alamy, p70 © British Museum/Eileen Tweedy/Art Archive, p71 © David Lyons/Alamy, p78 © Glenn Harper/Alamy, p90 © PA Photos, p94 © Visual Image Photographic Services/JORVIK Viking Centre, York Archaeological Trust, p101 © The British Museum/HIP/TopFoto, p104 © Cols Travel UK/Alamy, p105 © Photos12 SA, p115 © British Library/Art Archive, p117 © British Library/akg-images, p121 © akg-images, p123 © akg-images, p125 © akg-images

Contents

Chapter 4 Divided land

Chapter 5 Kings, monks and missionaries

Chapter 6 High kings and conquerors

Chapter 7 'Hero of the English'

Chapter 8 Life in Viking Britain

Chapter 9 Fighting for England

Chapter 10 The last Saxon kings

Appendices

Introduction

If you could travel back in time for 2000 years, what would you find in Britain? Towns? Big cities? Roads? Temples? Farms? Peaceful people or warring tribes? Teachers? Musicians? Invaders? Would the people you meet be friendly or hostile? Could you understand their language? What would you think about the way they look? Would you like to eat and live and work like them?

This book will help you to investigate life in the British Isles from around 50 BC to 1066 AD. It was a time of great change, great achievements, and – sometimes – great suffering. The people who lived then are all dead long ago, but they have not been forgotten. Their ideas, words, beliefs, designs and technology still have an impact on our lives. They helped create our present-day British language, government, landscape and laws.

Read on, and find out more ...

Fiona Macdonald
2008

Chapter 1

Britain and Rome

Unknown land

The Roman general **Julius Caesar** wanted to celebrate. At the end of 55 BC he had conquered Gaul (France), and then became the first Roman leader to invade Britain – and return safely! Caesar wanted to share his delight, so he gave the citizens of Rome twenty days of public holiday.

At this time Romans viewed the British Isles as a misty, unknown territory. A Roman historian, Cassius Dio, wrote that they lay 'beyond the realms of the known world'. Tacitus, another historian, told how survivors of a Roman ship wrecked off Britain returned with tales 'of marvels – furious whirlwinds, unheard-of beasts, strange shapes, half-human and half-animal'. Even Caesar's soldiers, famous for their loyalty, felt uneasy about crossing the English Channel and landing on British soil. Such stories made them nervous of what they would find.

But the sailors and traders who sold goods between Gaul and Britain could have told them – Britain was a land of farmers, hunters, metal workers, and warriors. Long before Caesar invaded, British merchants had been selling wheat, slaves, furs and hunting dogs to traders from Gaul, who sold them on to the Romans. The Romans were also keen to get hold of tin, which was essential for making bronze, and used by them for all kinds of items – from hairpins and helmets to chariots and cooking pots. Tin was mined and smelted in Britain. Caesar himself had seen some British warriors – in his battles to conquer Gaul, many fierce British warriors had been recruited by the Gauls. In his written account of the wars Caesar commented that they looked 'very frightening in battle'.

Painted people

The Romans called the unknown islands '**Britannia**'. The name was first written down by a Greek explorer, **Pytheas**, around 330 BC. He may have based it on the Egyptian word for tin: *pretan*, or the Latin word *picti* ('painted people'). Caesar had seen the Britons 'paint themselves … which gives their skin a bluish colour.' But in 55 BC people in the British Isles did not think of themselves as one single, united, nation. Instead, Britain was divided into over twenty different kingdoms and each was the home of a separate **tribe**. Families were proud of the tribe they belonged to, called themselves by its name, and looked to its leaders to guide and protect them.

VOTADINII
SELGOVAE
CARVETII
BRIGANTES
PARISI
DECEANGLI
CORNAVII
CORITANI
ICENI
ORDOVICES
CATUVELLAUNI
DEMETAE
DOBUNNI
TRINOVANTES
SILURES
ATREBATES
BELGAE
CANTII
DUROTRIGES
REGNI
DUMNONII

The Celtic tribes of southern Britain

Protection was necessary as some tribes could be bitter enemies. But others built up friendships and helped each other against bigger threats. Tribes often had similar religious beliefs, customs and ways of decorating themselves and their surroundings. A tribe's way of life depended on where the people lived. In sheltered, lowland areas with good fertile land, they would be farmers who grew grain. On cold, bleak hills and mountains, as Caesar told his friends, 'they do not sow corn but live on meat and milk, and dress in skins'. People in the British Isles mostly spoke **Celtic** languages, which were like Scottish or Irish Gaelic or Welsh. But members of a tribe called the **Belgae**, who settled in southern Britain between 100 BC and 100 AD, may have spoken a language more like German.

Why invade Britain?

The British Isles were not the easiest place for a Roman general to conquer. They were around 1500 kilometres (about 900 miles) from Rome – a long way away from the place where all important decisions about the Roman empire were made. The rough, stormy seas around the British Isles made it difficult and dangerous to get into or out of Britain quickly. The tribes were

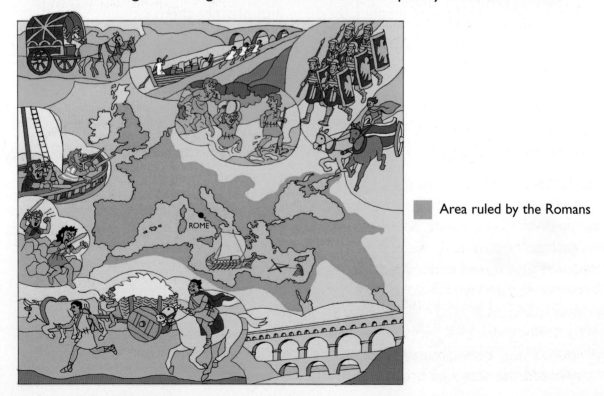

Area ruled by the Romans

How people travelled through the Roman Empire

unfriendly, with customs and beliefs that were all very different from the Romans' own. And – for Romans used to sunny Mediterranean weather – the wet, windy British climate was very unpleasant. Yet the Romans invaded three times, in 55 BC and 54 BC, then again in 43 AD. Why did they bother?

Power and glory

The answer is because two ambitious Roman men wanted to win power and glory. Julius Caesar, who led the first two invasions, was a brave and brilliant army commander who also wanted to become leader of the government in Rome. Caesar hoped to find silver-mines and get rich, giving him the funds to persuade Roman people to vote for him. At that time, Caesar's enemies in Rome were trying to put him in prison – so invading Britain was a good excuse not to return home. Naturally, Caesar did not speak about these reasons in public. Instead, he said he had to invade the British Isles to stop British tribes helping the Gauls fight against the Romans.

Caesar invades: 55 BC and 54 BC

Caesar began to plan his first invasion in 57 BC. He sent a Roman warship to spy along the south-east coast of the British Isles, and held talks with **Commius**, the king of the **Atrebates** tribe in Gaul. Commius was a friend of Rome, but was also related to the British tribal leaders. He tried to persuade the Britons to accept Roman rule peacefully, but he failed – and they took him prisoner! The Romans had a name for foreign leaders like Commius who worked for them. They called them **client kings**, and used them to get information and advice about lands they hoped to conquer.

In August 55 BC, Caesar gave orders for his army to set sail from Gaul. He arrived at a beach in Kent with about 10,000 soldiers. As the Romans approached the coast, British warriors hurled spears at them. At first, Caesar's men did not want to wade ashore. They knew that their heavy armour would slow them down, making them easy targets for the Britons. But one standard-bearer leaped over the side of his ship, daring the rest to follow. Caesar later wrote that he had said: 'Leap, soldiers, unless you want to betray our standard to the enemy. I will perform my duty to my country and my leader!' This sounds very brave; but we do not know whether it is true. Caesar might have invented the story to boast about how his men respected him.

'Leap, soldiers!'

Most of Caesar's soldiers reached the shore safely, and the British warriors retreated. But just three days later, the Roman ships that carried the army's horses were wrecked in a sudden storm. Unable to ride into Britain to explore, the Romans mended their ships as well as they could, and sailed back to Gaul.

The next year, 54 BC, Caesar invaded again. This time the attacking force was much larger, with 800 ships, 20,000 foot-soldiers and 2000 horses. The Romans landed, set up their camp, then marched 12 Roman miles (around 18 kilometres) into Britain – all on the same day, fighting off attacks from British warriors. Caesar's army far outnumbered the British. His soldiers were a better-trained, better-armed, better-organised force and much more disciplined. The British retreated to a hill fort, and the Romans surrounded it. They built a ramp of earth beside the fort and, lifting their shields above their heads, charged up the ramp and killed the Britons.

But once again, the British weather seemed to be fighting against Caesar. Another storm blew up and wrecked forty of his ships. His soldiers hurried back to drag the rest on to dry land, for safety. While they were busy doing this, **Cassivellaunus**, king of the powerful **Catuvellauni** tribe, sent messages to other British tribes. He persuaded them to join him in his fight against the Romans.

Roman soldiers in a 'testudo' formation attack a hill-fort

Caesar's invasions of 55 and 54 BC

Once their ships were safe, the Romans marched north, and crossed the River Thames into the land of the Catuvellauni. As they marched on, Cassivellaunus's warriors made hit-and-run attacks in horse-drawn chariots. Charging towards the Romans, they hurled deadly spears, then leapt to the ground and fought with long swords before driving quickly away. Cassivellaunus also ordered his people to move their farm animals away from the advancing Romans, and set fire to the crops growing in their fields. He hoped the Roman army would run out of food and starve. But the Romans got supplies from five weaker British tribes, who made peace when they realised that they could never defeat the Roman soldiers. Caesar's army marched on, fighting all the time, and managed to surround Cassivellaunus. But the British chieftan had one last trick up his sleeve. As the Romans closed in, he cleverly sent men to attack their ships on the shore. Caesar and his soldiers did not want to find themselves trapped, with no way to travel home, so they rushed back to defend them.

In September 54 BC, Caesar received an urgent message from Gaul. He was needed there, straight away, to fight tribes that were rebelling against Rome. Caesar made an agreement with Cassivellaunus: British kings would still rule the British Isles but they had to pay tribute to Rome and promise not to fight the Romans. The mighty Roman army sailed away – and stayed away – for the next 97 years.

Claudius invades: 43 AD

Almost 100 years later, the emperor **Claudius** launched another invasion of Britain. Like Julius Caesar before him, Claudius wished to prove that he was the right man to rule Rome. He had become emperor two years earlier, after the previous emperor was murdered, and still needed to win support from the Roman people and the Roman army. Claudius also wanted to help the British members of the friendly Atrebates tribe. They were ruled by relatives of Commius, and were being attacked by the Catuvellauni tribe. A victory would prove Rome's strength to foreign enemies, and show that Claudius would come to help friends of Rome.

So, in 43 AD, Claudius sent a huge army of 40,000 Roman soldiers to Britain. Led by the general **Aulus Plautius**, they landed safely at **Rutupiae** (now Richborough in Kent) and marched westwards. Their first aim was to defeat the Catuvellauni, who lay in wait beside the River Medway. The battle lasted two whole days. First, the Romans sent 'special agents' to cross the river unseen and attack the Catuvellauni from behind. Next, about 10,000 men marched towards the Catuvellauni, packed tightly together and crushing everything in their path. Finally, close ranks of Roman troops attacked from either side. The Catuvellauni fought fiercely, but the Romans were stronger and far outnumbered them.

British tribes surrender

The Romans then marched north, heading for the Catuvellauni capital, **Camulodunum** (now Colchester). British warriors attacked all the way but the Romans overpowered them. By now, Aulus Plautius thought it was safe enough to call Claudius to join in the fighting. Claudius was not a strong man or a warrior like Caesar but, as emperor, was still the official leader of the Roman army. He landed in Kent with fresh troops, heavy war-machines – and thirty-eight war-elephants to terrify the Britons. He stayed in Britain for just sixteen days, to accept the surrender of the Catuvellauni and eleven other tribes.

An early Roman version of the tank!

The conquest continues

By defeating the Catuvellauni, Rome won control of all the land in what is now south-east England. But many Britons were still enemies. The Romans turned Camulodunum into their army headquarters and set out to conquer the rest of the British Isles. In just four years, the Romans controlled all the land south of the River Humber, except for Wales. They also began to build a great new trading port, **Londinium**

Part of the skeleton of a British warrior killed by a Roman ballista bolt

(London), and a network of roads so that merchants, and the Roman army, could travel quickly and safely throughout the British Isles.

One man who was not prepared to lie down and let the Romans walk all over him was **Caratacus**, the last king of the Catuvellauni. He fled to the land now called Wales, and joined with the **Silures** and **Ordovices** tribes to carry on the fight against the Romans. Although the Romans defeated Caratacus in battle in 51 AD, he escaped to northern England. There, he asked **Cartimandua**, queen of the **Brigantes** tribe, to shelter him. But Cartimandua was a client of Rome and did not dare to risk the Romans' anger. Reluctantly, she handed Caratacus over. He was sent to Rome in chains, where he was put on display, shamed and tortured. When Caratacus saw the grand buildings of Rome, he said, 'With all these fine belongings, why do you want to take our poor little huts as well?'

Boudicca's revolt: 60–61 AD

Another famous Britain to resist Roman rule was **Boudicca**. In East Anglia, the Romans ruled with the help of the **Iceni**, another client tribe. Their king, **Prasatugas**, agreed to give half his land to Rome as long as his wife, Boudicca, could keep the other half. But when Prasatugas died in 60 AD, the Romans took all his kingdom. Boudicca was outraged and protested. Not used to such open defiance, particularly from a woman, Roman soldiers beat her in public and assaulted her daughters. Boudicca asked for help from her neighbouring tribe, the **Trinovantes**, and declared war on Rome.

Boudicca's rebellion caused some of the most savage fighting the Romans had ever seen. First, she led her army to Camulodunum, where the Romans had built a huge temple to celebrate the Emperor Claudius's invasion. There was also a government meeting house, a market square and a theatre, all in grand Roman style. The Roman historian **Tacitus** reported strange events in Camulodunum as Boudicca approached the city: 'Without any cause, the

A 19th century statue of Boudicca, queen of the Iceni tribe

statue of Victory toppled over and turned its face away, as if it was trying to escape … Ghostly voices cried out in the meeting-house … Wailing echoed through the theatre …' The Romans sent 5000 men to defend the city. In a ferocious battle, Boudicca's army killed them all.

Next, Boudicca passed through the city of **Verulamium** (now St Albans). Tacitus described the fury of her army: 'The Britons took no prisoners … without delay, they began their gruesome business of hanging, burning and crucifying …' Boudicca's army reached Londinium and set fire to the whole city. Today, archaeologists can see the remains of this massive blaze – as a layer of black ash and baked soil about 3.5 metres below the city streets. When Boudicca's revolt began, **Suetonius Paulinus**, the top Roman commander, was fighting in north Wales. As soon as he could, he hurried south with his troops. He finally came face to face with Boudicca at a place north of London.

Paulinus's army was smaller than Boudicca's, but he was an expert at planning battles. He marched his men to the top of a hill, then challenged Boudicca to attack. Boudicca's army was tired after so much fighting but her warriors rushed boldly up the hillside. They were soon forced down again by Roman spears and trapped against their own baggage wagons. Tacitus reported that 80,000 Britons were

Boudicca's last battle

killed, but only 400 Romans – these figures are probably exaggerated but they can give us some idea of the slaughter. When Boudicca saw that she was defeated, she took poison rather than be captured by the Romans.

Rome in control: 60–90 AD

Boudicca's revolt had angered the Romans. After her death, they punished rebel tribes by destroying their towns, forts and farms, and selling their people as slaves. In 70 AD they put down a revolt led by Cartimandua's headstrong new husband, and in 76–77 AD they finally conquered all of Wales. After this, led by general **Julius Agricola**, Roman soldiers fought their way northwards. They cruelly attacked local tribes, terrorising them into surrendering, and built roads, army camps and forts to keep tight control of the newly-conquered land.

In around 79 AD, Roman troops advanced into the country now known as Scotland. At the same time, Agricola sent ships to explore Scotland's wild coastline. In 84 AD, the Romans won a great battle against the **Caledonii** tribe at a place called **Mons Graupius** (probably near Bennachie in Aberdeenshire). According to Tacitus, **Calgacus**, chief of the Caledonii, made a bitter comment about Roman warfare: 'They make a wasteland, and call it peace.'

An artist's impression of one of Agricola's forts

Despite their early success, the Romans found Scotland to be harsher than they had expected. The climate was too cold, and the land too wild and mountainous, for Roman soldiers to keep hold of the land they had won. By 90 AD, they had retreated back into England. Apart from this setback, almost all the British Isles were now part of the Roman empire. The Roman invasion had succeeded.

Exercise 1.1

Read the information on pages 2 to 11 about the Roman invasions of the British Isles, and answer the following questions:

1. To what extent was the British Isles one united kingdom before the Romans invaded?

2. Which languages did British tribes speak before the Romans arrived?

3. When were the first two Roman invasions of Britain?

4. Where did the third army of Roman invaders land?

5. How many Roman soldiers did Emperor Claudius send to invade Britain in 43 AD?

6. Who was Queen Boudicca and when was her rebellion?

7. Who led Roman armies into Scotland around 79 AD?

8. Which great battle did the Romans win in Scotland in 84 AD?

. . . .

Exercise 1.2

Read the information on pages 5 to 11 and then complete the following sentences:

1. Before the Roman invasion, British warriors had helped the _____ to fight against the Romans.

2. _____ led the first Roman invasion of the British Isles in 55 BC.

3. The ships carrying the first invading Roman army's horses were _____ in a storm.

4. King _____ led the British tribes to fight against the second Roman invasion in 54 BC.

5. The emperor _____ brought war-elephants with him to the British Isles.

6. After fighting the Romans, King Caratacus escaped to _____.

7. Boudicca's army burned the city of _____ in 60 BC.

8. The Romans retreated from _____ because of the harsh conditions there.

. . . .

Exercise 1.3

Explain what is meant by the following:

1. Gaul

2. client king

3. standard-bearer

4. in close ranks

5. hill-fort

6. Londinium

. . . .

Exercise 1.4

Look at this photo of the statue of Julius Caesar. The statue was made shortly before 44 AD, when Caesar died. The sculptor would have seen Caesar and may even have met him.

Now read this description of Caesar written by Roman author **Suetonius Tranquillus**. Suetonius was not born until 70 AD, but he read documents written in Caesar's time, and may have spoken to old people whose parents remembered seeing the emperor.

Julius Caesar

'He is said to have been tall with a fair complexion, shapely limbs, quite a round face, and keen black eyes... Quite healthy, except towards the end when he had fainting fits and nightmares ... His was greatly troubled by his baldness... he used to comb his thin hair forward from the crown of his head ...'

1. Write down two ways in which the evidence from the statue and from the written description agree.

2. Write down one piece of evidence that we get only from the statue.

3. Write down one piece of evidence that we get only from the written description.

Exercise 1.5

Imagine that you are a boy or girl from a British tribe, living in Camulodunum (now Colchester) in 60 BC. In the past fifteen years, the city has been taken over by the Romans. They have brought hundreds of tough Roman soldiers to live there and built huge new buildings in their own Roman style. Your parents say that the city has been changed, and that their old way of life is being destroyed by the Roman invaders. On the other hand, the Romans run the city fairly and peacefully, on the whole. They bring trade, make money, improve housing, drains and water supplies, and employ many local workers – including your father.

One day, you hear that Boudicca and her army are approaching, ready to fight the Romans. Write an entry in your diary describing your feelings, and the reasons for them.

Chapter 2

Romans in Britain

By around 90 AD, the Romans had conquered almost all of the British Isles except for Scotland and Ireland. But how could they keep control of the tribes and territory they had won? And how could they link the **province** (region) of Britannia more closely with the other lands they ruled, now that it was part of the mighty Roman empire?

Keeping control

The Romans relied on their army to control their empire and guard its borders. This was the world's first full-time, paid, fighting force – and it was always ready for action. In 64 AD, the Jewish historian, **Josephus**, who saw many Roman soldiers in the Middle East, commented that they '... do not wait for war to begin before getting to grips with their weapons, nor they do nothing in peacetime ... but, as if born with weapons in their hands, they never stop fighting.'

In 90 AD, the Roman army was made up of about 150,000 **legionaries** (Roman citizens) and around 200,000 **auxiliaries** (soldiers recruited from non-Roman peoples). There were also thousands of Roman sailors sailing the ships that carried the invading armies, or patrolling the coasts of the empire, looking out for pirates and enemies. About 55,000 Roman soldiers were stationed in Britannia by 150 AD. They were mostly auxiliaries, and came from lands known today as Germany, the Netherlands, Luxembourg and northern France. Later, they were joined by men from Syria, Spain, North Africa and Bulgaria. The army even recruited men from British tribes that were friendly to Rome. Archaeologists think that there were between three and four million people living in Britannia under Roman rule. This means that one person in about every sixty or seventy was a soldier in the Roman army.

Tough training

How did soldiers survive in enemy territory such as Britannia? Their army training taught them how to fight, of course, but also many other useful skills. They were sent on long route marches, until each man became tough enough to walk 30 kilometres a day. They learned to cook easy meals: every

Romans were trained to be tough!

soldier carried a water flask, a cooking pot, some salt and several days' rations of dried grain, to boil with water to make porridge. He also carried his weapons and armour, a warm cloak, and a leather bag containing personal items such as a comb and a razor.

Roads and camps

Roman soldiers were taught many different kinds of building skills. They had to know how to clear rough ground, measure straight lines across it, and build stone roads and wooden bridges so that they could march quickly to danger spots. Agricola's men completed an astonishing 2100 kilometres of roads in under twenty years – plus seventy army forts! Soldiers also learned how to build temporary **marching camps** where they could shelter safely every night, sleeping in tents made of leather. Each camp was surrounded by a deep ditch and earth **ramparts** (steep banks, like walls) made by the soldiers. In dangerous places, like the British Isles, half the soldiers in each legion stood on guard, while the other half got the camp ready.

Each **contubernium** (a group of eight men sharing a tent) carried a set of building tools between them: a pickaxe, ropes, chains, hooks, a spade, a saw, and baskets for carrying earth.

Forts and walls

Once enemy tribes had retreated, the soldiers had to build **forts** to stop them returning so easily. These were strong, permanent bases where soldiers could live for many years while patrolling and guarding conquered land. Forts were made of wood and stone, and were laid out like army camps. At the centre of the fort there was a house for the legion commander and

Building a Roman road

his family, as well as workshops, barns to store food, a hospital, a headquarters building with a meeting hall, weapons stores, a treasury (to keep money and valuables), offices for army clerks, a shrine (a place for worshipping gods) and a room where the legion's battle-standards were stored.

In places where the local tribes were a real danger, the Romans built massive walls of wood, turf and stone to protect their border, and to stop enemies invading Roman lands. The greatest example was **Hadrian's Wall**, in the north of Britain. It was built after the Roman Emperor **Hadrian** visited Britain in 122 AD. It took 15,000 men about four years to build, and stretched for 117 kilometres. It had look-out posts every Roman mile (1480 metres) and a fort about every 10 kilometres.

Hadrian's Wall, with (inset) Vindolanda Fort, and the Antonine Wall (which marked the most northerly point the Roman army reached)

Between 139 and 142 AD, the Romans made a second attempt to conquer Scotland. They reached the central lowland region (where the cities of Edinburgh and Glasgow are today), and built a second great wall, named after **Antoninus Pius**, who was then emperor. But still the enemy tribes resisted, and when the Romans found that they could not defend it effectively, the **Antonine Wall** was abandoned in around 160 AD.

Frontier life

Men who joined the Roman army could receive rich rewards. There was excitement, adventure, comradeship, regular pay, good training, a share of the treasure captured from enemies and, when they retired, a government pension, or a gift of land and citizenship. Even so, all Roman soldiers knew that their lives would be hard. They had to serve in the army for twenty years if they were legionaries, or twenty-five if they were auxiliaries. They lived far away from their home towns, friends and families, and only legion commanders were allowed to marry. Army discipline was strict and the punishments were severe. The soldiers had to cope with loneliness, boredom and miserable living conditions, especially in cold, remote northern places like the British frontier.

The Vindolanda Letters

We know how some Romans felt about British frontier life because their words have been preserved. Between around 90-120 AD, soldiers stationed at the **Vindolanda Fort**, close to the frontier, wrote letters on thin sheets of wood. Incredibly, these have survived for almost 2000 years, buried in the damp ground. Some '**Vindolanda Letters**' are official reports, giving details of troop movements, or listing the food brought to feed the soldiers. Others are more personal. One is an invitation to a birthday party from a legion commander's wife, desperately longing for a friend to talk to. Another complains about local tribes, calling them *Brittunculi* ('nasty little Brits'). A third letter asks for woollen socks and two pairs of underpants!

A new government

While the Roman army kept order in Britannia, Roman officials set up a new government. The historian Tacitus described their aim: 'to make divided,

A reconstruction of the palace of the Roman governor in Britain

rough and warlike people get used to the pleasures of peace and idleness'. Or, in other words, to stop them fighting against Rome.

Roman rule in Britannia was headed by a **Governor**. He was the top politician, senior judge in the law courts, and supreme army commander. The next most important official was the **Procurator**, who was the head of finance. He was in charge of collecting taxes (paid as money) and tribute (paid as farm produce, and used to feed the army). The Governor and Procurator were both helped by teams of secretaries, clerks, messengers and advisors. The more important posts were given to their friends or to Roman politicians. Less important posts were often filled by slaves.

The new government was based first in Camulodunum (now Colchester). After 61 AD it moved to Londinium (London). Archaeologists have discovered the remains of a huge governor's palace, covering 13,000 square metres, under the present-day city of London. It had offices, meeting halls, rooms to entertain important visitors, private apartments for the governor, a bath house and a courtyard garden with a large ornamental pool.

Part of the empire

The governor and his staff ruled Britannia like any other province of the empire. They expected people to be obedient to Roman officials, to respect the Roman emperor and the Roman gods, and to generally follow the civilised Roman way of life. The Romans regarded the Britons as **peregrini**: lower class men and women who did not have equal rights with the citizens of Rome. In general, however, Roman rulers did not interfere with Celtic customs and traditions, though they thought that some were barbaric and disgusting – like human sacrifice.

As you probably know, Roman rulers spoke and wrote their own language, **Latin**. Anyone wanting to meet or do business with the Romans had to learn Latin. Speaking and writing the same language helped people from all over the Roman empire to understand and work with each other. They were encouraged to think that they were all part of the same Roman community.

Roman officials counted using Roman numbers and measured using Roman units of length and weight. They made payments using Roman coins made from bronze, silver and gold, and set up mints in British towns. Roman coins had political messages printed on them: on one side was the head of the

A coin from the time of the Emperor Septimus Severus (193-211 AD)

ruling emperor, and on the other were proud symbols of Roman power, such as the goddess of victory.

New arrivals

Under Roman rule, people from many parts of the empire came to live in Britannia: soldiers, sailors, traders, government officials, teachers, doctors, writers and artists. Although their ways of doing things were all very different, Roman rule brought them together. They traded in the same market places, watched the same entertainment, set up businesses together, and sometimes married each other. Inscriptions and tombs record the names of several multicultural couples living in Britannia. They included Julia Fortunata, from Sardinia (an island near Italy), and her husband Marcus Verecundus, who came from south-west France; and Barates, a merchant from Syria, and his wife Regina, from the Celtic Catuvellauni tribe.

Free-born and slaves

According to Roman law, all peoples of the empire were either **free-born** or **slaves**. Citizens of Rome were always free. Slaves belonged to their owners and were regarded as their property. Some slaves, who worked in mines or did heavy labour on farms, might be very badly treated. Others, who served as private secretaries, nursemaids or tutors, were trusted and cared for by their owners. There were also **freedmen and women**. These were slaves who had enough money to buy their freedom, or had been set free by their owners. This often happened when a slave owner died, or because a free man wanted to marry a slave woman.

Town life

The Celts were country people and they didn't have towns as such – only trading settlements and royal palaces. The Romans believed that a well-run town or city was the most civilised place to live, so it was the Romans who built the first real towns in the British Isles. In new Roman towns, the laws and way of life were very similar to Rome's, with public services such as running water, and town councils chosen by the citizens. Some towns, called **coloniae**, were for retired Roman soldiers. Other towns were for anyone from the Roman empire, including conquered Celts.

To make town life comfortable, the Romans planned carefully. Each new town was laid out around a central **forum**, which was an open-air meeting place. There might also be several indoor shopping malls. A fine **basilica** (a town hall, with government offices and law courts) was built near the town centre, and a **temple**, to honour Roman gods. Dead Roman emperors also had temples, where their spirits were worshipped. At Camulodunum (Colchester) the Romans made the conquered Britons pay for the emperor's temple and attend ceremonies there once a year. It was a good way of reminding them who was in charge!

A model of the Roman port of London

New town streets were straight and paved with stone, with raised sidewalks, and stepping-stones across muddy gutters. Fresh water for drinking and cooking came from pipes or fountains; there were public lavatories and splendid, heated baths. Rich families lived in large houses built around private courtyards. Poorer families ate and slept in rooms behind shops and workshops. For entertainment, there might be a theatre, a race track, and an arena for shows with gladiators and wild beasts. For security, the towns were surrounded by a wall of wood or stone, with massive gates that were locked every night.

An artist's impression of a Roman street

Roman religion

At home in Rome, the Romans worshipped many different gods and goddesses. They built temples that contained statues of the gods, and made offerings to please them, hoping that the gods would send favours in return. The Romans also believed in nature-spirits, ghosts and magic, and carried amulets, or lucky charms, for protection. The Roman religion spread to all the furthest parts of their empire. But the Romans also learned to worship many new, local gods. For example, Roman soldiers honoured **Mithras**, a god of light from Persia, and prayed to **Serapis**, the Egyptian god of the Underworld.

In Britannia, the Romans began to worship Celtic gods and goddesses, such as **Nodens**, god of thunder, **Epona**, the horse-goddess, and the **Three Mothers**, who were ancient goddesses of birth, life and death. In London, a Roman inscription recorded how the citizens 'rebuilt the shrine in honour of the Mothers, at their own expense'.

Romans in Britannia also took over many Celtic holy places, realising that the gods the Celts worshipped were very similar to their own. You may remember from *Junior History Book 2* that at **Bath**, in south-west England, there were natural springs of hot water, sacred to the Celtic goddess, **Sulis**. The Romans believed that Sulis was the same as **Minerva**, their own goddess of wisdom, and built a temple to them both. People visited Bath, hoping to be cured of their illnesses, and they became known as **Aquae Sulis** ('the waters of Sulis'). People threw offerings into the holy springs – and little scraps of metal with prayers written on them, asking the goddess to curse their enemies!

A plaque showing the three mother-goddesses which can be seen in the Museum of London

'A curse on you, Marcus!'

Christianity

Some Romans in Britain also began to follow a new faith – **Christianity** – that began in the empire province of **Judea** (which is today Jordan, Israel and Palestine). At first, Christians in the Roman empire were persecuted and killed. But in 313 AD, the Roman Emperor **Constantine**, who spent part of his early life in Britannia, gave them complete freedom to worship. We do not know when Christianity first arrived in Britain, or how popular it was. However, around 200 AD, the Roman writer **Tertullian** wrote: 'the word of Christ had been preached in areas of Britain beyond Rome's control'.

At about the same time, a Roman soldier named **Alban** was martyred, or killed for his faith, because he sheltered a Christian priest. (The town where this happened was named after him: St Albans, in the present-day county of Hertfordshire.) From around 350 AD, Christian symbols were used to decorate floors and walls in Roman buildings. Silver bowls and dishes with Christian designs have also been found.

How do we know?

We know about the Romans' arrival in the British Isles from several different sources. All our written evidence comes from the Romans themselves and describes events from a Roman point of view. The most important account of the Roman invasion is by the historian Cornelius Tacitus. In **Agricola**, completed in 98 AD, Tacitus recorded the life and times of his father-in law, Roman governor Agricola (see page 11), and the events in Britannia, where he ruled. Before Tacitus, the famous Roman general Julius Caesar (see page 2) wrote down his observations of the Celtic people in **De Bello Gallico** ('On the War in Gaul'), around 55 BC. Later, around 180 AD, **Cassius Dio** wrote a history of the Roman Empire that described the invasion and occupation of the British Isles, and some powerful Britons, including Boudicca. He based parts of his account on important writings by Tacitus that no longer survive today.

The Romans also left a great deal of evidence in the form of the structures they built. Some are still standing, like Hadrian's spectacular Wall. Many more Roman remains have been carefully uncovered by archaeologists over the last 300 years: stone and metal statues, stone carvings and inscriptions, glass, pottery, metalware, coins and burials. The complete tomb of a high-born Roman lady was discovered in London in 1999 and is still being analysed. Traces of long-lost Roman buildings have also been found, such as stone foundations or mosaic floors.

Much evidence of Roman rule in Britain is still being used in the English-speaking world today. Old Roman measurements, such as miles, feet and pounds, are still used by many people. The English language contains many Latin words. Some British towns, such as Chester, Lancaster, Manchester (whose names are all based on *castra*, which means 'camp'), and Lincoln (originally Lindum Colonia), still have names based on Roman ones. So do many people: for example, Marcus and Julia are both Latin names.

Exercise 2.1

Read the information on pages 15 to 26 about Romans in Britain, and answer the following questions:

1. How many Roman soldiers (approximately) were stationed in Britannia in 150 AD?

2. Where did the Roman soldiers in Britannia come from?

3. What did soldiers carry as they marched?

4. Where did Roman soldiers in Britannia live?

5. How long is Hadrian's Wall?

6. Which two towns were capitals of Britannia?

7. Who was head of the Roman government in Britannia?

8. What kept Roman towns safe at night?

9. Who did the Romans worship at Bath?

10. What did St Alban protect?

. . . .

Exercise 2.2

Read the information on pages 15 to 25 and then complete the following sentences:

1. About _____ or _____ million people lived in Roman Britannia.

2. Roman legionary soldiers served in the army for _____ years.

3. The Romans spoke and wrote in a language called _____.

4. Roman people might be free, or slaves, or _____ men and women.

5. The Romans built _____ because they thought life was more civilised there.

6. Retired Roman soldiers lived in towns called _____.

7. The head of Roman government tax collecting in Britain was called the _____.

8. *Peregrini* were people who were not Roman _____.

9. The Roman soldiers' god, Mithras, came from _____.

10. _____ was the Celtic god of thunder.

. . . .

Exercise 2.3

Explain what is meant by:

1. legionary

2. auxiliary

3. *contubernium*

4. mint

5. propaganda

6. forum

7. basilica

8. martyred

Exercise 2.4

The Vindolanda Letters provide us with very important evidence about Roman army life.

1. Write down at least two different types of information that would have been lost for ever if the Vindolanda Letters had not survived.

2. Imagine that you are either a Roman soldier stationed at a fort close to Hadrian's Wall, or the wife or daughter of an army commander living in the only family house in the same fort. Write a letter to a friend saying what your life is like. How do you spend your days? What do you like about the fort, and Britannia? What don't you like?

Exercise 2.5

Do you or any of your friends have a Roman name? Here's how to find out.

Go to a library and find a book listing personal names and their meanings, or look up a site about names on the Internet.

Make a list of Roman names for boys and girls that are still used today. See if you can find out what each name means, and add the meanings to your list. If you like, you could decorate your list with Roman-style patterns. Look at the photos in this book for some Roman design ideas.

Chapter 3

British peoples

Roman rule brought new people, words, buildings, money, technology and beliefs to the British Isles. How did these change the lives of the Celtic people who lived there?

As we saw on page 3, before the Romans arrived, the British Isles were divided into many different Celtic kingdoms. After the invasion, Roman governors let the Celts go on living in these tribal lands, although they made sure to build new towns there, to show off Roman power and help to encourage the Roman way of life. But in the countryside, the Romans left the Celts alone, as long as they did not challenge Roman rule.

Kings and warriors

Celtic kings and queens were proud, powerful people who impressed foreigners who saw them. The Roman writer Cassius Dio, who lived from around 160 to 230 AD, described Queen Boudicca as 'terrifying to look at, and with a harsh voice'. Celtic kings were very rich and powerful but also had many duties to carry out. They had to protect their kingdoms, command armies in battle, uphold the law and give rewards to loyal fighting men. These rewards were gifts of jewellery and weapons, and invitations to rich, lavish feasts.

Many Celtic stories and poems were not written down until 700 to 800 AD. They can give us an idea of the Celts from even before the Roman invasions. They describe splendid feasts given by Celtic rulers for warriors and other guests. Diners sat in a circle, with the bravest man in the seat of honour. Eating and drinking might go on all night. The Greek writer **Athenaeus** said that Celts drank 'from a shared cup, a little at a time, no more than a mouthful, but they do it rather frequently.' Drunken quarrels were common and might result in rival warriors fighting for the 'champion's portion', for example, which was the best helping of meat.

The next important people, after the kings and queens, were the clan chiefs. They guarded their family's fields and farms, and recruited men to form armies. They also led troops of keen young warriors on raids to steal animals, slaves and treasure from rival Celtic clans. Some chiefs were famous as great warriors who boasted about their own brave deeds, and dared anyone to stand against them.

Life and death

The mythical chief **CuChulainn** (pronounced 'Coo-hull-in' or 'Coo-shull-in') was a hero of many tales from Celtic Ireland. He was said to have proudly declared to his friends, 'As long as I am famous, I don't mind living just one day in this world.' Like many Celtic warriors, he believed that it was better to die gloriously and win fame and praise, than to survive and be defeated. He hoped that his spirit would live on after death, in the mysterious **Otherworld**.

Celtic warriors liked to enjoy life!

We do not know how these beliefs about life and death came about. Possibly because life was short and dangerous for many people in Britannia. Archaeologists have discovered that the average age of death at this time was thirty-six for men and twenty-eight for women. Men often died from injuries, and women in childbirth. Anyone – especially children and babies – might be killed by disease.

Battle tactics

Celtic warriors rode into battle on fast, horse-drawn chariots, then leaped off and fought on foot with heavy swords and spears. Their aim was simply to kill as many men as possible – and cut off their heads, as battle trophies. Caesar later told how a Celtic chariot charge had deadly effect: 'Many of the first line [of Roman soldiers] were trodden underfoot by the rush of horses …' Some Celts wore chain-mail tunics, bronze helmets and iron breastplates, but others fought naked. The Celts believed that their blue war-paint and gold torcs (heavy neck-bands) gave them

A Celtic warrior shown on a Roman coin. This can be seen at the Ashmolean Museum, Oxford.

magical protection, and this puzzled foreigners. The Greek writer, **Dionysus of Halicarnassus**, was amazed: 'Their breasts, sides, thighs, legs are all bare, and they have no armour except for their shields.'

Safe places

To protect their families, animals and treasure from enemy attack, Celtic tribes built strong forts in safe places. These forts also showed the wealth and power of the tribes who made them. Most forts

Mousa broch, Shetland

consisted of rows of steep earth banks, or walls of wood and rough rocks, surrounding a stronghold on a hilltop. Defenders at the top could throw spears and hurl stones at the enemies who were struggling to climb up and attack them. In Scotland, Celts also built massive **brochs** (tall round stone towers) and **crannogs**, which you may remember from *Junior History Book 1*. These were shelters on artificial islands, safely surrounded by water.

Celtic farms

Before the Romans invaded the British Isles, most Celtic people were farmers. They planted crops and raised animals to provide food for their families. They also had to produce enough to pay tribute to Celtic kings and chiefs, and later, tax to Roman tax-collectors.

Celtic families lived in scattered farmsteads, with a farmhouse, grain stores, animal shelters, haystacks and racks for drying fish and curing (cleaning and preserving) animal skins, all surrounded by a strong wooden fence. Celtic houses were large and often circular in shape. Usually, they were built of wooden poles with walls made of **wattle and daub** – a mat of woven twigs covered with a layer of mud and clay. They had steep, sloping roofs, so that

Village life

the rain ran off, which were thatched with straw or turf. For magical protection, the Celts would hang over their doorway an animal's skull – or an enemy's head, captured in battle! Inside a Celtic farmhouse it was dark and smoky, but warm and dry. There were woollen rugs and sheepskins for beds, weapons and farm tools, a loom for weaving cloth, a fire for heating and cooking and, sometimes, a dome-shaped clay oven for baking bread.

Crops and animals

The most important Celtic farm crops were wheat, oats and barley. These were planted in fields ploughed by oxen pulling heavy iron-tipped ploughs, and harvested by men and women with sickles (sharp curved knives).

A Celtic shield, on show at the British Museum

Women ground the grain between stones to make flour for baking bread, or boiled it whole to make porridge. Farmers kept pigs for meat, sheep for wool, and cows and goats for milk and butter. The men also went hunting for wild deer and boar, and caught fish from rivers and streams. In late summer, children were sent into the woods to gather berries, mushrooms and nuts.

Skilled workers

After feeding their family, Celtic farmers hoped to have enough spare produce to be able to trade with craft workers. In that way, they could get items that they could not make themselves, such as shoes, knives or mirrors. All these items – and more – were made by expert craftsmen and women, skilled at metalwork, pottery, jewellery making and leatherwork, as well as spinning, weaving and dyeing wool and smooth **flax** (a tall plant whose stems were used to make linen cloth). Metalworkers made the objects that Celtic people valued most, from bronze weapons and armour to drinking cups and gold jewellery. Only rich people could afford these. All these items and simpler, cheaper objects, such as pottery bowls or iron fastenings for horse harnesses, were decorated in swirling Celtic designs.

A Celtic warrior chief

Looking good

Celtic fabrics and clothes were decorated with bright checked or striped patterns. The Celts loved fine clothes and jewellery, and took great pride in their appearance. Women wore shawls and sleeveless tunics over long, loose dresses; men wore cloaks, tunics and trousers. A piece of a broken metal statue, found in Roman North Africa, shows a captured British warrior wearing checked trousers and a woollen cloak held in place by a big metal brooch. Rich people wore flat leather shoes; poor people went barefoot.

A Celtic woman

Strabo, a Greek geographer, wrote that Celtic men and women 'wear bracelets on the wrists and arms, and necklaces of solid gold, and rings of great worth.' He added that Celtic men liked to stay slim, and that a warrior could be fined by his chief if he grew too fat to fasten his belt! Other Roman writers were surprised at how tall Celtic men and women were, how pale they looked compared with suntanned Romans and Greeks, and how much care and attention they lavished on their hair. They said that many British Celts had red hair, which men and women wore long. We are told that Boudicca's hair reached to her knees! Other Celts, who were naturally dark-haired, bleached and stiffened their hair to make it stand on end like a horse's mane. Many Celtic men had beards, but the chiefs shaved their faces except for long, drooping moustaches – which trapped crumbs from meals, and got soggy when they drank!

Druids and bards

Religious leaders were very powerful in Celtic society. **Druids** (priests) spent twenty years studying secret religious knowledge, tribal history, magic and law. They were then qualified to say prayers, foretell the future, and offer sacrifices of gold, animals, and – in times of danger or disaster – even the finest young humans too. They celebrated four great festivals at natural turning-points in the year: **Beltane** (1st May, for warmth and sunshine); **Lughnasad** (1st August, for growth and ripeness); **Samhain** (1st November, for death and darkness); **Imbolc** (1st February, for spring fertility).

Druids (Celtic priests), gathering mistletoe which, to them, was a sacred plant

Sacrifices were gifts to the gods, to ask for help or to thank them. Each Celtic tribe worshipped its own gods and goddesses, who, they believed, gave them victory in battle and brought fertility to farms and fields. Other gods were worshipped by Celts all over Europe, such as **Lugh** (god of the arts and intelligence), the **Daghda** (lord of plenty) and the **Divine Mother** (a goddess who appeared in three different shapes, sometimes kindly, sometimes cruel). Celts thought that gods lived in the sky and goddesses lived on earth.

Celtic people also thought that there were spirits living in mountains, trees and rivers. They believed that certain animals, places, patterns and numbers (especially 'three') had magic powers.

Bards (poets) sang or chanted at religious ceremonies. At feasts, they told exciting stories about enchanted lovers, monsters who could change shape and kings who became gods. They recited poems praising the victories of great chiefs and heroes. They rode with Celtic warriors into battle, playing harps, pipes or drums to encourage the men to fight bravely.

Celtic mysteries

There are many things that we do not know about Celtic beliefs and ideas. Because they believed it was too holy to share with foreigners, Celts kept no written records of their religion. But later versions of old Celtic poems and stories still survive, as do Celtic statues, carvings, grave goods (treasures buried with dead bodies) and holy objects. Much of our understanding of Celtic religion comes from these artefacts. They show that for the Celts, this world, and the Otherworld, were full of mystery and magic, terror and delight.

There is one other reason why we know so little about Celtic religion and ideas. Druids were respected and feared by all Celtic people, and were trusted advisors to Celtic kings. The Roman conquerors of Britannia thought that the Druids were the most serious threat to peaceful Roman rule. So, in 59 AD, Roman armies launched a deadly attack on the British Druid headquarters on the island of **Anglesey**, North Wales. The Roman historian, Tacitus, tells us that female Druids prowled furiously on the shore, howling curses at

An image of a Celtic goddess, which can be seen in the National Museum of Scotland, Edinburgh

the invaders. The Romans also destroyed many sacred groves (clumps of trees) throughout Britannia, where Druids said prayers and made sacrifices.

Living like Romans

Most Celtic families in the British Isles continued their traditional way of life, without Druids, for hundreds of years after the Romans invaded. But the lives of rich, important Celtic leaders were dramatically changed by Roman rule.

Even before the invasions, friendly British client kings had begun to live more like Romans. They imported wine to drink and Roman luxuries such as sweet dried figs and raisins. After Claudius's invasion of 43 AD, it became fashionable among friendly Celtic tribes to wear Roman **togas** (half-circle cloaks, a traditional sign of Roman citizenship), and to buy goods such as silk, spices and olive oil from Roman empire lands. These 'Romanised' Celts also built **villas** (grand country homes) in Roman style, with bath-houses, underfloor heating, mosaic decorations and ornaments. They began to introduce into Britain new crops brought from Rome that we still eat today: cherries, walnuts, grape, peas, parsnips, carrots and celery. Rowdy, drunken Celtic feasts were replaced by elegant Roman-style dinner parties. Celtic kings and their guests spoke in Latin, and even discussed Roman ideas and politics.

The ruins of several of these villas still survive today. One of the finest is at **Fishbourne**, in Sussex. It was probably built for King **Cogidubnus** of the Atrebates tribe around 50 AD, and later enlarged for the family members who ruled after him.

The Roman conquerors also recruited friendly, powerful Celts to work for their government, or to serve on the new local councils that they set up to run Roman towns. They volunteered to teach young Celtic princes the Roman way of life, to encourage the next generation of Celtic rulers to be friendly to Rome.

Next to the fort

The Roman invaders also changed the lives of a few ordinary Celtic people. These Celts moved to live and work in the **vicus** (village) that grew up close to each Roman army fort. Celtic farmers and traders sold grain, meat, hides, timber and other useful goods to Roman fort officials. Celtic workers provided transport services with their horses and carts, and worked for the Romans creating new buildings or making repairs. Celtic brewers and bakers set up taverns and food shops where off-duty Roman soldiers could relax and enjoy meals and drinks. And, although Roman soldiers were not allowed to marry, many met Celtic women and set up homes in the *vicus* next to their fort for their 'unofficial' wives and children.

Side by side

Slowly but surely, a new way of life developed in Britain in the places where Roman and Celtic peoples lived and worked side by side. By around 200 AD, people in towns, villas and villages next to forts were living 'Romano-British' lives. And many people in Britain also had mixed ancestry: part Celtic, part Roman.

A tavern in a *vicus*

How do we know?

Although the Celts of Roman-ruled Britannia left no written records, we can learn about their lives from several different sources. Celtic craftsmen were expert metalworkers, and many objects they made have survived until today. We can see the Celts' appearance from the images of conquered Celts on Roman carvings and coins, and gather more clues from the written descriptions by Roman authors.

Archaeologists have uncovered the remains of Celtic farmhouses and barns. These have then been rebuilt in museums, so that we can visit, walk inside, and experience what it would have been like to live in Celtic buildings.

It is more difficult to discover about the Celts' religious beliefs. But a few images of Celtic gods have been found in Britain, and in other Celtic lands in Europe. There are also descriptions of Celtic holy places by Roman authors (see page 36). We can piece together clues about Celtic gods and heroes from the stories written down by monks in Ireland around 300 years after the Romans left Britain. They are also full of magic and monsters – and very exciting to read!

Exercise 3.1

Read the information on pages 29 to 39 about the Celts and then answer the following questions:

1. What were the duties of Celtic kings and queens?

2. How did Celtic warriors use chariots to fight?

3. What were the main crops grown by Celtic farmers?

4. What did Celtic clothes look like?

5. Why don't we know very much about Celtic religion?

6. Which Celts built villas, and lived in Roman style?

7. What was a *vicus*, and who lived there?

8. Why did the Romans attack the druids?

9. Where did 'Romano-British' culture develop?

10. How do we know what the Celts looked like?

Exercise 3.2

Complete the following sentences:

1. Romans thought some Celtic kings and queens looked _____.

2. Celtic warriors liked to _____ about their bravery.

3. The Celts collected the _____ from dead enemy warriors.

4. Celtic warriors who grew too fat were _____.

5. Most Celtic families lived in the _____ and were _____.

6. Celtic craftworkers were very skilled at_____, _____ and _____.

7. In dangerous times, Celts sometimes sacrificed _____ to their gods.

8. Celtic brewers set up _____ in which the Roman soldiers could drink.

Exercise 3.3

Explain what is meant by the following:

1. champion's portion

2. battle trophies

3. chain mail

4. torcs

5. brochs

6. crannogs

7. curing (of animal skins)

8. loom

9. druid

10. bard

Exercise 3.4

Look at the photo of the wooden statue of the Celtic goddess shown on page 36.

Now read this description of a Celtic holy place, by Roman writer **Lucan** in his poem ***Pharsalia***. It was composed about 60 AD to celebrate Caesar's wars against the Celts:

> 'There was an ancient, sacred grove of trees. Its wild, tangled branches arched high overhead; below, all was cold, dark and shadowy. Gods were worshipped there in savage ceremonies. There were altars heaped with horrible sacrifices, and every tree was sprinkled with human blood. Birds were too scared to perch there; wild animals would not seek shelter. But there were statues of fierce, grim gods roughly carved from fallen tree-trunks…'

1. Write down at least one problem we might have when we use the statue to find out about Celtic religion, and one problem we might have when we use the poem.

2. How does the poem help us understand the statue?

3. How does the statue help us to trust the poem as evidence?

. . . .

Exercise 3.5

Before starting this exercise, try to find out more about Roman villas or Celtic farms from a library or a museum, or even by going to visit one.

Now imagine that you are a Celtic country boy or girl, sent to deliver a message to a grand Roman villa OR that you are a young Roman slave, visiting a Celtic farm with the local tax collector. In either case, it is your first visit.

Draw a big picture, with captions and labels, to record your impressions. What do you see? What's new? What's different from your own life? What amazes you? What don't you understand?

Chapter 4
Divided land

The end of Roman rule

Roman rule in Britannia lasted for over 300 years but was rarely peaceful. From around 180 AD, the Roman army had to put up with repeated invasions from the Celtic tribes north of Hadrian's Wall, and attacks from across the North Sea by **Saxons**. These were German tribes from the lands now known as Denmark, the Netherlands, Germany and south Sweden. At the same time, invaders were also attacking the city of Rome and its empire in Europe. Seizing their chance, several powerful Romans took part in political plots to overthrow emperors in Rome or seize power for themselves. These troubles at home kept Roman soldiers away from Britannia.

By 410 AD, there were not many Roman army leaders or high-ranking Roman government officials in Britannia. In 409 AD, the last few appealed to Emperor **Honorius** in Rome for help against invaders. But Honorious and his army were busy fighting the **Vandals** and other enemy tribes. These tribes had crossed the frozen River Rhine and swarmed into Roman empire lands. Honorius's reply to the Roman leaders was alarming. He had no troops to spare; the British Isles must defend themselves. Roman power in Britannia had ended.

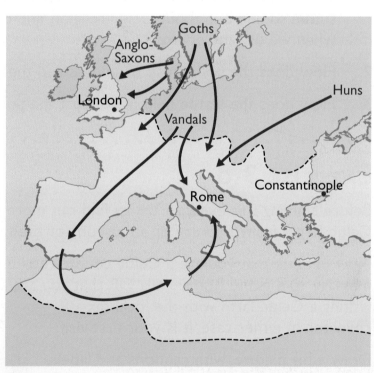

The invaders who attacked the Roman Empire

Who stayed behind?

Only a few documents survive to give us facts and figures about the British Isles in the years after 410 AD. But archaeologists have found that the largest group of people living there were Britons descended from Celtic tribes. They belonged to around thirty **civitates** (tribal kingdoms), each led by a king or chief. They spoke Celtic languages or a little Latin, and their way of life was a mixture of Roman and Celtic customs.

Many Britons were farmers but others lived in grand villas or Roman-built towns. Some were merchants, trading tin and slaves with customers from the Middle East or North Africa. Some were craftsmen, making jewellery, weapons and stone carvings in a mixture of Roman and Celtic styles. Some worshipped Roman and Celtic gods; some had even become Christians.

We do not know how many Britons who had joined the Roman army stayed in the British Isles when other Roman troops sailed away. Others friendly to Rome may have chosen to remain after the Roman armies left, such as merchants or government clerks from distant parts of the Roman empire. There were also groups of Saxon **mercenaries** (warriors who fought for money), recruited by the Romans to guard British frontiers.

Who ruled the Britons?

After 410 AD, Saxons and hostile Celtic tribes all continued to attack the British kingdoms. Each tribal king or chief organised his own army. Some kingdoms were richer and more powerful than others, and their kings began to control the weaker kingdoms. We know the names of just five or six of these powerful British kings. One of the earliest, **Vortigern**, may have lived around 450 AD. **Bede**, a Saxon monk who wrote a history of Britain in 731 AD, tells us how Vortigern invited some Saxons to come to Britain to live and fight against other invaders. But it was a big mistake – the Saxon settlers fought against Vortigern as well, and defeated him.

Ambrosius or Arthur?

The greatest early British king we know about is **Ambrosius Aurelianus**. He might have come from a Roman family, or a Celtic tribe loyal to Rome. He was called 'perhaps the last of the Romans' by **Gildas**, a British monk writing around 550 AD. A Welsh writer, **Nennius**, who lived around 800 AD, described him as 'king among all the kings of the British people'.

Timechart – the end of Roman power

c.200 AD: First known raids on the British Isles by Saxons. The Romans start to build 'Saxon Shore' forts, and send camouflaged ships (with ropes and sails dyed blue!) to patrol North Sea and English Channel coasts.

c.205 AD: Hadrian's Wall is rebuilt.

260–273 AD: Gaul, Britannia, Germany and Spain try to break away from the Roman Empire, but fail.

287–293 AD: Carausius, commander of the British fleet, declares himself emperor of Britain and North Gaul. He is murdered.

342–343 AD: Rebellion by tribes close to Hadrian's Wall.

367 AD: Celtic **Picts** attack from north Scotland; Celtic **Scots** attack from Ireland.

369 AD: Hadrian's Wall is rebuilt again.

383–388 AD: Magnus Maximus declares himself emperor of Britain. He is killed.

401 AD: Roman army leader **Stilicho** recalls many Roman soldiers from Britannia.

406–407 AD: Marcus, then **Gratian**, then **Constantine** (all soldiers based in Britannia) claim to be Roman emperor.

407 AD: Constantine leads most remaining Roman soldiers out of Britannia, to help him fight for power. (He fails.)

407 AD: British Isles are attacked by Saxons. Other tribes from north-east Europe also threaten to attack.

409 AD: Britons start to organise their own armies, for defence.

410 AD: End of Roman power in British Isles.

460–570 AD: Groups of Britons leave the British Isles to settle in **Brittany** (north-west France) and **Galicia** (north-west Spain).

A Victorian impression of King Arthur

Gildas recorded that Ambrosius defeated Saxon invaders at a place called **Mount Badon**, in around 500 AD. Today, nobody knows where this legendary place is. Gildas adds that Ambrosius's victory stopped Saxons attacking British kingdoms for the next fifty years.

The stories about King Ambrosius and his battles may have inspired legends about a magical British hero, King **Arthur**. Arthur might have been another powerful early king – or he might never have existed at all! We do not have enough evidence to be certain. But the legend goes that, if Britain is ever threatened, Arthur will magically return to defend his old kingdom against enemies.

Survival and decay

In 410 AD people were still using some buildings and structures that the Romans had built, such as roads, forts, walls and planned towns. For example, **York**, a Roman town for old soldiers, became the capital of a British tribal kingdom. But many more Roman structures were abandoned or dismantled so that their materials could be used for smaller, less well-made houses. By around 450 AD, the Roman capital city, Londinium (London) was a deserted ruin.

In a few places, new structures were built on old Roman sites. At **Wroxeter**, in present-day Shropshire, archaeologists have uncovered traces of a large, Roman-style house, with stables and outbuildings, that might have been made for a rich British tribal king. At Verulamium (St Albans) they have discovered a town water-pipe, laid after the Romans left. Some Britons made homes on the sites of deserted Roman army forts. But most new buildings at this time were made of timber, not stone. They were cheaper, quicker and less impressive than Roman stone buildings – and did not last as long.

In the countryside, some British kings rebuilt ancient Celtic forts to use as their headquarters. At **Tintagel**, in Cornwall, archaeologists have found stone buildings, imported glass and jewels, and vast amounts of pottery from jars containing wine and oil from Mediterranean lands. At **South Cadbury**, in Dorset, there are the remains of stone walls, a massive timber gate, and a large hall for feasting, all built between 400 and 500 AD, together with Roman coins and fine jewellery. According to later legends, what is at Cadbury are the remains of **Camelot**, the home of King Arthur. Whether we believe this or not, the hall and its treasures must have belonged to a powerful British king.

Who were the Saxons?

Around 470 AD, **Sidonius Apollinaris**, a Christian church leader in western France, described an attack on his homeland by a gang of Saxon slave-catchers. He wrote, '… they outdo all others in brutality.

A British settlement in an old Roman fort

Ungovernable, entirely at home at sea, they attack unexpectedly.' The Saxons were also pagans, who worshipped gods as brutal as themselves. In Sidonius's eyes this was just as bad: 'When they are ready to sail home, they drown or crucify one in ten of their captives as a sacrifice.'

Similar groups of raiders had attacked the British Isles from around 200 AD. From 407 AD, they began to settle there, in the east and south-east. Looking back, in 731 AD, Bede recorded what he knew about the attackers: 'Those who came over were three of the more powerful peoples of German lands: the **Saxons**, the **Angles** and the **Jutes**.' We now know that these different groups of invaders were closely related, spoke similar languages and shared the same way of life. Historians usually group them together and call them '**Anglo-Saxons**' or just 'Saxons'.

Fierce Saxon invaders

Why did the Saxons invade?

As we saw on page 43, some Saxons came to the British Isles because they were invited. British kings needed their fierceness and fighting skills. Others came because their own Saxon kings and chiefs had led them over the sea in search of new, better places to live. Compared with cold, bleak Saxon homelands, the British weather was milder and British farmland was richer and more fertile. Also, by around 500 AD, rising sea levels were flooding Saxon lands near the coast.

Once the Saxons found British land that they liked, they took it over and settled there. Without the strong, well-organised Roman army, it was very difficult to stop them. Sometimes this takeover led to fighting but sometimes it just happened peacefully. There were probably not many Saxon settlers and they were mostly chiefs and warriors.

Some Saxons may have married British wives and settled close to their new families. British kings and chiefs were probably driven out or killed, but ordinary British people stayed in their homes and farms, under the control of the Saxons. We know very little about these new rulers, but Bede records the names of two: **Hengist** and **Horsa**. Bede says that they helped British kings in Kent to fight, but rebelled and seized power for themselves in 449 AD.

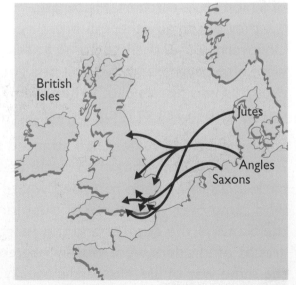

This shows the Anglo-Saxons' homelands and where they settled

Saxon life

Wherever these Saxon kings and their followers settled, they introduced their own customs and beliefs, and the Saxon language. The Britons slowly copied these, and began to live and speak like Saxons – just like they had with the Romans many years before. Names for everyday things became Saxon, such as 'man', 'land', 'work', 'war', 'weapon', 'farm' and 'house'. So did some of the days of the week: Tuesday, Wednesday, Thursday and Friday are named after Saxon gods or goddesses. Saxon, or 'Old English', became the most widely-spoken language in the British Isles.

Most Saxon families lived as farmers. From around 500 AD, most new buildings in Saxon-ruled lands were built in the Saxon style. They were wooden, rectangular and thatched with straw. We can learn more about Saxon settlers by looking at modern place names based on Saxon words. For example, **Finglesham** in Kent means 'Prince's Farm', and **Whittinghame** in south-east Scotland means 'the settlement of Hwita's people'.

A picture of reconstructed houses from West Stowe, Suffolk

Farmers and fighters

In return for the right to farm land, British men and women had to work for the local Saxon chief or king, or pay tribute to him. A later Saxon book, written around 1000 AD, lists many different skilled jobs for farmworkers, such as cowherd, goatherd, pig keeper, shepherd, beekeeper, forester, grain-store worker and cheesemaker. Men also had to fight for their king whenever he commanded. The most dishonourable thing a Saxon man could do was to desert his leader in battle.

Saxon ceorl, king and thane

Saxon laws divided people into slave or free. Slaves might be captured enemies: Britons, Picts, Scots or rival Saxons. They could also be criminals, or people who were too poor to survive as farmers. Some slaves were purchased, mostly from Saxon slave-raiders. As in Roman times, slaves could buy their freedom, or be set free by their owners.

Among free families, there were several different classes. At the top were kings; next came **thanes**, or chiefs, who were rich and led armies in battle. **Ceorls** (pronounced 'churls') were free men and the largest group in society. Some had large farms, or worked as craftsmen and traders. Others had only a little land and had to spend several days each week working for their king or thane.

Powerful women

Saxon women shared the rank of their father or husband. They had much more freedom than women had been allowed by Roman rulers. They could own land and goods and, when they acted as witnesses in the law courts, were treated as equal to men. Often, they had to manage farms while their husbands were away fighting. We know the names of several powerful Saxon women, such as **Abbess Hilda of Whitby** (in present-day Yorkshire). She became head of a monastery there in 657 AD and led a religious community of men and women.

Clothes, jewels and weapons

Splendid rings, brooches and buckles have been found in the graves of Saxon men and women. Spears, shields and helmets were buried alongside Saxon men. But there is little evidence to tell us about Saxon or British clothes between 400 and 600 AD. Later carvings and documents show that Saxon men wore knee-length tunics, trousers and cloaks, made of wool or linen. Saxon women wore long, loose dresses and cloaks, and covered their hair with scarves.

Graves of rich Saxons contain fine glass imported from Germany, together with gold and silver coins, bronze dishes and elephant-ivory combs from the Middle East and North Africa.

Apart from metalwork, Saxon technology in the British Isles was less developed than British or Roman. Before 600 AD, craftworkers did not use wheels to make pottery, or stone for building. Ordinary people in Saxon-ruled lands had also stopped using coins for trading. Instead, they bartered (swapped) farm produce for other useful items.

Mother goddess

Saxons worshipped **Nerthus**, the Earth-mother. They believed she made crops grow and protected farm animals. They also honoured **Freya**, the goddess of love; **Thunor** or **Thor**, god of storms; and **Tiw**, god of the sky. **Woden**, lord of battles and magic, was the most powerful Saxon god. Many Saxon kings claimed to be descended from him. Like the Celts, the Saxons worshipped their gods in open-air holy places, such as woods and lakes. Some of these still have gods' names, such as **Wednesbury** (Woden's Mound), which is in present-day Shropshire.

A gold buckle showing the god Thunor (also called Thor)

Saxon people celebrated festivals to mark the seasons of the year, especially **Yule**, at midwinter, when warriors burned Yule logs and sacrificed boars (male wild pigs – which, to the Saxons, were magic animals). In late March, they also honoured **Eostre** (Easter), goddess of spring, and her sacred symbols of new life, eggs and hares.

How do we know?

There are only two history books by writers living in the British Isles surviving from before 750 AD. The first author, Gildas, a British monk, wrote ***De Excidio Britanniae*** ('On the Fall of Britain') around 550 AD. He believed that the Saxon invasions were God's way of punishing the British people for being wicked. The second writer, the Saxon monk, Bede, did not complete his ***Historia ecclesiastica gentis Anglorum*** ('Ecclesiastical [Church] History of the English People') until 731 AD, but he based it on earlier reports of the Saxon invasions that are now lost.

The Welsh writer, Nennius, who lived around 800 AD, also collected and reported earlier information about Saxons. So did the writers of the ***Anglo-Saxon Chronicle***, a list of important events compiled by Saxon monks from around 892 AD.

Archaeologists have uncovered around 1500 Saxon cemeteries, where rich people were buried with grave-goods beside them. However, we know much less about poorer Saxon people, or about Britons.

The early Saxons built in timber and almost all their buildings have disappeared. But patterns of **post-holes** (areas of earth containing rotted wood where timber wall-posts and roof-posts once stood) have helped archeologists to work out what Saxon halls and smaller homes looked like. Sometimes, these layouts can allow us to build reconstructions of the original building.

Exercise 4.1

Read pages 42 to 52 about the arrival of the Saxons and answer the following questions:

1. Who attacked Roman-ruled Britannia from around 180 AD?

2. When did Roman power in Britannia end?

3. Who was the greatest early British king that we know about?

4. When did London become a ruin?

5. Which days of the week have Saxon names?

6. Who did the Saxons worship?

7. Who was Bede?

8. How do archaeologists know about the presence of wooden buildings that have since rotted away?

Exercise 4.2

Read pages 42 to 52 about the Saxons and the end of the Roman rule in Britannia and complete the following sentences:

1. The Romans built _____ to defend the Saxon Shore against raiders.

2. Most people living in Britain in 410 AD were _____ descended from _____ tribes.

3. Famous British hero, King _____, might never have existed!

4. Saxon women had the right to own _____ and _____.

5. We know about Saxon weapons and jewellery because they were _____ in _____.

6. _____ was the Saxon goddess of spring.

Exercise 4.3

Read pages 42 to 52 about Saxon life and explain what is meant by the following:

1. Saxons

2. mercenaries

3. rectangular

4. cowherd and goatherd

5. forester

6. thanes

7. ceorls

8. elephant-ivory

9. bartered

10. boars

. . . .

Exercise 4.4

This is part of a poem by a Saxon writer, describing a ruined Roman town:

> '*Splendid this rampart is, though fate destroyed it*
> *The city buildings fell apart, the works*
> *Of giants crumble. Tumbled are the towers.*
> *Ruined the roofs, and broken the barred gate,*
> *… all the ceilings gape,*
> *Torn and collapsed and eaten up by age.*'

Write your own short poem about Roman ruins OR about how a Roman soldier or governor might have felt as they sailed away from Britannia soon after 400 AD.

Exercise 4.5

If possible, visit a heritage centre or museum with displays of Saxon objects. You can also look on the Internet for sites run by 'living history' or re-enactment groups, or visit a library and look at books about Saxon history and archaeology.

Draw pictures of Saxon men, women and children, to show their clothes, weapons and jewellery. Add captions and labels to identify each Saxon item in your drawing, and to explain why they were worn and what they were made of.

Chapter 5

Kings, monks and missionaries

Changing kingdoms

The Saxon raiders did not arrive all at once, or settle in all parts of the British Isles. Between 400 and 600 AD, some parts of the north and west remained under British rule. Other British kingdoms kept their old names, such as **Bernicia** and **Deira**, even though the Saxons ruled them.

A map showing how Britain was divided in around 600 AD

The rulers of all these kingdoms had enormous power. They encouraged trade, passed new laws and sent ambassadors to countries in Europe. They also decided on the religion of their kingdoms. Between 600 and 800 AD, many Saxon, British, Scottish and Pictish kings chose a new faith: Christianity. This brought great changes to the British Isles.

Old and new beliefs

As we saw on page 25, the Romans first brought Christianity to the British Isles some time before 300 AD. When the Romans left, some Christian communities remained, in Roman-built towns or large country villas, and in the countryside of western and northern regions. But other people in the British Isles continued to follow the old Celtic religion or, after around 410 AD, to copy the new pagan beliefs from the Saxons.

St Patrick

Christianity had also spread from the British mainland to Ireland. According to legend, it was carried there by **St Patrick**, who died around 490 AD. Patrick was a Briton from a Christian family, probably living in Cumbria. As a child, he was captured by slave-traders and taken away to Ireland. After six years, he escaped, sailed back home and studied to become a Christian priest.

St Patrick has a dream

One night, in a dream, Patrick saw a letter sent by the Irish people, where they begged him to teach them. He returned to Ireland and spent the rest of his life there, preaching.

Many tales were told about Patrick's adventures: some miraculous, some magical. These were great stories, but they may not be historically accurate – after all, that was not their aim! Historians now think that other British people had taken Christianity to Ireland many years before Patrick, but their names have since been forgotten.

Back from Ireland

Around 500 AD, **missionaries** from Ireland carried the Christian faith back to the British mainland. They left their homes hoping to become **martyrs** (people who die for their faith) but they were also inspiring teachers. The first-known Irish missionary was **St Ninian**, who died around 432 AD. He built a monastery at **Whithorn** (in the far south-west of Scotland) and preached to the Picts and Britons living near **Din Eidyn** (now called Edinburgh).

Columba meets the Loch Ness monster

Shortly afterwards **St Columba**, another Irish monk, arrived in Britain. In 563 AD, Columba set up a monastery on **Iona**, a tiny, rocky island off the far west coast of Scotland. From there, he and his fellow monks travelled through the northern British Isles, telling the Picts and Scots about Christianity.

Legends told how Columba challenged Pictish priests to perform magic tricks, and even encountered the Loch Ness monster! The story goes that Columba saw a Pict swimming in the loch who was about to be attacked by the monster. Raising his hand, Columba shouted 'You will go no further; do not touch the man, and go back with all speed!' Like the stories about Patrick, these tales were told to show the spiritual powers of the missionaries.

Alone with God

In Ireland and Iona, monks lived alone or in clusters of rough little huts in wild, remote places. They stayed away from villages and towns, and spent their time praying, writing, meditating and studying the Bible and other holy books. They kept themselves alive by gathering nuts and berries, keeping animals, fishing and growing vegetables.

Little angels

At around the same time as Columba and Ninian were busy in the north, Christian missionaries from Rome were arriving in the far south of the British Isles. A story, famous for 1400 years, tells us why they travelled there. Around 595 AD, **Pope Gregory**, in far-away Rome, saw some captured children on sale as slaves. Feeling sorry for them, he asked the slave trader who they were. He was told that they were Angles and Saxons, from the British Isles. '*Non Angli sed angeli*', the Pope declared. 'Not Angles, but angels!' Pope Gregory decided that he must tell the Angles and Saxons in the British Isles about the Christian faith.

Foreign queens

Pope Gregory may also have been encouraged to send missionaries by **Ethelbert**, a Saxon king. Ethelbert ruled Kent, in the south-east, from around 560 to 616 AD. This was a very long reign for the time, and suggests that Ethelbert must have been really powerful to stay in control of a kingdom for over 40 years.

As a young man, Ethelbert worshipped the old Saxon gods, but he married a Christian princess, **Bertha**. She came from the kingdom of the **Franks** (in northern France), and brought a Christian priest with her. She gave orders to rebuild the old Roman church in **Canterbury**, which was then Kent's capital city, and she worshipped there.

Christian kings

In 597 AD, Pope Gregory sent a monk, **St Augustine**, to Kent. A team of missionary priests travelled with him. They persuaded King Ethelbert to become a Christian. He was the first Saxon king in the British Isles to change his religion. Soon the Saxon kings in nearby Essex and East Anglia followed Ethelbert's example. They also commanded the men and women in their kingdoms to become Christians.

However, when King Ethelbert died in 616 AD, many people in Kent and East Anglia went back to worshipping Saxon gods. They felt suspicious of Christianity, thinking it was a dangerous, foreign faith. But in 619 AD, one of King Ethelbert's daughters married **Edwin**, the Saxon king of Northumbria. She took her Christian faith with her. After several years of doubts and delays, Edwin became a Christian in 627 AD. Bede later claimed that it took thirty-six days to teach and baptise all of Edwin's followers.

Lindisfarne

Edwin was killed fighting in 633 AD, and his people went back to their old ways again. Christian missionaries had either to hide or leave the kingdom. But two years later, a famous Saxon warrior prince, **Oswald**, became the new king of Northumbria. He had learnt Christianity while sheltering at a monastery in Scotland. Oswald invited monks from Iona to come and live at **Lindisfarne**, an island off the north-east coast (near today's city of

Newcastle). Northumbria became a new centre of Christian teaching, sending missionaries over a wide area, from south-east Scotland to the region known today as Yorkshire.

St Cuthbert, the first **bishop** (Church leader) of Lindisfarne, was the most famous northern missionary. Bede reported that Cuthbert worked miracles, healed the sick, saw angels, and spoke with birds and animals. These claims may not be true but Cuthbert obviously impressed everyone who saw him.

An artist's impression of monks opening the tomb of St Cuthbert

Cuthbert died in 687 AD and was buried at Lindisfarne, like a Saxon noble, with magnificent grave-goods beside him. But Cuthbert's goods were Christian treasures: a cross made of gold and precious stones, a silver altar and a beautifully-bound Gospel Book. Eleven years later, Cuthbert's tomb was opened by the Lindisfarne monks. They claimed that his body was miraculously preserved.

Pagan or Christian?

The last pagan Saxon king in the British Isles, **Penda of Mercia**, died in 655 AD. Most other British kings became Christians before 800 AD.

Kings changed their religion partly for personal reasons. Life for everyone at that time was short and dangerous, and what happened after death was uncertain. In famous lines from his *History*, Bede described human existence as: 'like the swift flight of a sparrow through a banqueting hall … While he is inside, he is safe from the winter storms. But, after a few moments of comfort, he vanishes from sight …' Christianity offered the hope of a new, peaceful life after death. The Christian God seemed kindly and forgiving, unlike the Saxons' own fierce, unpredictable gods who demanded human sacrifices.

Ordinary people followed the beliefs of their kings, and some were forced to become Christians. Others were persuaded to change their faith by Christian preachers, who were often very convincing. For example, **St Wilfred**, who lived around 660 AD, was said to have a 'sweet and marvellous' way of speaking. The Church also won people's support by offering help and charity.

Church and state

Christian kings protected priests, monks and nuns living on their lands, and gave money to build churches and monasteries. In return, Church leaders supported kings by becoming royal advisors. Sometimes, they helped to make peace between warring kingdoms. They also taught ordinary men and women that they should be peaceful and honest, and obey royal laws.

Different traditions

When missionaries sent by the Pope in Rome arrived in the British Isles, they were surprised to discover that Christians who had been taught by

Irish monks worshipped in their own, unusual style. They even celebrated Easter – the most important Christian festival – on a different day from Roman Christians. In 664 AD, the 'Roman' and 'Irish' Church groups met at the monastery of Whitby, in Northumbria. After long discussions, King **Oswy** of Northumbria made the final decision: all Christians in the British Isles should worship in the 'Roman' way.

Community living

New monasteries, paid for by Christian kings, were also organised in 'Roman' style. Instead of living in small, isolated huts, as in Ireland and on Iona, monks and nuns now belonged to large, busy communities. For example, the twin monasteries at **Jarrow** and **Monkwearmouth** in Northumbria, where Bede wrote his *History*, had 600 members between them. Archaeologists have found the remains of both monasteries, and even the room in which Bede died. It seems that the buildings there were made by craftsmen hired from Gaul.

A model of a monastery in Jarrow, Northumberland

Monasteries like Jarrow had large churches where monks or nuns could pray and sing hymns, surrounded by big, shared buildings where they worked, studied, ate and slept. There might also be private rooms for the head of the monastery and for guests, a hospital, a library, storehouses, a kitchen, a garden and a burial ground.

Words and pictures

Whichever way they lived or worshipped, Christian monks and nuns were the best-educated people in the British Isles. Unlike most kings and warriors, they could read and write, and loved to study. For example, **Benedict Biscop**, the first head of the Jarrow monastery, travelled to Rome and back six times in order to bring important manuscripts back to Britain.

Some monks worked as **clerks** (secretaries) for Christian kings, helping them to write letters to important people, make lists of taxpayers, and copy out **charters** (documents recording gifts of land, often to the Church).

All these texts were written in Latin, the language used by the Pope in Rome and by scholars throughout the western half of the old Roman empire. This meant that monks, Church leaders and Christian kings could communicate easily with each other, and share ideas.

Other skilled monks worked as artists, copying holy texts slowly and carefully by hand, then decorating them with beautiful pictures and patterns to show respect and reverence. Some monasteries, like Lindisfarne, became great centres of book production. Monks drew and painted in a new artistic style, based on a mixture of Celtic, Anglo-Saxon and Roman traditions.

A page from The Lindisfarne Gospels, showing Matthew the Evangelist writing

How do we know?

Some of our most important evidence for the years 600 to 800 AD comes from the texts written by monks. As well as Bede's *History*, biographies of famous leaders such as Cuthbert and Wilfred have survived. So have poems about all kinds of religious subjects.

Bede's writings even changed the way we use the date and time. He was the first writer to count years starting from the time when Jesus Christ was born. He described each date after Jesus's birth as being 'AD' or *Anno Domini* (in the year of our Lord). Most countries still use this calendar system today, over 1300 years after Bede died.

Although few early monastery buildings are still standing, archaeologists have found many traces of their remains, plus a few early Saxon churches. We can still see many stone-carvings decorated with religious images, and tall crosses, where people met to listen to Christian preachers.

. . . .

Exercise 5.1

Read pages 56 to 63 on monks, nuns and missionaries, and answer the following questions:

1. Who first brought the Christian faith to the British Isles?

2. Where did Christian beliefs survive after around 410 AD?

3. Where did St Patrick preach?

4. Who sent missionaries from Rome to Kent?

5. Who was the first Christian Saxon king in the British Isles?

6. How many people lived at the twin monasteries of Jarrow and Monkwearmouth?

7. What language did monks write in?

8. Why did monks decorate Christian holy texts?

Exercise 5.2

Read pages 56 to 63 and complete the following sentences:

1. After 410 AD, some parts of _____ and _____ of the British Isles were still ruled by Britons.

2. Monks in Ireland liked to live in _____, _____ places, to be 'alone with God'.

3. St Columba set up a monastery on the island of _____.

4. King Oswald of Northumbria asked monks to build a new monastery, at _____.

5. St _____ was the most famous northern missionary.

6. Some ordinary people chose to become Christians. Others were _____ to change their faith by kings.

7. Kings helped the Church by _____ monks and nuns, and _____ for churches and monasteries.

8. Church leaders helped kings by serving as _____ _____.

· ·

Exercise 5.3

Read pages 56 to 63 about Christianity during Saxon times and explain what is meant by the following:

1. pagan

2. missionaries

3. baptise

4. altar

5. Gospel

6. monastery

7. manuscripts

8. clerks

Exercise 5.4

Around 900 AD, one Irish monk wrote a poem, describing his life in a remote hut in a forest. Here is part of it:

'I have a hut in the wood, no-one knows it but my Lord …

Excellent fresh springs – a cup of water, splendid to drink …

Tame pigs lie down around it, goats … tall deer … a badger's brood … foxes come to the wood … It is delightful …

Fruits … A clutch of eggs … honey … God has sent it … sweet apples … a patch of strawberries, delicious abundance …

A beautiful pine makes music to me …

Without an hour of quarrel, without the noise of strife which disturbs you … [God gives me] every good in my hut'

EITHER

Write your own poem about a place where you would like to go to be alone to think deeply.

OR

Make a painting or collage to show the Irish monk in his lonely hut.

. . . .

Exercise 5.5

Go to a library or search the Internet to see whether you can find stories about the following Christian missionaries and preachers: St Patrick; St Columba; St Cuthbert.

Choose some of the stories you like best, and tell them in your own words. If you like, you can decorate them with pictures and patterns, as monks did.

Chapter 6
High kings and conquerors

In 600 AD, there were seven strong Saxon kingdoms in the British Isles, and many weaker ones. None of these kingdoms stayed the same for very long. They grew larger or smaller, richer or poorer, depending on the strength and leadership skills of their rulers.

Bretwaldas

The most powerful Saxon king in the British Isles claimed the title **Bretwalda** (meaning 'overlord', or 'high king'). We do not know all the kings who held this title, but in 731 AD, Bede recorded the names of the first seven. They came from five different Saxon kingdoms. This tells us that no Saxon king had yet found a way of keeping power once he had got it.

The seven kingdoms of the Heptarchy

The earliest overlords whose names have survived ruled Sussex, Wessex and Kent. We know very little about the first two, **Aella** (died around 514 AD) and **Ceawlin** (died around 593 AD), except that Ceawlin of Wessex conquered land in the south-west of the British Isles.

Ethelbert of Kent (see pages 58 to 59) was the third Bretwalda. He was certainly rich, powerful and respected, but he did not rule all of Britain.

Respect and rewards

What made a great king? First and foremost, a Saxon ruler had to be a fighter. He needed to be tough and determined, and prove that he was strong enough to rule. The eldest son of a Saxon king did not automatically take over when his father died. Any young male warrior from the royal family could make a claim. Then he had to take control, either by peaceful persuasion or, more usually, by plotting and fighting. There were very often battles between royal brothers.

A 7th century gold brooch which may have been worn by a king

To stay in power, kings had to win respect from their warriors and keep them loyal. They did this by becoming as rich as they could, conquering land and seizing treasures. Then they rewarded the warriors with gifts of land, plus weapons and jewellery plundered from enemies. In the most famous Saxon poem, *Beowulf* (written around 800 AD), kings are called 'treasure-guardians', 'gold-lovers' and 'ring givers'.

A warrior given gifts by his king was honoured by his friends. Many warriors were prepared to die in return for getting praise, fame and treasure. They also might leave their home to serve a foreign overlord, and fight and die alongside men from different kingdoms.

Royal laws

As well as fighting, kings had a duty to uphold law and order. Crimes were punished according to the victim's rank in society. The more important the person who was attacked or robbed, the harsher the punishment. Each person had a **wergild**, or 'man-price', that was paid to the family of a murder victim. Attackers also had to pay fines to anyone they injured. If they had no money, they might be sold as slaves.

Blood feuds between families were common, and could carry on for years. Each death was punished by another, over and over again. Revenge attacks for insults or injuries were also common and very violent. Nearly everyone carried a knife, and men also had swords, spears or wooden clubs.

Feuds could go on for generations

A king gives judgement over a feud

Saxon communities could also make local laws and chase local criminals. All free men living in Saxon lands had to attend the **moot** (village assembly) to discuss important local issues and report local crimes and problems.

Saxon kings also began to make new laws to keep control of the lands they ruled. They needed to make everyone in their kingdoms obey them, and hoped to stop powerful rivals challenging them or fighting against each other. They wanted people to settle quarrels without feuds or bloodshed, and encouraged everyone to live peacefully. They also had to organise and pay for useful community projects, such as town or village walls, and bridges. Some of the earliest documents to survive from Saxon kingdoms are lists of laws, made in Kent (before 619 AD) and Wessex (around 700 AD). Church leaders helped to draft them and wrote them down.

A long struggle

For centuries, British and Saxon kings went on fighting each other, to win more land, wealth and power. Occasionally, one or two joined forces against a common enemy such as the Picts who invaded from north-east Scotland. As rival kings fought and died, four Saxon kingdoms grew stronger than all the others: the first was East Anglia, then Northumbria, then Mercia, then Wessex.

East Anglia

East Anglia (present-day Norfolk and Suffolk) was not a safe place to live. The kings who ruled it between about 590 and 627 AD had short, violent

Imprint of the burial ship at Sutton Hoo – the actual timbers have rotted away

lives. Five out of six of them died young and in battle. We do not know how long the sixth king reigned, or what killed him. But we do know his name, **Redwald**, and that he claimed to be Bretwalda.

Archaeologists have found the place where King Redwald was buried. It was at **Sutton Hoo**, in Suffolk, beside a river flowing out to sea. There, Redwald's body was laid in a wooden ship, surrounded by rich treasures. These were covered with a tent-shaped wooden roof, then buried under a mound of soil.

The Sutton Hoo burial survived untouched until the 1930s and has been excavated twice since then, revealing wonderful treasures. King Redwald's burial ship was

A modern reconstruction of King Redwald's burial chamber at Sutton Hoo

27.5 metres long and over 4.25 metres wide, and is the largest vessel from Saxon times that has been discovered so far. The ship's timbers have rotted away, but we can still see the nails that held them together, and the shape of the hull.

King Redwald's body has also decayed completely away in the acidic soil. But his splendid helmet, sword and shield have survived, together with his jewellery, silver bowls and spoons, his ceremonial whetstone (sword-sharpening stone) and his purse full of solid gold coins. All are magnificent; they show that King Redwald, and his kingdom, were enormously wealthy. The metalwork and jewellery are wonderfully well made. They prove that there must have been some very skilled craftworkers living in Saxon times.

The helmet from Sutton Hoo

What else does Sutton Hoo tell us?

The ship burial is unusual for the British Isles but similar to those found in southern Sweden. It suggests that the East Anglian royal family came from Sweden and had stayed in touch with their homeland for almost 200 years. The kings of East Anglia were part of a network of Saxon rulers stretching across large areas of northern Europe. The East Anglians also traded with distant lands. For example, Redwald's gold coins came from France, but his silver bowl was made in **Byzantium** (now Istanbul in Turkey).

The silver spoons found at Sutton Hoo were marked with Christian symbols but buried in a pre-Christian way. They confirm a story told in Bede's *History*. Bede tells us that Redwald allowed Christian priests to worship in his kingdom, but also protected pagan Saxon holy places. He could not decide which faith was best.

After Redwald died, East Anglia slowly became less powerful. Strong Saxon kings from Mercia (see page 72) controlled and finally conquered it in 775 AD.

Northumbria

The Saxon kingdom of Northumbria was the largest in the British Isles. It was formed when **Ethelfrith**, Saxon king of Bernicia, conquered the neighbouring Saxon kingdom of Deira. Ethelfrith also fought against, and defeated, Scots and British kings.

In 616 AD, Ethelfrith was killed in a revenge attack by Prince **Edwin** of Deira. Edwin had escaped Ethelfrith's invading armies and found refuge with King Redwald of East Anglia. Later, Redwald helped him defeat Ethelfrith. Edwin became king of Northumbria, then claimed the title of Bretwalda. As well as being friendly with East Anglia, he also had links with Saxons in Kent, and married King Ethelbert's daughter (see page 59).

Edwin was killed fighting Saxon King Penda of Mercia and British King **Cadwallon** of Gwynedd (north Wales) in 633 AD. He died very horribly: his head and hands were cut off, stuck on spears and displayed on the battlefield. After this battle, Edwin's nephew, **Oswald**, returned from exile in Scotland. He had gone there for his own safety after Edwin became king: mighty rulers like Edwin did not want rivals living so close to them! King Oswald won Northumbria back from King Penda, and like Edwin, became Bretwalda. Also like Edwin, he was killed fighting Penda, this time in 642 AD.

Pictish carved stone from Aberlemno, Scotland showing Pictish warriors

Oswald won praise for paying for the new monastery at Lindisfarne. The kings who ruled after him continued to support the Church and its scholars, and Northumbria became a great centre of art and scholarship that was famous throughout Europe.

Royal halls

In Northumbria, archaeologists have discovered the remains of great halls built for Saxon kings like Edwin and Oswald. These halls were places where kings rewarded their followers with gifts, food and entertainment. Halls were often surrounded by royal villages, with homes for farmers and the king's officials.

When they were not fighting, Northumbrian kings travelled from one royal hall to another with their wives, priests, favourite warriors and advisors. They collected taxes and tribute, settled disputes, checked up on local officials, went hunting, and showed off their royal wealth and power. They held feasts with music, poems and story-telling, and handed out gifts and rewards. The unknown Saxon poet who wrote *Beowulf* described the mood at such celebrations: 'the brave words of a happy people and the clamour of a conquering nation resounded in the hall.'

The most famous royal hall is at **Yeavering** in Northumbria, close to Hadrian's Wall. It was built on the site of a Roman settlement, using massive, heavy timbers. Nearby, there stood an unusual building, looking rather like a grandstand at a sports arena. Archaeologists think that villagers met there to hold *moots*, and to listen to Christian missionaries. Bede reports that the famous Christian preacher **Paulinus** visited Yeavering with King Edwin.

The royal hall at Yeavering fell out of use around 670 AD. After that time, most Northumbrian kings were more interested in art and learning than conquering extra land.

Mercia

The Saxon kingdom of Mercia, in what is now known as the English Midlands, was Northumbria's chief rival. It first became really powerful when Penda was king (633 to 655 AD). As well as killing two Northumbrian kings, Penda also conquered the neighbouring Saxons known as the **Hwicce**. He died fighting King **Oswy** of Northumbria in 655 AD, but his kingdom of Mercia stayed strong. **Wulfhere**, the next king, led his armies south to conquer new land. Later, the Mercians captured the city of London and invaded Wales.

Offa the Great

The greatest Mercian king was **Offa**, who ruled from 757 AD. He called himself 'King of the English' and won control of almost all southern Britain, including the Saxon kingdoms of Kent, Wessex and East Anglia. But Offa was more than just a good fighter. He encouraged trade and reorganised the coinage of Mercia, issuing the first ever British pennies, made of silver. They were stamped with his portrait, and were used throughout the British Isles and abroad.

Offa was the first Saxon king to hold regular meetings of all the important Church leaders, to discuss religion and politics. He also learned new ideas about government and kingship from other European rulers. The mighty Emperor **Charlemagne** of France, who ruled many lands in the old Roman empire, treated Offa with respect. In 796 AD he praised Offa as 'a most strong protector of your earthly country, and a most devout defender of the holy faith'. Offa also sent scholars and artists from the British Isles to travel throughout Europe, where their work was admired.

Offa's Dyke

King Offa's biggest project was a deep ditch and massive wall of earth, known today as **Offa's Dyke**. It was around 190 kilometres long and over seven metres high – about as tall as a house – and most of it still survives. Today we think that Offa's Dyke was built to mark the western boundary of Mercia, and protect it against attack from the Welsh. It tells us that Offa could command

The building of Offa's Dyke

thousands of men to work for him, and had the money to pay them. It also shows that he knew how to recruit good organisers and expert engineers, and keep them working for him for many years.

Wessex

After Offa's death in 796 AD, the rulers of Mercia could not manage to control all the lands that he had conquered. Mercia still stayed powerful for the next hundred years. But after then it was not strong enough to challenge Wessex, which became the most powerful Saxon kingdom.

In 802 AD, **Egbert** became King of Wessex. He was a fearsome warrior, and soon began to attack and conquer Mercian lands. Around 830 AD, Egbert forced the huge kingdom of Northumbria to submit to him and recognise him as Bretwalda. With the help of his son Ethelwulf, he took control of Kent, and fought and conquered kings of the Britons in the south-west, including Cornwall. This was a real achievement, and for the first time, almost all the land now known as England was ruled by just one Saxon king. But Egbert, and his sons and grandsons, now faced a new problem: **Viking** invaders!

In 836 AD, Vikings from Denmark attacked Egbert and defeated him. He fought back and drove them off two years later, but they did not stay away. Egbert died in 839 AD and was succeeded by his son Ethelwulf. Three of Ethelwulf's sons then followed him as King of Wessex, and continued the fight. At the same time, the Vikings attacked further to the east and north. In 865 AD a 'great army' of Vikings invaded and conquered East Anglia. The next year, the Vikings captured the great Northumbrian city of York. This was a crisis! Who could save Saxon lands?

Viking warriors

How do we know?

As we have seen in this chapter, many impressive objects remain from the years between 600 and 800 AD. As well as Offa's Dyke, the Yeavering royal halls and the Sutton Hoo ship burial, decorated swords, gold jewellery, silver bowls, stone and ivory carvings and many religious items have survived. Archaeologists have also found evidence that large quantities of cloth were being made and traded with other countries.

The *Anglo-Saxon Chronicle* (see page 52) is one of the main sources of evidence for this time, together with many charters and letters from kings like Offa. There are also letters written by **Alcuin**, a great scholar who went from England to teach at the court of Emperor Charlemagne, and who also wrote a history of his own times in verse.

Exercise 6.1

Read pages 66 to 75 about Saxon kingdoms and answer these questions:

1. How many strong Saxon kingdoms were there in the British Isles around 600 AD?

2. How did a Saxon prince become king?

3. How did Saxon kings stay in power?

4. What was buried at Sutton Hoo?

5. Which Saxon kingdom was the largest in the British Isles?

6. Where did Saxon kings hold feasts for their followers?

7. Why was Offa's Dyke built?

8. Which powerful people attacked Wessex in 836 AD?

Exercise 6.2

Read pages 66 to 75 about the way the Saxons ruled their kingdoms and complete these sentences.

1. A Saxon kingdom's power depended on the _____ _____ and _____ _____ of its ruler.

2. Saxon kings rewarded their followers with gifts of _____, _____ and _____.

3. In Saxon times, crimes were punished according to the victim's _____.

4. Saxon kings made new _____ to help control their kingdoms.

5. King _____ was buried at Sutton Hoo. The ruling family he belonged to originally came from _____.

6. The kingdom of Northumbria was formed when the Saxon king of _____ conquered the neighbouring kingdom of _____.

7. King Penda of Mercia killed two Northumbrian kings, named _____ and _____.

8. King Offa of Mercia's silver coins were stamped with his _____.

. . . .

Exercise 6.3

Read pages 66 to 75 about Saxon life and explain what is meant by the following:

1. Bretwalda

2. *wergild*

3. blood feud

4. whetstone

5. *moot*

Exercise 6.4

Guthlac (who died in 714 AD, aged thirty-nine) was a typical prince, from the Saxon kingdom of Mercia. He described his life as a young royal warrior to **Felix**, a monk, who recorded it. Felix wrote that Guthlac had:

> '*a noble love of leadership … He devoted himself to fighting, wrecked the towns, houses, villages and forts of his enemies, recruited comrades from different peoples, and seized vast treasure …*'

EITHER

Imagine that you were a Saxon king, wanting to become Bretwalda. Create a job advertisement calling for young warriors to come and fight in your army. Use Felix's description of Guthlac to help you.

OR

Imagine that you are Guthlac's mother or girlfriend. How do you feel as he marches or rides away? You do not know how long it will be before you next see him, or whether he will ever return alive. If he dies, will it be important to you, knowing that he fought bravely and became rich and famous? Write a letter to a friend, explaining your thoughts and feelings.

Exercise 6.5

Go to a library and find a copy of a translation of the famous Saxon poem *Beowulf* or a book that tells the poem's story.

Tell Beowulf's story in your own words or as a comic strip, in words and pictures. Or, if you like, you could work with some friends or the rest of your class to act the story of Beowulf, as a play.

Chapter 7

'Hero of the English'

A 19th century statue of King Alfred which can be seen in Winchester

Alfred was the youngest son of Ethelwulf of Wessex. He became king in 871 AD, after his father and three older brothers had all ruled, and died, before him. He is usually remembered as a great hero, who defended Wessex and other southern Saxon kingdoms from Viking attack, and helped create the nation now known as England. Alfred was the first Saxon ruler to call himself 'King of all the English'.

Today, historians think that Alfred's glorious memory might be rather exaggerated. He did not win all the battles he fought. The land now called England was still divided when he died, and the kings of Wessex only managed to rule it all a hundred years later. But, even so, most historians agree that Alfred was a very great ruler, in peacetime as well as in war.

A strong, rich kingdom

The kingdom of Wessex was the strongest and richest in the British Isles. Wessex kings had won fame and wealth by controlling weaker Saxon kingdoms. And, by drawing up his will very carefully, Alfred's father, Ethelwulf, had made all his sons agree to wait for their turn to rule, rather than fight their brothers.

New towns and churches were being built in Wessex, and trade was flourishing. Coins issued by Wessex kings – a sign of their wealth – were pure, heavy silver. Wessex merchants and nobles were also wealthy. We know this because many documents survive that record their business deals. The nobles' wealth came mostly from the land and the people who worked on it. Wessex farmers had to work very hard. As well as labouring on their lord's land, they also had to pay tax or tribute to the king, and be ready to fight in his army.

Powerful friends

The kings who ruled Wessex before Alfred were good friends with Church leaders. By around 800 AD, the Church had grown very powerful, thanks to rich gifts from kings and nobles all over the British Isles. Church leaders sometimes disagreed with kings, and some kings wanted to take back Church land. All this led to quarrels. But in Wessex, kings regularly consulted a council of wise men, including Church leaders, for advice.

Wessex was also friendly with powerful countries in Europe. King Alfred's stepmother, **Judith**, was a French princess. Together with Church leaders, she encouraged links between Wessex scholars and artists and their European colleagues. Throughout his reign, from 871 to 899 AD, Alfred continued to encourage these links, and strengthened them.

Weaker rivals

Compared with Wessex, all other Saxon kingdoms were weaker, though in different ways. East Anglia was smaller, though quite wealthy: archaeologists have found traces of a busy pottery industry there. Mercia and Northumbria had both suffered fights between rivals wanting to be king. In Northumbria, there were also disagreements between kings and Church leaders. Low-quality coins found in Mercia suggest that its kings and people were growing poorer from around 800 AD.

In spite of these problems, Saxon kingdoms in the British Isles were still tempting targets for Vikings to attack.

Viking raiders

Vikings were pirates from the countries known today as Norway, Denmark and Sweden. (You can read more about them in Chapter 8.) The first recorded Viking raid on Wessex came in 789 AD, almost a hundred years before Alfred became king. At that time, three ships arrived on the beach at **Dorchester**, and Vikings leapt out and killed the Saxon royal official who went to meet them. Soon afterwards, Viking raids were reported from northern Saxon kingdoms, and from lands ruled by Irish, Scots and Britons.

Viking raiders came in search of loot – anything valuable that they could carry away. Some of their main targets were churches and monasteries, which were often the largest and best buildings in any community. They also contained rich treasures which had been given to the Church by Christian believers. Vikings knew nothing about Christian beliefs. The raiders did not understand that attacks on holy buildings caused enormous offence to Christians, as well as anger and sorrow.

Vikings looted and set fire to the great Northumbrian monastery at Lindisfarne in 793 AD, and raided Iona (see page 57) and Ireland the next year, robbing churches as they went.

As well as wrecking churches and monasteries, raiders also caused hardship in the countryside by destroying houses, stealing food crops and livestock, killing farmworkers and looting towns.

Where Viking raids took place in the British Isles

News of the Viking raids spread throughout Europe, causing horror and shock. An Irish chronicle reported: 'If a hundred heads of iron could grow on one neck, and if each head possessed a hundred sharp indestructible tongues, and if each tongue cried out incessantly with a hundred loud voices, they would never be able to count the griefs which the people of Ireland have suffered at the hands of these warlike, ruthless, pagans.'

But the separate kingdoms of the British Isles were still rivals. They had no way of working together to defend their lands. And a few Irish and Saxon kings were friendly with groups of Vikings. They even invited Vikings to the British Isles to help fight rivals or defend their lands.

Each kingdom fought off the Vikings as well as it could, but Saxon, British, Irish and Scots armies could not possibly defend the whole British coastline. Viking raids were swift, sudden, unpredictable and savage. Sometimes it seemed as if the only hope of safety came from bad weather. As one monk wrote, thankfully: 'the wind and waves are wild tonight; I shall not fear the fierce Vikings.'

The Great Army

Until around 850 AD, most Vikings came as small groups of raiders, grabbing what they could, then sailing away. Later, their tactics changed. In 865 AD, as we saw on page 74, Viking war-bands joined together and attacked as a **Great Army**. Unlike earlier raiders, these Vikings came to stay – at first for a short while, then for ever. We do not know for sure how big the army was, but it probably consisted of hundreds or even thousands of men. It was made up of lords and their followers from several different Viking lands. They all had one aim: to conquer the British Isles.

A Viking army was a formidable force. Viking warriors were strong, well trained and well armed, and fiercely loyal to their leaders. Viking commanders sent warriors in fast warships to attack coasts and sail inland along rivers. The warships carried horses as well, so that the warriors could ride quickly towards important targets.

The Great Army set up camp in Kent and stayed there over the winter of 865 to 866 AD, ready to move further inland in the spring. In the next three years, it conquered East Anglia and Northumbria, and sacrificed the Saxon kings there, **Edmund** and **Aelle**, to the Viking war-god, **Odin**.

In the summer of 870 AD, a second army of Vikings arrived and marched into Wessex. Alfred was not yet king; his fourth brother, **Ethelred**, was ruler. Together, Ethelred, Alfred and their men fought furiously against the invaders. They won a few battles, the most important being at **Ashdown** early in 871 AD, when Alfred led his men very bravely. But the fighting continued and the Vikings proved stronger. Ethelred was killed in April, and Alfred became king of Wessex, aged just twenty-one.

The next year, there was a rebellion against Viking conquerors in Northumbria. This gave Alfred valuable breathing space, as the Viking armies were kept busy in the north. He also paid the Vikings to stay away from Wessex – for a while, at least. From 873 AD to 875 AD, the Vikings attacked and took control of Mercia. After this, Alfred's Wessex was the only large Saxon kingdom still unconquered by Viking armies. For the next two years, Viking armies attacked from the sea along the south coast of Wessex, and advanced westwards, inland.

Alfred and the cakes

Losing no time, Viking armies led by King **Guthrum** of Denmark marched from Mercia towards Wessex. They invaded suddenly from the north, at the end of 876 AD. The writer of the *Anglo-Saxon Chronicle* said that Wessex people were overpowered and ran away. The Vikings seized their food and goods and set fire to their homes. Alfred and a small band of followers took refuge in the woods and wild marshland around **Athelney**, which is now part of Somerset. They built a fort there to hide in while Alfred tried to work out how to defeat the Viking invaders.

'Can anyone smell burning?'

A later chronicler, writing around 1100, told a story that has since become famous about King Alfred at Athelney. One day, Alfred took shelter in a poor woman's cottage, close to the marshes. She did not recognise him and, because she was busy, told him to look after some cakes that she was baking. But Alfred's mind was full of worries about how to fight the Vikings. He forgot the cakes, and they were burnt.

The cake story may not be true, but it tells us how dangerous and desperate Alfred's situation had become. He no longer controlled Wessex or the rich treasures that had belonged to his father and brothers. He was facing Guthrum's well-trained army, which was many times larger than his own. He was young and inexperienced. The Viking leaders were older and very tough, and had seen much more fighting. How could he – and Wessex – survive?

Peace at last

From his fort, Alfred gathered as many loyal soldiers as he could find in Wessex. Using their local knowledge, small groups of these men then made hit-and-run attacks on the Viking army. In May 878 AD, Alfred's soldiers trapped the Vikings at **Edington** (in present-day Wiltshire), and fought a battle against them. **Asser**, a Welsh monk who met King Alfred and wrote his life-story, reported that: 'Alfred attacked the whole Viking army, fighting ferociously in thick rank, and by divine will, won the victory… Alfred's men caused great slaughter, and chased the Vikings back to their fortress… After 14 days, the pagans were brought to extreme depths of despair by hunger, cold and fear, and they sought peace'.

The Battle of Edington was a great, unexpected success, but Alfred and Guthrum both realised that neither of them could hope to defeat the other completely. Alfred had won back Wessex, but he could not make the Vikings leave the lands they had conquered in Northumbria, Mercia and East Anglia. Guthrum saw that he could not control lands in the north and east if he had to keep fighting against Alfred. So they made peace, recorded in a famous document: the **Treaty of Wedmore**. Guthrum agreed to lead his army out of

Alfred's army besieging Vikings at Edington

Wessex, leaving important Vikings behind as hostages – they would be killed if the Vikings attacked again. Guthrum also agreed to become a Christian, with King Alfred as his sponsor.

Soon afterwards, in 886 AD, King Alfred and the Vikings made another important agreement: to share power in the British Isles. Wessex stayed free, ruled by Alfred. Kent and south-west Mercia also became part of Alfred's kingdom. But all land to the north and east was to be ruled by Vikings. This British Viking kingdom later became known as the **Danelaw**.

Strengthening Wessex

In spite of this agreement with Guthrum, Alfred set his soldiers and farmers to work straight away, strengthening Wessex against the Vikings. He did not trust the Viking leaders and felt sure they would attack again. He organised his army so that half its men were always ready to fight, while the other half were busy working. This meant that Alfred had soldiers whenever he needed them to defend Wessex from attackers. It also meant that ordinary life continued without too much interruption. Alfred did not want the people of Wessex to grow poor or go hungry whenever war threatened.

Next, Alfred ordered new market towns, with strong walls and gates, to be built throughout Wessex. He called them **burhs** (meaning forts, or fortress towns), and encouraged people to move to them to live in safety. Within town walls there was also space for farmers and their families from the countryside to shelter from invading armies.

Alfred stationed troops of soldiers to defend each burh. Traces of some of Alfred's well-planned burhs can also still be seen, reflected in the way some old Wessex towns still have their streets laid out.

To defend the coast of Wessex from Viking attack, Alfred ordered a new navy. Each warship was big – crewed by about sixty sailors, rowing with oars – and could sail very fast. Alfred also gave orders for low bridges to be built across rivers, to trap Viking ships heading inland.

Alfred's defence of Wessex was a great success. When a Viking Great Army attacked again, from 892 AD to 896 AD, they did not advance far into Wessex. Viking raiders attacked Wessex coasts but were driven off by Alfred's navy.

Alfred oversees a lesson

God's punishment

Like many people at the time, King Alfred believed that the Viking raids were a punishment, sent to the Saxon people by God, 'because we neither loved wisdom ourselves nor allowed it to others'. To prevent further punishment of his kingdom, Alfred decided that he must study and help his people to become better educated. He announced that he wanted 'all the youth in England now born of free men to be devoted to learning until they can read English…' Aged nearly forty, he himself began to learn Latin, the language of the Church.

Alfred also arranged for many religious texts and books on government to be translated from Latin to everyday English, so that everyone could understand them, and made a collection of old Saxon laws that he thought were useful for his own times.

To improve law keeping, Alfred ordered all the judges in his kingdom to learn to read, or else lose their jobs. He invited some of the best scholars in Europe to live at the Wessex royal court, to teach future scholars and Church leaders, discuss religion, law and philosophy, and create beautiful manuscripts.

The death of Alfred

King Alfred died in 899 AD, aged fifty. He had achieved more than any other Saxon king by saving Wessex from invaders, and leaving it larger and stronger than it had been when his reign began. He had won a great battle, then made peace with the Vikings at a time when defeat looked certain. He reorganised his towns, his army and his navy. He worked alongside Church leaders, writers and artists. He thought and prayed and wrote about his hopes and duties as king. In short, his reign was remarkable.

After Alfred

Alfred's son **Edward** (nicknamed 'the Elder') became the next king of Wessex. He spent the first three years of his reign fighting his cousin **Ethelwold**, who had rebelled and joined forces with the Vikings. Ethelwold was killed in 903 AD, and now Edward controlled Wessex, he decided it was time to get rid of the Vikings.

In 909 AD Edward defeated the Viking kingdom of York; the next year he won a great victory at **Tettenhall** (in present-day Staffordshire). Three Viking kings

Edward and Ethelflaed's campaigns 909 to 919 AD

and eleven **jarls** (warlords) were killed on one day. By 918 AD, Edward controlled the southern Danelaw.

Edward was helped by his sister, **Ethelflaed**, the brave 'Lady of the Mercians'. In 884 AD King Alfred had arranged for her to marry the chief nobleman of Mercia, to strengthen the friendship between their kingdoms. After Ethelflaed's husband died, in 911 AD, she ruled Mercia alone, setting up burhs like her father had done, and sending her soldiers to attack Vikings. She died in 918 AD, just as her men, and Edward's, were completing their conquests in the Danelaw.

Edward took control of Mercia in 919 AD, and of its western neighbour, Wales. He was now the strongest king in the British Isles. But his triumph did not last long. Later that year, the Vikings who had settled in Ireland retook York, and then the old ruling families of Wales and Mercia rebelled against Edward's kingship. Edward died fighting them in 924 AD.

How do we know?

We know about King Alfred from many surviving written sources. There is his biography (written by Asser), the *Anglo-Saxon Chronicle* which may have been started on Alfred's orders, Alfred's **Law Code** and several **prefaces** (notes) written by Alfred himself at the beginning of religious texts translated by Christian scholars. Almost all of these sources are rather one-sided, as they were produced by Alfred or people who admired him. But the letters to Alfred from important people, and collections of his charters, show that he was respected, and that his kingdom was well run.

Exercise 7.1

Read pages 78 to 86 about the beginning of Alfred's life, and answer the following questions:

1. Why is King Alfred famous?

2. Whom did the kings of Wessex, including Alfred, rely on for advice?

3. When was the first Viking attack on Wessex?

4. What did Viking raiders want?

5. How old was Alfred when he became king? How old was he when he died?

6. Where did Alfred defeat King Guthrum's army?

7. What was agreed at the Treaty of Wedmore?

8. Why did Alfred learn to read Latin?

Exercise 7.2

Read pages 78 to 86 about King Alfred's reign, and complete the following sentences:

1. Alfred was the first king to call himself _____ of all the _____.

2. Vikings looted the great monastery at Lindisfarne in _____ AD.

3. Vikings attacked in fast _____.

4. King Alfred hid from Viking invaders at _____.

5. The story of Alfred and the cakes is probably _____ _____.

6. In 878 AD, Alfred's army surrounded the Vikings in their fortress at _____ for _____ days until the Vikings _____.

7. Alfred reorganised his army and built new towns called _____.

8. Alfred believed that the Viking attacks were a _____ sent by God.

9. Alfred wanted all the free-born young men in England to learn to
_____.

10. Alfred's son _____ _____ _____ and his daughter _____ continued his fight against the Vikings.

. . . .

Exercise 7.3

Read pages 78 to 86 about the later part of Alfred's reign and explain what is meant by the following:

1. will (document)

2. Viking

3. indestructible

4. incessantly

5. chronicler

6. Great Army

7. divine will

8. Danelaw

9. *burh*

10. *jarls*

Exercise 7.4

Compare these two accounts of Viking raids, both written soon after 793 AD:

A. From the writings of Archbishop Alcuin of York

'It is nearly 350 years that we and our fathers have inhabited this most lovely land, and never before has such terror appeared in Britain as we have now suffered from a pagan race, nor was it thought that such an inroad from the sea could be made. Behold the church of St Cuthbert spattered with the blood of the priests of God, robbed of all its ornaments.'

B. From the *Anglo-Saxon Chronicle*

'In this year, dire warning signs appeared over Northumbria and sorely frightened the people. They consisted of immense whirlwinds and flashes of lightning, and fiery dragons were seen flying in the air … On 8th June, the fierce attacks of heathen men miserably destroyed God's church on Lindisfarne, with plunder and slaughter.'

1. Write down three facts that each writer tells us.

2. Write down two opinions that each writer gives.

3. Write down at least one thing that makes you doubt the total accuracy of these sources.

4. Do you think one text is more useful than the other in telling us how people in Northumbria felt about the Viking invaders? Give your reasons.

Exercise 7.5

Asser, Alfred's biographer, described him as:

'… an unshakeable pillar of the western people, a man full of justice, vigorous in warfare, learned in speech, above all instructed in divine learning.'

Imagine that you are a journalist or a biographer. Your job is to interview King Alfred. Write down a list of questions you would like to ask him. Write down the reason for asking each question, too.

Chapter 8
Life in Viking Britain

As we saw in Chapter 7, the Vikings came from lands known today as Norway, Sweden and Denmark. For many years, families there made a peaceful living as farmers, fishermen, hunters, craft workers and traders. The Vikings were also bold seafarers and expert ship builders. They travelled long distances, by land and sea, to trade in far-away places such as Russia (which is named after the 'Rus', who were Vikings from Sweden) and Byzantium (now Istanbul in Turkey).

Raiders and settlers

From around 800 AD, Vikings began to use their splendid ships to make raids on lands throughout Europe, not just the British Isles. Their targets were mostly places close to the coast. They took gold and silver treasures,

A reconstructed Viking ship

coins, weapons and slaves. Anywhere they raided, the Vikings killed people who protested, or dragged them away as prisoners to be sold.

Between around 850 and 1000 AD, groups of Viking warriors and their families found new homes in the British Isles and elsewhere in northern Europe. Historians think that Viking settlers left their homes to seek new fields and farms, and also to gain more freedom, out of reach of Viking kings. In the Viking homelands, these kings were growing stronger and taking tighter control of warlords – and their land.

Hard to find

King **Ethelred the Unready**, who reigned from 978 to 1016 AD, described the Viking settlers as 'sprouting like poisonous weeds'. This suggests that Viking settlement was widespread. But it is difficult for historians to find out precisely where the Vikings settled, because most of them did not read or write. Very few Viking burials or ruins of Viking-style farms have been found in England. Many more have been uncovered in Scotland, Ireland and the Isle of Man.

Place names and tombstones

Although there are few remains of Viking settlements in the British Isles, hundreds of Viking place names still survive. These include **Grimsby**, **Scunthorpe**, **Scafell** and **Kettleston** in England, and **Helmsdale**, **Cape Wrath** and **Stromness** in Scotland. These names tell us where Vikings once lived, or gave names to the landscape around them. There are also many carved tombstones decorated with Viking images and designs.

Looking at all this evidence, historians think that the Vikings settled in two main areas. Vikings from Norway made their homes around the northern and western coasts of the British Isles, including Ireland. Vikings from Denmark went to live in the Danelaw – the land that Alfred and Guthrum had agreed should be ruled by Viking kings. Groups of Danish Vikings also settled on the north-west coast of France. Today, that region – **Normandy** – is still named after these Vikings, or 'north-men'.

Takeover

Most Vikings settled in the far north and north-west of the British Isles. It took them only forty-eight hours to sail from their homelands to islands off north Scotland, but almost twice as long to reach the southern Danelaw. On **Lewis**, the largest island in the Outer Hebrides, off Scotland, about three-quarters of all the village names are Viking. The settlers in the far north seem to have driven away or overpowered many of the people who had been living there before them. Elsewhere in Scotland and in Ireland, the communities mixed and married each other.

An artist's impression of a Viking farm on a Scottish island

In the north and west, settlers built clusters of stone houses, in Viking style, for each Viking *jarl* and his followers. Archaeologists have excavated the **middens**, or rubbish tips, close to these Viking homes. From the remains found there, they can tell which crops the Vikings grew, and which foods they ate. The main plants grown were barley and oats (for food), as well as flax, which the Vikings brought from Norway – its stalks were woven into linen cloth. Viking farmers in the north and west also kept long-horned cattle for milk, very hairy sheep for wool, pigs and small, tough horses. They hunted deer (for meat and antlers) and otters (for fur) and went fishing. They used meat, fat and bone from whales that had been washed up on beaches, but probably did not hunt them.

Viking settlers in the far north and west did not build towns. Instead, they met at big open-air markets. Archaeologists have found traces of a busy market on the beach at **Westray**, Orkney. Traders and customers would have travelled there by boat.

Side by side

Further south, in the Danelaw, Vikings and Saxons lived side by side. Viking *jarls* took over large areas of land belonging to defeated Saxon lords, churches and monasteries, or cleared woodland to make new fields for farming. *Jarls* kept some land for themselves, and handed out the rest to their followers. Ordinary Saxons now had to pay tax or tribute to Viking *jarls* instead of Saxon landowners. Many Viking warriors settled down with Saxon wives. Soon, families as well as communities were a mixture of Saxon and Viking.

Viking settlers also learned Christian beliefs from the Saxons around them. In the Viking homelands, people worshipped **Odin** (lord of war and wisdom), **Thor** (god of thunder and metalworking) and **Frey** (who brought fertility), together with many other gods, goddesses and spirits. They admired and honoured warrior values, such as strength, boldness and bravery, and believed that heroes who died in battle would enjoy a new life of feasting and fighting in Odin's great hall, **Valhalla**. Mythical female warriors, called **Valkyries**, would choose the dead who had earned entry into Valhalla, and serve them at lavish feasts.

Vikings in their 'heaven'

In the Danelaw, most Vikings had become Christians by around 1000. Further north, Vikings on the mainland of what is now Scotland did not all become Christians until around 1100. In Orkney and Shetland, they continued their old pagan beliefs until around 1200.

Towns, crafts and trade

The first Viking raids damaged Saxon trade in the south of the British Isles. But by around 1000, when Viking settlement had almost ended, there were many more trading towns there than there had been two hundred years earlier. There were also many more craftworkers making goods for sale. How and why did this happen?

Firstly, Viking raids led to the building of new burhs (fortress towns), as Saxon villagers sought shelter from Viking attackers. Burhs soon became centres for making craft goods and for trading.

A model of a Viking marketplace, which can be seen at the Jorvik Centre, York

Secondly, the Vikings in the Danelaw built new towns for craftworkers and traders, or rebuilt and expanded old Roman ones. Thirdly, the Vikings brought new manufacturing techniques with them, or re-introduced old ones that had been lost since Roman times. The most important was making pots using a wheel, rather than moulding pottery by hand.

Jorvik

The most famous British Viking town was **Jorvik**, which is now called York. Archaeologists have discovered the remains of Viking houses there, together with over 15,000 Viking objects, including coins, jewellery, pottery, amber, bones and antlers (used to make combs), metalwork, leatherwork and wood-carvings. Some of the most exciting Jorvik finds are scraps of clothing, preserved for over 1000 years in the waterlogged ground. These include shoes, socks – and a silk cap, which shows that Viking merchants had trading contacts with the Middle East. Precious ivory from walrus tusks and valuable amber (fossilised tree resin) also tell us that Viking traders dealt in goods from icy Arctic waters and the shores of the Baltic Sea.

Viking homes

The houses at Jorvik were similar to those found in Denmark, and in other British Danelaw towns. They were built of timber, and were just one storey high, with roofs made of straw thatch or slabs of turf. Some houses had wood-lined cellars, used for storage; others had solid floors of clay or pounded earth. Doors were wooden and there were very few small windows, closed with wooden shutters. Only the very grandest houses had glass in the windows.

Inside, a fire for heating and cooking burned on a hearth in the middle of the floor; its smoke escaped through the roof. Low beds and benches were built around the inside of the walls, and covered with straw mattresses, woollen rugs and sheepskins. Most Viking homes had just one room, for eating, sitting and sleeping, but the better houses were divided into two rooms by a light wall of timber planks or woven twigs. Family clothes and other valuable items were stored in wooden chests; perishable foods, such as salt or grain, were stored in big pottery jars.

Food and farming

In the Danelaw, Vikings copied the way Saxon farmers managed their fields and animals. This made good sense. Conditions in south Britain were very different from the cold Viking homelands, and settlers had to adapt to British conditions to survive. Saxons and Vikings grew wheat to make bread, and oats for porridge. They also grew peas and beans, planted apple and plum trees, and gathered wild nuts and berries. Many poor farmers could not afford much meat, but they hunted wild birds in woods, and went fishing in streams. Saxons and Vikings also fished around the coast, where some of their catch was covered in salt and sent to towns for sale. Viking warriors were famous for drinking lots of ale, which Viking women brewed from barley.

Saxon and Viking farmers kept horses for transport, sheep for wool, and cows and pigs for meat. The bones found in their middens show that Vikings preferred to eat cattle. They also show that many townspeople had pet dogs, and fattened pigs or kept chickens in their back gardens. In the countryside, Viking farmers kept big, fierce dogs to guard and herd sheep, and for hunting. Wild cats were trapped and killed for their fur.

A Viking man and woman

Viking words, Viking styles

To the Saxons and Celtic-speaking Britons, Viking settlers must have looked and sounded strange – at least, to begin with. The Viking settlers spoke **Old Norse**. It was distantly related to Old English, but the Saxons could not understand it. Nor could the peoples living in the lands now called Scotland, Wales and Ireland, who spoke Celtic languages.

Viking clothes and jewellery were different from Saxon or British designs, and so were Viking hairstyles. Viking women wore long dresses with pinafores over the top, held in place by heavy brooches. Viking men wore loose breeches plus shirts, cloaks and tunics, and heavy neck rings and arm rings.

Viking women arranged their hair into buns or long ponytails, while Viking men trimmed their hair neatly at the back. Many Saxons were surprised to discover how clean the 'savage', 'heathen' Vikings liked to be. Even rough, fierce warriors regularly combed their hair and bathed once a week, on Saturdays – which was more often than the Saxons did! One chronicler complained that, because of this, Saxon women preferred Viking husbands.

North-west kingdoms

In the far north and west, Viking settlers continued to speak Norse for hundreds of years, and to carve inscriptions in Viking runes. They also followed traditional customs, for example, holding **things** (local parliaments) to punish criminals and make new laws. On the Isle of Man the parliament set up by Viking settlers, the **Tynwald**, still survives today.

'Vikings are cool'

Viking areas of the far north and west of what we now call Scotland became part of the kingdom of Norway. It was ruled sometimes by Norwegian kings, and sometimes by warlords who were part Celtic and part Viking. It was not until 1266 that Norway handed over all its land on the mainland of Scotland and the Hebrides islands to the Scottish king. The Orkney and Shetland Isles were ruled by Denmark until 1469.

In Ireland, the Viking rulers of Dublin were defeated by the Irish king, **Brian Boru**, in 1014. But many Viking settlers stayed in Ireland, married Irish women and became Christians.

Saxons and Vikings together

In the Danelaw, Viking traditions slowly became lost as the Danelaw was re-conquered by Saxon kings. By around 1066, the end of the Saxon era, most Viking settlers in the south were speaking Old English like the Saxons, and dressing and working like Saxons too. Even so, Viking words did not disappear completely. Some were copied by the Saxons, and are still part of English today, such as 'sky', 'sister', 'window', 'knife' and 'egg'. Viking names such as Eric and Harold were given to children throughout the Danelaw.

This blend of Saxon and Viking in the Danelaw can clearly be seen in the stone memorials left by Viking settlers. They show that Vikings soon began to follow Christian beliefs, although these were often mixed with old, half-remembered Viking myths and legends.

How do we know?

As we have seen in this chapter, most of the evidence about Vikings who settled throughout the British Isles comes from archaeological investigations. Thanks to these, we have evidence of many different areas of Viking settler life, from rich warriors' burials and carved memorial stones to crowded town houses in Jorvik and poor farmers' rubbish pits. In the far north and west of the British Isles, standing buildings also provide evidence. Poor farmhouses, sometimes called **black-houses**, continued to be built in Viking style until the mid-19th century.

There is also some evidence in words and names to tell us where the Vikings settled, and charters made between around 850 AD and 1000 record the ownership and sale of land by Vikings.

• •

Exercise 8.1

Read pages 90 to 98 about Viking settlers arriving in Britain, and answer these questions:

1.   Where were the Viking homelands?

2.   Name two places where Viking long-distance traders travelled.

3.   When did Vikings settle in the British Isles?

4.   What do Viking place names tell us?

5.   Where did Vikings from Norway settle? Where did Vikings from Denmark settle?

6.   What is the name of the most famous Viking town in the British Isles?

7.   What have archaeologists discovered there?

8.   Did all Vikings change their way of life when they settled in the British Isles?

Exercise 8.2

Read pages 90 to 98 about Viking raiders, and complete these sentences:

1. Viking raiders took _____, _____, _____ and slaves from the British Isles and lands throughout _____.

2. In the Danelaw, Vikings and Saxons lived by _____ and _____.

3. Viking raids encouraged Saxon people to build and live in new _____.

4. Viking houses in towns were built of _____.

5. Viking farmers grew wheat to make _____ and oats to make _____.

6. Viking women wore long dresses and _____.

7. _____ was bath day for Viking settlers.

8. There is still some Viking _____ being spoken today.

. . . .

Exercise 8.3

Read pages 92 to 96 about Viking lifestyles and say what is meant by the following:

1. seafarers

2. Rus

3. Normandy

4. middens

5. flax

6. linen cloth

7. antlers

8. Jorvik

9. walrus tusks

10. amber

Exercise 8.4

Did Vikings settle near you?

For this exercise, you will need a detailed map of the area around your home or your school. Or you might like to look at a map of part of the Danelaw, or of the Orkney and Shetland Isles.

Look at this list of some of the Viking word parts found in British place names, and their meanings:

by = farmstead

thorpe = outlying farm

thwaite = bracken clearing

side = shieling (summer hut on the hillside)

beck = stream

fell = hill

dale = valley

garth = enclosure

setter = place where animals grazed

bister, *bost* = share of a field

ting = place where a *thing* (assembly) met

Now look at your map and see if you can find any place names containing these word parts.

EITHER

Make a list of the Viking place names you have found, and what they tell you about the countryside shown on your map.

OR

Draw your own map of the area you have investigated and add little pictures based on the Viking place names.

Exercise 8.5

A hoard of treasure from c. 900 AD

This photo shows looted treasure – mostly silver – found at **Cuerdale**, in present-day Lancashire. It was found on a riverbank, and had been left there, probably by a Viking settler, around 900 AD. The **Cuerdale Hoard** is the largest ever found in Europe. It weighs almost 40 kg and contains brooches, arm rings, scrap silver (used for trading with) and over 7000 coins.

EITHER

Imagine you are a Viking *jarl*, carrying this treasure with you to England. Write down what you plan to use it for when you arrive.

OR

Imagine that you are one of the pieces of silver jewellery (many in this hoard come from Ireland). Write down your life history, from first being made to being displayed in a museum today.

Chapter 9
Fighting for England

While Viking settlers were making new homes in the Danelaw and the north-west British Isles, new groups of raiders were arriving. First, from around 919 AD, Vikings from Dublin in Ireland attacked Jorvik (York) and northern Britain. Next, from around 980 AD, ruthless warriors from several Viking lands made raids all round the British coast.

These new Viking raiders, led by Danish kings, plundered towns and villages and killed many of the people living in them: Saxons, Scots, Britons, and even peaceful Viking settlers. Their raids caused death and destruction but had a surprising side effect. To fight well against the Vikings, the Saxon kings of Wessex also had to win – and keep – control of all the land now known as England. Because of their battles, the kingdom of England was created. Since then, it has stayed united, ruled by just one king or queen, for over a thousand years.

The kingdoms of the British Isles in the late 900s AD, with the routes the Viking invaders took

King Athelstan

As we saw on page 86, King Edward the Elder died in 924 AD. The task of defending Wessex passed to his eldest son, **Athelstan**, who had been brought up by Ethelflaed, Lady of the Mercians. Athelstan was friendly with the peaceful Vikings of York: his sister married **Sihtric**, the Viking king there, in 926 AD. But Sihtric died the next year, and his young son by an earlier marriage became king of York. Sihtric's brother, **Guthric**, the Viking king of Dublin, arrived in York to help the boy rule.

Athelstan had to act fast to stop this Viking takeover. He attacked and conquered Viking York, and forced rulers of lands to the north of it – King **Constantine** of the Scots, and the kings of **Strathclyde** and **Bamburgh** (next to Northumbria) – to accept him as overlord. Next he forced **Hywel Dda**, the ruler of south Wales, and five other Welsh princes, to pay him tribute of gold, silver, cattle, hunting dogs and hawks. The Welsh also agreed not to attack across the boundary between their lands and Athelstan's. The new boundary was fixed at the River Wye.

The Battle of Brunanburh

In 934 AD, Athelstan sent armies to attack and intimidate the Scots, to stop them raiding his kingdom. But the Scots joined forces with Britons from Strathclyde and Vikings from Dublin, and invaded England. In 937 AD, their army met Athelstan's troops at the Battle of **Brunanburh**. No one has yet found where this battle took place, but the *Anglo-Saxon Chronicle* reported that Athelstan won a great victory: 'King Athelstan, lord of warriors, ring-giver of men, won undying glory with the edges of swords … The Scots and the Vikings from the ships fell, doomed …'

King of the English

Athelstan now ruled all the land from the English Channel to what is now southern Scotland. In his royal charters he proudly called himself 'King of the English'. To keep hold of his kingdom, he appointed royal deputies, known as **ealdormen**, in each region, and passed new laws to punish criminals, deter theft and encourage trade. He also made regular journeys throughout England to hold **councils** with important local leaders, including churchmen.

Athelstan also worked to make good relationships with other countries. He arranged marriages for his sisters with powerful rulers in lands known today as France and southern Germany. He also made friends with European Church scholars, and made a cautious peace with Norway. When Athelstan died in 939 AD, aged forty-four, he was famous and respected all over Europe.

Edmund loses – then wins

Athelstan's half-brother, **Edmund**, became the next king. He was strong, keen and brave – but lacked experience, being only eighteen years old.

The tomb of Athelstan, which can be seen at Malmesbury Abbey, England

The Dublin Vikings attacked him at once. Led by their king, **Olaf Guthricsson**, they quickly captured the city of York and the Danelaw. They were helped by the Northumbrians and by the king of Strathclyde. Many Northumbrian leaders had Viking ancestors, or were friendly with Viking settlers. They didn't like being ruled by a king based in southern England.

Olaf died in 841 AD, after ruling York for less than two years. King Sihtric's son, also called **Olaf**, became king of York and Dublin after him. But before the new king Olaf had a chance to settle in, Edmund attacked, and won back the Danelaw in 942 AD. The next year, Edmund forced King Olaf to become a Christian and accept him as overlord.

However, Olaf's armies continued to attack English lands so, in 944 AD, Edmund conquered the city of York. Olaf had to flee for his life to Dublin. Edmund also sent armies north, to attack Olaf's allies in Strathclyde. To put further pressure on Olaf's friends, Edmund announced that he supported King **Malcolm** of the Scots, who was the enemy of the people of Strathclyde.

King Edmund died in 946 AD, in a typically bold, brave way, while helping his steward (palace manager) who was being attacked by an outlaw. He was only twenty-five years old.

A new threat – Erik Bloodaxe

Edmund's brother, **Eadred**, became king and soon faced yet another attack by Vikings. This time, they were led by **Erik Bloodaxe**, the ex-King of Norway. As his nickname suggests, Erik was a brutal pirate and killer. He led many Viking raids and murdered at least one of his own brothers.

In 946 AD, the Norwegians got rid of Erik as king and he sailed for Britain. He raided the Scottish islands, made friends with the Northumbrians, and seized control of York in 947 AD. He reigned there for two years, but was driven out by the Northumbrians who had become sickened by his violence. Olaf became king of York once again, and Erik went to raid more Scottish islands.

In 952 AD, Erik Bloodaxe captured York a second time and ruled it until 954 AD. But he was driven out by the Northumbrians once again – just as King Eadred's armies marched northwards. King Eadred's men killed Erik and the Northumbrians agreed to accept Eadred as king. Northumbria was now part of England again, as it had been in King Athelstan's time.

Viking raiders pictured on a manuscript that can be seen at the Bibliotheque Nationale, in Paris

Eadwig and Edgar

Eadred died, from illness, in 955 AD. He left England rich, peaceful and, most important of all, a single, united kingdom. But Eadred had no children, and his two royal nephews – the sons of King Edmund – were still only teenagers. What happened next is not clear but there was probably a quarrel. One group of powerful men at the royal court backed one of the boys; while their rivals, and Church leaders, supported the other.

In 956 AD, the older boy, **Eadwig**, was crowned king. His rivals spread stories claiming that Eadwig was wild and wicked, and involved in shameful scandals. He quarrelled with **Dunstan**, who was abbot of Worcester and the wisest man in the kingdom, and banished him from England.

After just one year of Eadwig's reign, the leading men in Mercia and Northumbria decided that they would no longer obey him. They wanted his younger brother, **Edgar**, to be king.

Peace, law and order

As things turned out, Eadwig died in 959 AD, after ruling for just three years. The new king, Edgar, was a very different character. Edgar had a strong Christian faith; he was also a skilful politician, and made good use of the Church to help him govern England. He called Dunstan back from exile, and invited him to serve as a trusted royal advisor. Edgar was also careful to stay friendly with powerful men from each region of his kingdom. He often asked their advice or asked for their opinions, and announced that he ruled 'for all the nation: Saxons, Vikings or Britons'.

Edgar reigned for sixteen years, and became one of the most successful Saxon kings. He continued to improve the government system as Athelstan had done (see pages 102 to 103), organised the boundaries of the English **shires** (counties), set up new local law courts, improved weights and measures which helped trade, and took steps to make sure that all coins made in England were genuine and trustworthy. All **moneyers**, or craftsmen who made coins, had to buy fresh **dies** (patterns) for coins from the king every six years.

Church reforms

To help the Church, Edgar made laws to force ordinary people to give their local church a ten percent share of their earnings. He encouraged Church leaders to set up a system of **parishes**, which were areas around each local church, with religious rights and responsibilities. Edgar also supported Church reformers like Dunstan who were trying to make monks and nuns follow a new, stricter way of life. Until around 950 AD, many priests and monks in England were married. Some also travelled far from their monasteries, meeting people and enjoying themselves, instead of devoting their time to prayer, hard work and study. Rich monks and nuns also took their own money and fine goods into monasteries with them and paid for special luxuries, such as extra food or more comfortable, private accommodation.

Edgar gave the Church land and money to set up new monasteries, where monks and nuns followed a strict rule drawn up by **St Benedict**, a monk from Italy. These reformed monasteries soon became very powerful. Men and women from rich and important families became monks and nuns there, as did royal princes and princesses.

Royal ceremonies

Edgar wanted all Europe to see him as a truly Christian king, chosen by God to be ruler of England. So, in 973 AD, when he reached the age of twenty-nine, Edgar arranged to be **crowned** and **anointed** (blessed with holy oil) in a magnificent ceremony.

Edgar crosses the River Dee in style

Next, Edgar sailed along the west coast of Britain to meet a group of less powerful kings and princes from many parts of the British Isles. Edgar climbed aboard a small boat, and was rowed across the River Dee, near Chester, by eight lesser kings. The rowers included King **Kenneth II** of the Scots, King **Maccus** of the Isle of Man, and King **Iago** of Gwynedd (in north Wales). It was a clever demonstration of how Edgar ranked above all other kings in the British Isles.

Edward 'the Martyr'

Just two years after these splendid public appearances, Edgar was dead. He died suddenly and unexpectedly, aged thirty-one, and leaving two sons:

Edward, who was thirteen, and **Ethelred**, aged eight. Both were too young to rule. The Church and many powerful men backed Edward, so he became king in 975 AD. But other strong families, who felt that the Church was growing too rich and powerful, made plans to rebel against Edward and place Ethelred on the throne. A monk named **Byrhtferth** recorded that: 'Strife threw the kingdom into turmoil … family against family, prince against prince …' In 978 AD, Edward was murdered while visiting his step-mother, Queen **Elfthryth**. She was young Ethelred's mother; the killers were Ethelred's supporters and enemies of the Church. Edward became known as Edward 'the Martyr'. Later, people said that miracles happened at his tomb.

Defeat and Danegeld

And so Ethelred became king, aged eleven. But England had been left weak after three years of political quarrelling. Taking advantage of this, the Vikings attacked again in 980 AD. At first, small groups of raiders arrived but every year the Viking fleets grew larger and stronger. In 991 AD, a huge fleet of ninety-three Viking warships arrived at **Maldon** on the coast of Essex. Its commander was **Olaf Tryggvason**, who later became king of Norway. He offered peace, in return for gold, saying: 'We need not destroy each other if you are sufficiently wealthy.' The *Anglo-Saxon Chronicle* records what happened next: 'Ealdorman **Brythtnoth** of Essex marched against the Vikings with his army and fought with them … they killed the ealdorman, and occupied the place of slaughter …'

After the disastrous Battle of Maldon, Ethelred felt that he had no choice: he must pay the Vikings not to attack England. The *Anglo-Saxon Chronicle* reported: 'It was decided that tribute should first be paid to the Viking men because of the great terror they were causing along the coast. The first payment was 10,000 pounds.'

Ethelred paid tribute to the Vikings for the next ten years, at great cost to his kingdom. The payments became known as **Danegeld** (Dane-money). Historians estimate that they totalled over 100 tonnes of silver, plus other valuable treasures. As more and more Danegeld was paid to the Vikings, the people of England protested and turned against Viking settlers living in the Danelaw. In 1002, Ethelred gave orders for all Danes in England to be killed on St Brice's Day (13th November).

Ethelred did not mean his soldiers to harm peaceful Viking settlers but many of them were killed nonetheless. A charter from Oxford tells how terrified Viking people sheltered in a church but Saxons set it on fire and burnt them alive. After the St Brice's Day massacre, Ethelred lost the support of Viking settlers in England, and provoked revenge attacks from Viking raiders. They looted and destroyed many towns, villages and farms, and even murdered the Archbishop of Canterbury.

Ethelred 'the Unready'

Ethelred built a navy to chase the Viking ships away, and sent his army to fight against the raiders. He married **Emma**, a princess from Normandy, who was descended from Vikings. Ethelred hoped this would encourage the Normans to join his struggle against Viking invaders, instead of supporting them.

The St Brice's Day massacre, 1002.

Ethelred's schemes had some success but it was impossible to defeat the Vikings. Ethelred also found – as his advisors had warned – that paying Danegeld just encouraged the Vikings to attack.

In 1013, new Viking armies arrived, led by King **Svein Forkbeard** of Denmark. He came not to demand Danegeld but to conquer Ethelred's kingdom. He led his men towards London, looting and killing as they advanced, 'doing the greatest evil that any raiding army could do'. Ethelred fled abroad to seek refuge with his wife's family in Normandy.

Worn out by fighting, the **Witan** (council of royal advisors) agreed to accept Svein as king. He reigned for just two months, then died in 1014. The Viking army chose his son, **Cnut**, to follow him. Cnut sailed back to Denmark, but returned the next year, ready to take control of his English kingdom. But while he was away, the Witan changed its mind. Ethelred was called back to England so that, together with his son Prince **Edmund**, he could lead the fight against Cnut. But Ethelred died soon afterwards, in 1016. Once more, the question of who should rule over the English was thrown open.

Soon after Ethelred's death, the *Anglo-Saxon Chronicle* commented: 'these disasters befell us through bad policy …'. Ethelred's name means 'wise advice', but later chroniclers gave him a much less inspiring nickname: 'Ethelred *Unraed*', which means 'Ethelred No-Advice' or 'Ill-Advised'. Today, he is often known as 'Ethelred the Unready'.

How do we know?

The *Anglo-Saxon Chronicle* is one of the main written sources for the years 925 AD to 1016. It records the names of many important people and what they did, but it sometimes gives a one-sided view. It was also written down several years after the events it describes. Its writers often used information that had been passed down by word of mouth, and so could be unreliable. They also had strong opinions of their own – inventing King Ethelred's nickname, for example.

Other sources of written evidence include royal charters and law-codes. Monasteries also kept collections of charters, recording gifts of land and money. Well-educated Church leaders, such as Archbishop **Wulfstan** and Abbot **Aelfric**, commented on public affairs in letters, sermons and **homilies** (speeches giving advice). Archbishop **Ethelwold** drew up new rules for life in monasteries in a document called **Regularis Concordia**. A famous poem, ***The Battle of Maldon***, describes how the English were defeated by Viking raiders.

Coins and illustrated manuscripts provide the best visual evidence for this time. Most Viking warriors left no written records of their raiding, but a few carved stones giving details of their adventures have survived in the British Isles and the Viking homelands. Loot captured in Britain has also been found in Viking warriors' graves, including almost 70,000 Saxon coins.

Exercise 9.1

Read pages 102 to 110 on the time when the new Viking raiders arrived, and answer these questions:

1. Who led the new troops of Viking raiders?

2. What did Vikings from Dublin want to do?

3. Who did King Athelstan fight at the battle of Brunanburh?

4. How did King Edmund die?

5. Who was Erik Bloodaxe?

6. When did Northumbria agree to be part of England?

7. How did King Edgar help the Church?

8. What did King Ethelred give to the Viking invaders?

. . . .

Exercise 9.2

Read pages 102 to 110 about the kings who fought the Viking raiders, and complete these sentences:

Complete the following sentences:

1. The new Viking raiders attacked _____, _____, _____ and _____ _____.

2. To fight Viking invaders, Saxon kings also had to win control of _____.

3. King Athelstan forced the kings of _____, _____ and _____ to accept him as overlord, and made the Welsh princes pay _____.

4. Erik _____ captured York in 947 AD, but was driven out by _____ and then killed by King _____'s armies.

5. King Edgar used well-educated _____ _____ to help him rule England. He also asked powerful people in each region for _____ and their _____.

6. King Edgar was _____ and _____ in a splendid ceremony.

7. Dunstan and other Church leaders made _____ and _____ lead pure, holy lives, full of hard work and prayer.

8. King Ethelred learned that paying Danegeld _____ Viking raids.

Exercise 9.3

Read pages 105 to 110 about the later Saxon kings and their rule, and explain what is meant by the following:

1. tribute

2. hawks

3. host

4. steward

5. shires

6. moneyers

7. dies

8. parishes

9. privileges

10. anointed

11. Danegeld

12. corrupt

Exercise 9.4

Ask whether your school or your family can borrow a video or DVD showing Queen Elizabeth II's coronation in 1953. The music will be different, but many details of the ceremony will be much the same as they were at King Edgar's coronation, almost 1000 years earlier.

1. As you watch, try to think of all the ways in which the coronation ceremony might have helped strengthen Edgar's power as king. Work as a group with your class or your friends to write down as many as you can.

2. At the ceremony, Edgar was anointed (blessed with holy oil). A man becoming a Christian priest was blessed with oil, to show his special status. Do you think that Edgar saw kings as special people, with holy duties, like priests?

Exercise 9.5

One legal document from King Athelstan's reign describes an old Saxon law and order system. All free-born men over twelve years old had to belong to a group of ten. The oldest or wisest (or strongest) among them was leader. Each man was responsible for the good behaviour of the other nine men in his group, and might be punished for their bad behaviour. Group leaders also had to report any crimes or criminals in their neighbourhood. They met together once a month to eat and drink and share news of what was going on locally.

1. How did this system help kings of England keep control of their kingdom? (Remember, there were no phones, radios, televisions, computers or other instant ways of communicating, and no civil servants, lawyers or police.)

2. Do you think this system would have made people behave better, and helped prevent crime or ward off invaders?

3. Can you think of any disadvantages to the system?

4. Would you like to have lived at a time when this system operated, or to have taken part in it? Give your reasons.

Chapter 10

The last Saxon kings

In 1014, Archbishop Wulfstan of York preached a stern sermon, telling English people – and their king, Ethelred – to lead better lives: 'Things have not prospered now for a long time neither at home nor abroad,' he declared, '… there has been destruction and hate in every district …' Wulfstan was right. In many ways, King Ethelred's rule had brought trouble and suffering to England (see Chapter 9). But, even so, Ethelred had survived for almost thirty-eight years. Considering all the violence he had faced, that was quite an achievement.

In the fifty years after Ethelred died in 1016, the Viking threat grew less, though it never went away completely. But England faced a new challenge: it was squabbled over by rivals, who were all keen to be king. Between 1016 and 1066, England had seven different rulers, from English, Viking and Norman families. How did each one win power?

Edmund 'Ironside' and Cnut

After Ethelred died, two great warriors fought to rule England. One was Ethelred's son Edmund, nicknamed '**Ironside**' because he was so brave and strong. Edmund was supported by the Witan, the council of royal advisors.

The other warrior was Cnut of Denmark. He was backed by other powerful nobles, English and Viking, and by a strong Viking army and navy. Edmund's and Cnut's men fought fiercely but neither side could win control of all England.

In 1016, Cnut and Edmund Ironside signed a treaty called the **Peace of Alney**, in which they agreed to divide England between them. Edmund was to rule Wessex, the rich home of all English kings since Alfred. Cnut was to rule England

The temporary division of England between Cnut and Edmund 'Ironside'

Cnut and Emma present an altar cross to the New Minster in Winchester. This picture can be seen in the British Library

north of London. But, later the same year, Edmund suddenly died. Cnut quickly took control of Edmund's half of the kingdom as well as his own.

Murdered men

Cnut was just twenty years old when he became England's king. He was clever, bold and ruthless. He knew that some powerful English men did not want him to rule, so he had them killed, before they attacked him. The *Anglo-Saxon Chronicle* lamented: 'the flower of the English nation' was gone. Cnut gave their lands to his Viking *jarls*, as a reward for fighting bravely.

In 1017, Cnut arranged the murder of Edmund Ironside's young brother **Edwy**. Horrified, royal servants smuggled Edmund's baby sons out of England to far-away Hungary for safety. Edmund's last two surviving brothers, **Edward** and **Alfred**, were already living as refugees in Normandy.

Powerful women

In the same year, 1017, Cnut married King Ethelred's widow, Queen Emma. He hoped that this marriage would persuade Emma's brother, Duke **Richard** of Normandy (known as 'the Devil'), to support him. But Cnut already had a companion, Lady **Aelfgifu**, who came from an English noble family. Cnut and Aelfgifu had two sons: **Harold** '**Harefoot**', and **Svein**. Queen Emma did not like Aelfgifu, and was jealous of her.

Cnut in the middle!

Like other important Saxon and Viking women, Lady Aelfgifu and Queen Emma both played an active part in politics. They arranged meetings, gave advice, hosted dinners, kept secrets, made plots, and charmed, flattered, bullied or bribed powerful men. They also schemed – and sometimes fought – to win the best future for their children, especially their sons.

Viking empire

In 1019, Cnut's brother, King **Harald** of Denmark, died unexpectedly. Cnut left England and went to Denmark to take over the kingdom. He announced that England and Denmark were now united in a new Viking empire. Later, in 1028, Cnut also conquered Norway.

Cnut tried to rule England in a way that would leave him free to look after the rest of his empire. He said that he would govern like a lawful English king, and protect the English from Viking and Scottish raids, as long as they obeyed him. He took advice from members of the English Witan, especially Archbishop Wulfstan. He became a Christian, gave treasure to the Church, and went on a pilgrimage to the holy city of Rome.

Keeping control

To keep control of England, Cnut divided it into four regions, based on the older kingdoms (Wessex, Mercia, Northumbria and East Anglia). He appointed trusted warriors in three regions as his **earls** (deputies), but kept Wessex for himself. By around 1020, Cnut was too busy to govern Wessex, so he made an English noble, **Godwin**, the earl. Godwin married a Viking princess and so joined Cnut's royal family and became extremely powerful.

Cnut's rule finally stopped Viking raids on England. Towns and farms were allowed to recover from Viking attacks, and trade could flourish again. But the heavy taxes that Cnut collected were much less welcome. He needed the money to pay for his wars.

Cnut's chosen heir

King Cnut died in 1035, aged forty, worn out by fighting. He left instructions for England and Denmark to stay united. He also gave orders that **Harthacnut**, his son with Queen Emma, should be their king. Norway no longer belonged to Cnut's empire. This was because, in 1030, he had sent Lady Aelfgifu, his companion, to govern it with their son Svein. But the Norwegians had rebelled and chased Aelfgifu and Svein back to Denmark.

Part of an Anglo-Saxon manuscript, showing everyday life during Cnut's reign

Cnut's chosen heir, Harthacnut, had no time to think about England. He was desperately busy, defending Denmark from attacks by King **Magnus** of Norway. Nonetheless, English people needed a king to lead their army, head their government and keep control of rival nobles.

Ethelred's family tree

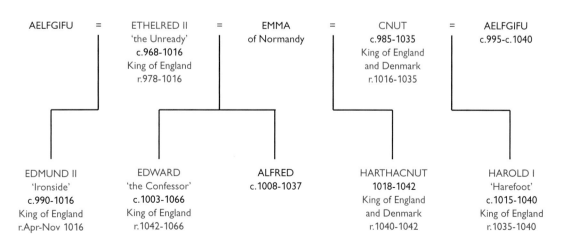

One group of nobles in England, led by Queen Emma and Earl Godwin, decided to wait for Harthacnut to finish fighting in Norway. Emma was Harthacnut's mother, so she wanted power for her son. Earl Godwin did not want to provoke fresh Viking raids by ignoring Harthacnut's claim to be king.

A temporary king?

However, Emma's rivals, Earl **Leofric** of Mercia and Earl **Siward** of Northumbria, wanted another man to rule – at least until Harthacnut was free to come to England. That man was Harold Harefoot, Cnut's son with Aelfgifu. Leofric and Siward were both related to Aelfgifu, so Harold Harefoot was part of their family. They also wanted to stop Queen Emma (and her royal relatives from Normandy and Denmark) becoming too powerful.

Betrayed!

Harthacnut stayed in Denmark, still fighting. For over a year, England had no king at all. But Emma's two surviving sons from her marriage to King Ethelred were still alive. In 1036, Prince **Alfred**, the younger, led an invading army to England. Emma probably encouraged him. At first, Alfred was welcomed by Emma's ally, Earl Godwin. But then Godwin changed sides. Harold Harefoot arranged for Alfred to be attacked and blinded, and Godwin did nothing to protect him. A few days later, Alfred died from his injuries. Shocked and angry, Emma fled from England.

King Harold Harefoot

Why did Godwin betray his friendship with Queen Emma and let her son be killed? He did it to stop the Vikings invading and to protect his own power. Godwin feared that Harthacnut would punish the English (including him) if anyone else became king. But the confusion following Alfred's murder gave Harold Harefoot and his supporters their chance. In 1037, Harold Harefoot seized power, claiming that he had been the rightful king since 1035. Harold seems to have been a weak character; his mother Aelfgifu ruled for him. Like Queen Emma, she wanted power for her family.

King Harthacnut

Harold Harefoot, and his mother, did not reign for long. He died in 1040, aged about twenty-six. Soon afterwards, Harthacnut arrived from Denmark with a Viking army to claim his place as English king. Before Harthacnut left Denmark, he made an agreement with his rival, Magnus of Norway. If either of them died without a son, the other would inherit his kingdom.

When Harthacnut became king of England, there was still one son of Queen Emma and King Ethelred left alive, in Normandy. His name was **Edward** (see page 117). In 1041, Harthacnut invited Edward to England and welcomed him as a half-brother. Harthacnut still had no son, and he feared that Edward might want to rule next, after him. Harthacnut needed to know what Edward was like, and whether he would challenge King Magnus.

Edward 'the Confessor'

To a Viking like Harthacnut, Edward must have seemed a most unusual character. In 1041, Edward was thirty-seven: few warriors lived that long. He was peaceful and gentle, and had no skills as a fighter. He was deeply religious and spent his time praying and studying, like a monk. He was not married, and had no children. Later, chroniclers gave him a nickname, '**the Confessor**', which meant 'devoted to religion'. Today, Edward is still remembered for giving money to build one of the most important churches in Britain: **Westminster Abbey**, in London.

Who should be king?

In 1042, Harthacnut collapsed and died at a wedding feast, after drinking too much wine. Now the English faced another difficult choice. Who should be king? The choice was between the monk-like Edward the Confessor, or Harthacnut's rival warrior, Magnus of Norway. Magnus was already trying to conquer all of Cnut's old empire. And, because of his bargain with Harthacnut (see above), he believed he had the right to rule England. Queen Emma agreed with him, even though Edward the Confessor was her son. Understandably, Edward was horrified.

In spite of Magnus's claim, the Witan chose Edward the Confessor, and in 1042 Edward became king. The reason for their choice was that Edward's father, Ethelred, had been English. They did not want a king from Norway. In 1044, Edward forgave his mother, Queen Emma, for supporting King Magnus. The following year, he agreed to marry **Edith**, Earl Godwin's daughter. This marriage linked the Godwins with the English royal family, and made sure that they stayed powerful.

The Last Saxon kings

1016: On the death of Ethelred, his son Edmund 'Ironside' and Cnut of Denmark fought for the throne. They agreed to divide it between them.

1016: Edmund died and Cnut seized the whole kingdom, marrying Ethelred's widow, Emma. This did not please Cnut's mistress, Aelfgifu.

1019: Cnut became King of Denmark and left England in the hands of Earl Godwin. Cnut died in 1035 and left the throne to his son by Emma, Harthacnut. This angered Aelfgifu, who wanted her son Harold 'Harefoot' to be king.

1037: Harold 'Harefoot' was crowned king, but died in 1040, leaving Harthacnut to claim the throne. Harthacnut promised to leave his kingdom to Magnus, the King of Norway, if he died before him.

1042: However, when Harthacnut died, the throne passed to the younger son of Ethelred and Emma, Edward 'the Confessor'. Edward promised to leave the throne to William of Normandy. This angered Earl Godwin and his sons, Harold Godwinson and Tostig, who did not want a foreign king.

1066: When Edward died, the throne should have gone either to Magnus of Norway's son Harald Hardrada; or to William of Normandy. But in fact it went to Harold Godwinson. The rest, as they say, is history…

Peace at last

Members of the Witan and Church leaders helped Edward to rule. He encouraged trade and law and order, and was a keen supporter of the Church. Scholarship and art flourished under his protection. Since he could not fight, Edward had to rely on the great earls to guard his kingdom. Earl Siward defended the north of England from the Scots, and Earl Godwin protected the Welsh border.

This part of the famous length of embroidered fabric known as the Bayeux Tapestry shows King Edward 'the Confessor' in his palace, consulting his nobles

Edward's only problems came when the English objected to the Norman churchmen and advisors that he brought with him. In 1051, a quarrel broke out between Edward and Earl Godwin over who should be Archbishop. Although Edward loved peace, he decided that Godwin's disobedience had gone too far. He outlawed Godwin and his sons, and they were forced to leave England. Because she was Godwin's daughter, Edward also sent his wife Edith away from his palace. She went to live in a nunnery.

Duke William's visit

Soon after this quarrel, as we learn from the chronicle of **William of Poitiers**, Duke **William** of Normandy arrived in England, and did **homage** to King Edward. This was a promise of loyalty and obedience. Edward knew William well, as they had spent years together in Normandy. Together, they made a deal. If Duke William supported Edward as king of England until he died, then Edward, who still had no children, would name William as his heir.

The Godwins come home

In 1052, Godwin came back to England with an army, ready to fight. Defying King Edward, he dismissed all the Normans in his earldom, and gave their jobs to his own, English, supporters. He also forced Edward to give the earldom of East Anglia to his son, **Harold Godwinson**.

The next year, Godwin died. Harold Godwinson took over the earldom of Wessex; Harold's younger brother, **Gyrth**, followed him as Earl of East Anglia. In 1055, another Godwin brother, **Tostig**, became Earl of Northumbria. A fourth brother, **Leofwine**, became a junior earl. Edith, Harold's sister, returned to the royal palace from her nunnery and was Edward the Confessor's queen once more. The Godwins were back in power!

A new, young prince arrives

By 1056, the Godwin family controlled most of England. Edward the Confessor was now fifty-two years old, and ill. The Godwins did not want his chosen heir, William of Normandy, to be king. They knew that there were still two of Edmund Ironside's sons left alive, far away in Hungary (see page 115). Could either of them be the next king of England? They helped one, nicknamed **Edward the Exile**, to travel back to England, but he died soon after arriving. However, his young son, **Edgar the Atheling** (meaning 'Young Prince'), survived. Edward the Confessor arranged for Edgar to be brought up in his royal palace. By blood, Edgar was King Edward's closest heir.

'Leader of the English'

In 1063 Harold Godwinson, still the most powerful man in England, led the English army to conquer North Wales. In 1065, he agreed peace with rebels in Northumbria and Mercia who were fighting his brother, Earl Tostig. Tostig was furious that his brother had gone behind his back to negotiate with the rebels. He left England for Norway, where he joined **Harald Hardrada** (meaning 'Ruthless'), the new Viking king. Harald Hardrada was related to King Magnus of Norway. He believed that Harthacnut's deal with Magnus (see page 119) now gave him the right to rule England. Together, Harald and Tostig plotted to seize power.

Harold Godwinson's promise

At around the same time, in 1064 or 1065, Harold Godwinson went to Normandy. He was probably sent there on royal business by Edward the Confessor. On the way, Harold was shipwrecked, rescued, then taken to meet Duke William. There – the Normans claimed – Harold swore loyalty to William as the next king of England. Harold probably had no choice. He was surrounded by William's soldiers!

Harold swearing loyalty to Duke William (from the Bayeux Tapestry)

King Harold II

In January 1066, King Edward the Confessor died, murmuring prayers as he did so. At his bedside was Harold Godwinson, now back from Normandy. Harold claimed that, with his dying breath, Edward also named him as the next English king.

Did Edward forget his promise to Duke William of Normandy? Or was Harold lying? We can never know for sure. But Harold had already shown that he was a brave warrior and good leader. He was popular with the English nobles. The English did not want to be ruled from Normandy or Norway. Edgar the Atheling was too young to rule, and no other English family was strong enough to defy the Godwins. For all these reasons, the Witan declared that Harold Godwinson should be king. He was crowned as Harold II, the day after Edward the Confessor died.

William wants war!

When Duke William of Normandy heard about the coronation he was very angry. He refused to believe Harold's claim about Edward the Confessor's dying wishes. If Harold wanted to be king, he would have to fight! From William's point of view, Harold had broken his promise. In 1066, this was a serious crime – but it also gave William a really good excuse to invade England. He got ready for war.

At the same time, the Viking King Harald Hardrada, helped by the Scots and Harold's angry brother Tostig, prepared to invade England from the north. Harold was trapped between two attacking armies. What should he do?

Loyal earls

King Harold lost no time. He sent soldiers to guard the south coast, the part of England closest to Normandy. Then he got married – for political, not romantic, reasons. His bride was **Edith**, sister of two powerful earls, **Edwin** of Mercia and **Morcar** of Northumbria. They defended all the north of England. Harold's marriage meant that they became his brothers-in-law, and ensured that they would help him to fight. He needed their help to fight off the Viking attack and they supported him bravely.

Defeated Vikings

On 20th September 1066, Earls Edwin and Morcar battled against Viking Harald Hardrada and rebel Earl Tostig at **Fulford Gate**, near York. They were defeated, but fought so fiercely that the Viking army was badly weakened. When King Harold arrived five days later, with his own men, he was able to defeat the Vikings at nearby **Stamford Bridge**. Harald Hardrada and Tostig were both killed.

Norman invaders

Meanwhile, Duke William's army was setting sail from Normandy. William knew that King Harold and most of the English army were far away, in the north of England. However, as soon as Harold's spies brought him news that the Normans had landed at **Pevensey** (in Sussex), he led an advance troop of about 7000 soldiers on an epic march south, covering 400 kilometres in just eleven days. He hoped to surprise Duke William, who would not be expecting to fight him so soon.

This part of the Bayeux Tapestry shows a man – probably Harold – being killed in battle

William the Conqueror

Harold's soldiers followed him loyally, but they were exhausted. To Harold's shock, they found Duke William's invading army ready and able to fight. The two sides met near **Hastings**, on 14th October 1066. It was a long, bitter battle. Harold fought bravely, but was killed — some said, by an arrow through the eye. On Christmas Day 1066, William the Conquerer was crowned King **William I of England**.

How do we know?

There is a famous saying: 'History is written by the winners'. That is certainly true of most of the evidence telling us about the Norman Conquest of 1066. Much of this was produced, after the Norman victory, by supporters of William the Conqueror, and was designed to prove his right to be king of England. It includes the **Gesta Normannorum Ducum** ('History of the Dukes of Normandy') written around 1070 by **William of Jumièges** (a Norman monk), and the **Gesta Guillelmi ducis Normannorum** ('Deeds of Duke William of Normandy') by **William of Poitiers** (another churchman, from France) around 1077.

Norman evidence also includes a splendid embroidered panel, 68 metres long, known as the Bayeux Tapestry (see pages 121, 123 and 125), which tells the story of the conquest in comic-book style. It was made around 1077 for Bishop **Odo**, Duke William's brother, by expert men and women craftworkers, probably in England.

For the years before the Norman Conquest, most of the written evidence is either confusing or one-sided. Copies of the *Anglo-Saxon Chronicle* have survived, but in several different versions, which do not all agree. The **Vita Regis Eduardi** ('Life of King Edward') was written in 1066 for his widow, Queen Edith. It strongly supports the Godwin family — except for Harold Godwinson, because Harold and Edith had quarrelled over their brother Tostig. The most balanced written source is probably the **Encomium Emmae Reginae** ('Praise of Queen Emma'), written by a monk in Flanders (now Belgium) around 1040. It favours Emma because she paid for it, but also records many events in Cnut's reign.

Exercise 10.1

Read pages 114 to 126 about the kings of England before 1066, and answer these questions:

1. How many kings ruled England between 1016 and 1066? (Make a list of them, in order.)

2. When did King Cnut murder young Edwy, and why?

3. What were the names of Cnut's and Aelfgifu's children? And Cnut's oldest son with Queen Emma?

4. Who were the next two kings after Cnut died?

5. Who promised his kingdom to King Magnus of Norway?

6. Why did the Witan choose Edward the Confessor as king?

7. Which was the most powerful family in England by 1056?

8. Which of Earl Godwin's sons became king?

9. Which king fought the battles of Fulford Gate and Stamford Bridge?

10. When was the Battle of Hastings?

. . . .

Exercise 10.2

Read pages 114 to 123 about the last kings before the arrival of William the Conqueror, and complete these sentences:

1. King Edmund Ironside ruled only one part of England, called _____.

2. Queen Emma had two husbands. The first was King _____. The second was King _____.

3. King Cnut joined England and _____ in his empire. He fought to add _____, as well.

4. King Harthacnut was too busy _____ to come to England in 1035.

5. Lady _____ took control of England while her son _____ was king.

6. King Edward the Confessor liked to spend his time _____ and _____.

7. In 1051, Edward the Confessor named the Duke _____ of _____ as his heir. Later, he may also have named Edgar the _____ and _____ Godwinson.

8. In 1064 or 1065, Harold Godwinson went to _____ and promised _____ to Duke William.

Exercise 10.3

Read pages 114 to 125 and explain what is meant by the following:

1. Archbishop

2. sermon

3. Witan

4. earl

5. heir

6. outlawed

7. earldom

8. allies

Exercise 10.4

You will need to do some research, in a library or on the Internet, for this exercise.

As we saw on page 116 King Cnut divided England into four regions, governed by earls. He also demanded heavy taxes from the English people, which were collected by the earls. Cnut gave the earldom of Mercia to Leofric. We know little about Leofric, but a very famous story is told about his wife, Lady **Godiva**. It was first written down in around 1200.

Find out what Lady Godiva's story is, and tell it in your own words. Explain why Lady Godiva and the people of Coventry behaved as they did. Say whether you think the story has a 'message' about politics and community life for people today.

Exercise 10.5

Another famous story about King Cnut's reign concerns the king himself. It was written down about a hundred years after he died; we don't know whether it is true. It tells how, after Cnut became a Christian, he took all the powerful people at his court down to the seashore. Then he commanded the waves to stop. Of course, they did not, but kept rolling in. Cnut turned to the onlookers, and said, 'Look, I am a strong king, but I can't do everything. I am only human. There is a greater power in heaven.'

EITHER

Work together with your classmates or friends to act out Cnut's famous story.

OR

Imagine that you are King Cnut, and write a poem or a song about your feelings as you face the waves. You could begin it like this:

> *'I'm just a king,*
> *I can't do everything …'*

Or you could choose your own words entirely.

Appendix 1 – Timeline: 100 BC to 1100

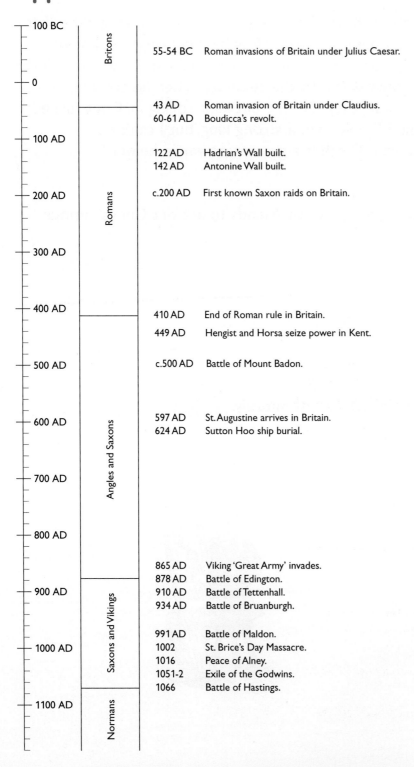

Britons

55-54 BC Roman invasions of Britain under Julius Caesar.

Romans

43 AD Roman invasion of Britain under Claudius.
60-61 AD Boudicca's revolt.

122 AD Hadrian's Wall built.
142 AD Antonine Wall built.

c.200 AD First known Saxon raids on Britain.

Angles and Saxons

410 AD End of Roman rule in Britain.

449 AD Hengist and Horsa seize power in Kent.

c.500 AD Battle of Mount Badon.

597 AD St. Augustine arrives in Britain.
624 AD Sutton Hoo ship burial.

Saxons and Vikings

865 AD Viking 'Great Army' invades.
878 AD Battle of Edington.
910 AD Battle of Tettenhall.
934 AD Battle of Bruanburgh.

991 AD Battle of Maldon.
1002 St. Brice's Day Massacre.
1016 Peace of Alney.
1051-2 Exile of the Godwins.
1066 Battle of Hastings.

Normans

Timeline scale: 100 BC, 0, 100 AD, 200 AD, 300 AD, 400 AD, 500 AD, 600 AD, 700 AD, 800 AD, 900 AD, 1000 AD, 1100 AD

Appendix 2 – Bretwaldas and Overlords of the English, 477 to 839 AD

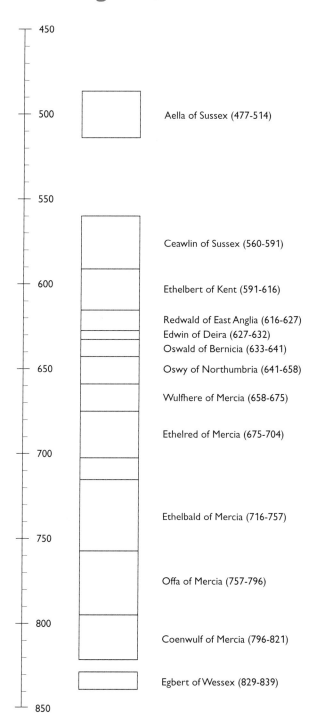

Aella of Sussex (477-514)

Ceawlin of Sussex (560-591)

Ethelbert of Kent (591-616)

Redwald of East Anglia (616-627)
Edwin of Deira (627-632)
Oswald of Bernicia (633-641)
Oswy of Northumbria (641-658)

Wulfhere of Mercia (658-675)

Ethelred of Mercia (675-704)

Ethelbald of Mercia (716-757)

Offa of Mercia (757-796)

Coenwulf of Mercia (796-821)

Egbert of Wessex (829-839)

Appendix 3 – Kings of England, 871 to 1087 AD

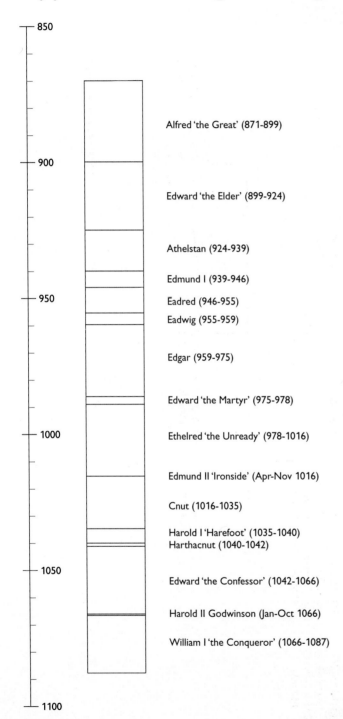

850

Alfred 'the Great' (871-899)

900

Edward 'the Elder' (899-924)

Athelstan (924-939)

Edmund I (939-946)

950

Eadred (946-955)

Eadwig (955-959)

Edgar (959-975)

Edward 'the Martyr' (975-978)

1000

Ethelred 'the Unready' (978-1016)

Edmund II 'Ironside' (Apr-Nov 1016)

Cnut (1016-1035)

Harold I 'Harefoot' (1035-1040)

Harthacnut (1040-1042)

1050

Edward 'the Confessor' (1042-1066)

Harold II Godwinson (Jan-Oct 1066)

William I 'the Conqueror' (1066-1087)

1100

Appendix 4 – Family tree of the Kings of England

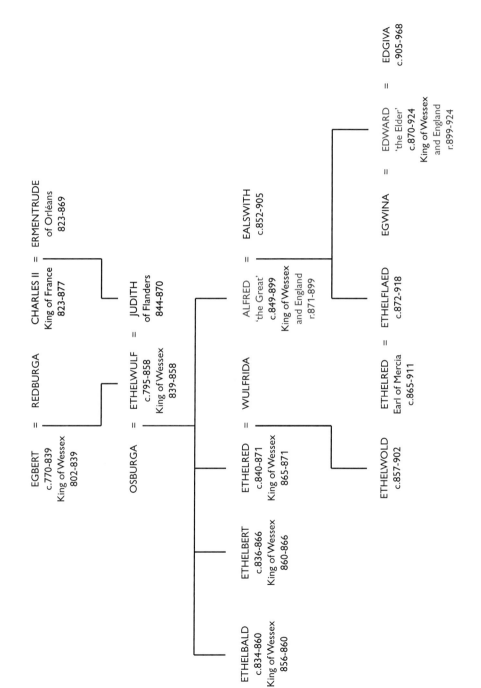

(continued on next page)

Appendix 4 – Family tree of the Kings of England (continued)

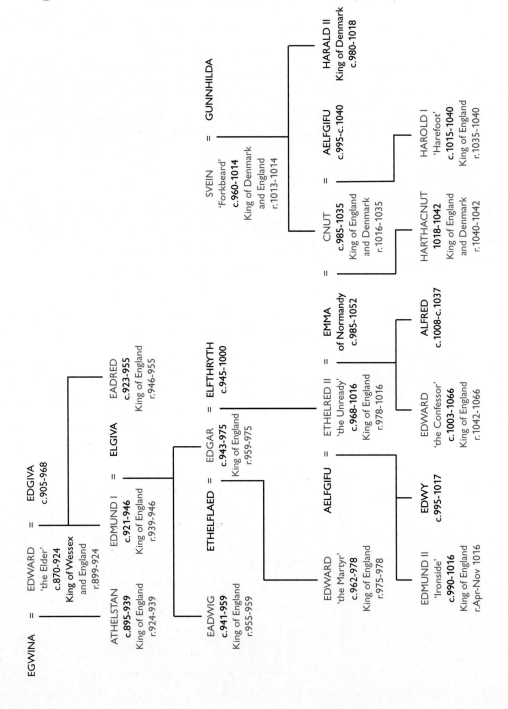

PORSCHE
THE ENGINEERING STORY

PORSCHE
THE ENGINEERING STORY

JEFF DANIELS

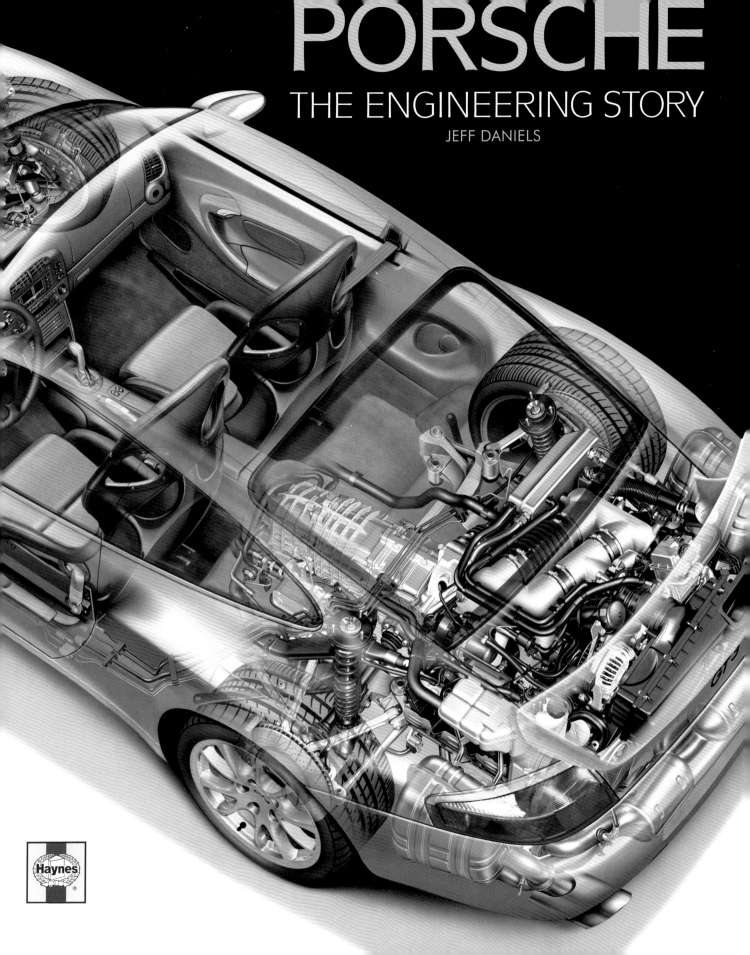

First published in August 2007

A catalogue record for this book is
available from the British Library

ISBN 978 1 84425 204 6

Library of Congress control no. 2005926171

Published by Haynes Publishing,
Sparkford, Yeovil, Somerset BA22 7JJ, UK
Tel: 01963 442030 Fax: 01963 440001
Int. tel: +44 1963 442030 Int. fax: +44 1963 440001
E-mail: sales@haynes.co.uk
Website: www.haynes.co.uk

Haynes North America Inc.
861 Lawrence Drive, Newbury Park,
California 91320, USA

Printed and bound in Great Britain by
J. H. Haynes & Co. Ltd, Sparkford

Contents

Introduction

Any motor industry journalist of my age must have his portfolio of Porsche stories. I still remember my first-ever 911 drive, when I was Assistant Editor of *CAR* magazine in 1967, when the car, like me, was still young and the engine was 2-litre – yet still powerful enough to give the feeling that the beast was always going faster than you thought it was. I remember hating the VW-Porsche 914, twitchy and cramped; being quietly invited, at the 1974 Geneva Motor Show, to have a quick test drive in something 'rather special' (the original Turbo). I recall falling wholly in love with a 911E 2.4 that I road-tested for *Autocar*, to such an extent that for several years I refused to acknowledge the merits of later, larger-engined, wider-tyred versions; of driving many thousands of miles in an early four-speed 924 without ever falling in love with it; of driving the Carrera 4 for the first time and realising that here was a car whose limits were, in any circumstance I could imagine, higher than mine (by this time, the 911 was 24 years old and I was 49). And these were just the salient points. How many different Porsches have I driven over the years? Really, I could no longer say with certainty.

There was also the archive. It was not just the books pulled straight off my library shelves, the 911 histories by my old friends Paul Frère and Michael Cotton, the huge and scholarly *Porsche – Excellence was Expected* of Karl Ludvigsen, and others. It was also the contents of well-stuffed folders: the proceedings of a symposium on fuel consumption technology held in the Weissach research centre in 1979, yellowed cuttings of that *Autocar* 911E 2.4 test but also of an article I wrote for *Motor* in 1980, surveying the then 17-year history of the 911. And of course the Porsche press kits, always well put together, always full of technical spec-ifications (thank goodness). Things I had squirreled away over time, as though knowing that one day I would come to write this book.

The point is, I am not alone in this. Of all the German car manufacturers, Porsche is the one which attracts the largest and most devoted enthusiast following. It was built on the engineering genius of one man, and its subsequent history has been full of contradictions. It has never built cars in large numbers – by the standards of fellow-Germans like Mercedes or BMW – yet, at least three times it has sought earnestly to produce a car which would reproduce its values in a much cheaper model, a 'people's Porsche'. By far its most famous product, the one which has sustained the company through its darkest financial times and won the near-fanatical support of rich enthusiasts, has long been a triumph of development over the basic drawback of its rear-engined layout.

Porsche's history, therefore, has a single thread of consistency provided by the 911, with all kinds of alternative activity woven around it. Not that the 911 story is in any sense straightforward. The 911 you see today has nothing in common with the 911 which was received with interest – but not much more than that – at the car's original announcement in 1964, except that the engine is in the same place and the general shape of the body remains visibly similar (which has become one of the most important points, no matter how many changes have been made beneath the skin).

The history of the 911 alone has been the subject of detailed study in many books through the last 25-odd years, the pick of them being Paul Frère's definitive study which has run into almost as many editions as the car itself. Yet Porsche is far more than the 911, vital though that model has proved. The purpose of

this book is to explore the technical thinking which went into the whole range of Porsche activities over the years, and which has seen the company today producing three very distinct models – the 'everlasting' rear-engined 911, the mid-engined Boxster, and the big front-engined Cayenne SUV. It is a story with some remarkable twists and turns, sometimes with a return to the same starting point. It is also a story which has been played out against a sometimes dark financial background, as the world economy has waxed and waned, and customers have retreated to more 'sensible' cars. As far as possible, however, this is a book about engineering, not financial analysis. It is, after all, the quality of its engineering which has seen Porsche through the dark days and into its present strong position.

As I said when writing the introduction to my companion book about Jaguar's engineering history, I was conscious of all the authors who had already written about Porsche. My excuse for writing yet another book is that I wanted to examine things as far as possible from an engineering point of view. For that reason, I have excluded any purely competition cars because they represent a different kind of engineering which often has little to do with the mainstream. Especially these days, it is far more a matter of how

Porsche photographed a prototype 911 with the complete development team. Ferry Porsche is nearest the camera; the original caption names all the others, and it is notable how many are survivors from Porsche's pre-war years, including Xavier Reimspeiss and Erwin Komenda. Loyalty to the company was clearly a quality inspired by its founder.

engineers interpret and work within the regulations governing any particular championship. Even then, there remained the potential imbalance between the 911 and the rest of the Porsche story – something I first tried to counter by splitting the 911 part into three chapters – the early cars, the post-3-litre cars, and the Turbos. Yet eventually, so constant a thread has the 911 been, the three chapters became seven. All the way through, my interest has been in engineering policy and the engineering decisions, rather than in the nitty-gritty detail which can be found elsewhere. Rather than simply record the changes which have been made to Porsche's cars – there are plenty of good books which do that – I have tried to analyse what lay behind the changes. Why was something done in a particular way, why were the alternatives ignored? Did it work? If it didn't, what did they do about it? To do that in 90,000 words was quite a challenge. I hope I have succeeded.

CHAPTER 1

The Porsches –
father and son

Ferdinand Porsche was born on 3 September 1875 in the town of Vratislavice, in what was then Austro-Hungaria and today, the Czech Republic. Because it was then Austria-Hungary, Vienna was the magnet for any young man of ability and ambition. The young Porsche clearly had both qualities in abundance. He learned basic engineering within the business of his father, who was a tinsmith, and worked to gain an understanding of electrical engineering, of which his father did not, it seems, approve. By the time he was 18, a local businessman had recommended him for a job with Bela Egger, a Vienna-based company which eventually evolved into Brown-Boveri. Having arrived in Vienna and established himself, Porsche apparently spent his evenings attending university lectures, although never appearing on the university rolls or gaining any formal degree. It seems that Porsche's was a native genius which needed no more than polishing.

The young Ferdinand worked for Bela Egger for five years, thus almost until the turn of the 19th century rising rapidly to become manager of the test section. If the company got value out of the Porsche, he probably returned the compliment, learning something new with every project he tackled. In 1898, he left Bela Egger to join the staff of the recently established vehicle manufacturer, Jakob Lohner, with premises in the Vienna suburb of Floridsdorf.

The final decade of the 19th century was of course one during which the motor car made the leap from an experimental toy to a practical means of transport. Its rapid pace of development, and its clear potential for the future, attracted many fertile engineering minds, among them that of Ferdinand Porsche. His capacity for original thinking was immediately applied to Jakob Lohner's products, first of all by designing a hub-mounted 2kW electric motor. By installing two such motors, Porsche was able to do away with conventional mechanical transmission – one of the more problematic aspects of the earliest cars. At the time, it should be remembered, electric traction was a more familiar technology than the new-fangled internal combustion engine, and Porsche's work at Bela Egger would have made him familiar with both the advantages and the limitations of electric motors. The electric driveline with its hub-mounted motors, the 'System Lohner-Porsche', was the first step in establishing the young engineer's reputation. It appeared, and was duly admired, at the Paris *Mondiale* of 1900, and established a number of Austrian national speed records.

The next remarkable stage of development was to create what was certainly the world's first hybrid petrol-electric car. Dissatisfied with the weight and bulk of the electric car battery pack, Porsche substituted an internal combustion engine – initially an Austro-Daimler flat-4 – driving a generator which supplied the power output for the hub motors. Thus, without sacrificing the advantages of the Lohner-Porsche system, Porsche freed the new vehicle from the constraint of limited range and the need for regular recharging. In 1905, his efforts were rewarded by the receipt of the Poetting Prize, awarded for significant achievement in the development of the Austrian motor industry. He had also gained something of a reputation as an early competition driver, plus a spell of compulsory military service which he had spent as chauffeur to the Archduke Ferdinand (he who was later to be assassinated at Sarajevo), driving one of his own cars!

The contacts which Porsche formed at Austro-Daimler, while adapting their engine as the primary power source for his 'mixte system' clearly bore additional fruit, because in 1906 he forsook Lohner in order to join the larger company as its technical director, remarkable recognition for a man who was yet to see his 31st birthday. Porsche immediately came to grips with all the aspects of conventional vehicle engineering and oversaw the design and development of many celebrated Austro-Daimler models of the Edwardian era, not least the *Modell* 27/80 competition car which took the first three places in the Prince Henry Trial of 1910. This was also the period during which Porsche became a family man, first fathering a daughter, Louisa, in 1904 and then a son, also christened Ferdinand, but invariably known as Ferry, who was born in Wiener Neustadt in 1909.

Doctor Ferdinand Porsche, motoring pioneer and engineering genius, in his creative prime in the 1930s, when he gathered the core team which contributed to the creation of the Porsche company.

Porsche was still in place at Austro-Daimler when the war clouds gathered, and during the conflict he applied his skills in particular to the challenge of moving heavy artillery and other items over virgin terrain, yet again using the 'mixte' principle but on a larger scale, often with the internal combustion prime mover in a separate vehicle linked by cable to a series of electrically propelled trailers. The company also moved into aero-engine development, and in 1916 Porsche became its managing director. It was then that he received official recognition for the time he had spent in the 1890s, sneaking into university

THE PORSCHES – FATHER AND SON

Above left: Porsche's first sensation – the Lohner electric car of 1900, complete with hub-mounted motors in the front wheels. These must have posed a question or two for the steering mechanism, but were arguably about a century ahead of their time.

Left: Nothing daunted, Porsche extended his hub-motor principle to all four wheels of this ungainly-looking device of 1904. He also added a petrol motor-

generator, to create what was not only the world's first 4WD car, but also the first petrol-electric hybrid – yet again, principles decades ahead of their time.

Above: Porsche was a first-class driver as well as an engineering genius. Here he sits at the wheel of the Austro-Daimler which carried him to outright victory in the 1910 Prince Henry Rally, a gruelling event of almost 2,000km.

lectures, the Vienna Technical University awarding him the honorary degree of Dr Ing. h.c.

Peace came in 1918 and the terms of the Armistice resulted in the former Austro-Hungarian empire being sundered into its constituent parts. Vienna became the capital of the new Austria and for a time, Austro-Daimler continued on its way. There were clouds on the horizon, however, because Porsche – at the height of his powers and with firm ideas about the direction in which he thought the company's products should

be developed – found himself increasingly at odds with his board of directors and shareholders. Porsche was of the opinion that performance should be gained through light weight and high efficiency, and sought to prove his point by developing a whole series of light-weight competition cars, which proved outstandingly successful. However, his board was determined that the future lay in the manufacture of large, heavy 'pres-tige' cars, and in the end Porsche resigned.

A man of his capabilities could not remain unem-ployed for long, however, and within months he had moved to Germany and become the technical director of Daimler itself, in Stuttgart. It was a successful period for Porsche in some respects, for he developed a long series of remarkable racing cars, including the straight-8 2-litre cars which dominated grands prix from 1925 to 1927, mainly in the hands of Rudolf Caracciola, and then fathered the hugely impressive series of 6-cylinder sports-racing cars up to and including the SS, SSK and SSKL. Meanwhile, in 1926, Daimler had merged with Benz, and the new Daimler-Benz board disagreed with Porsche's engi-neering and product planning philosophy, as had the Austro-Daimler board a few years previously. In 1929, Porsche once again resigned his position, and returned to Austria to work for Steyr, succeeding the almost equally celebrated Hans Ledwinka as chief designer.

Sadly, it took more than Porsche's genius to keep Steyr afloat during the years of the Great Depression. The company ran downhill until what remained of it was eventually merged with Austro-Daimler and Puch, to create Steyr-Daimler-Puch (SDP) which survived until 1990. But in 1930, Porsche was aged 55, had gained something of a reputation for being difficult to work with, and times were economically about as bad as they could be. In the circumstances, he took the most obvious option: he set up his own shop, offering product design and development facilities to the motor and allied industries.

In this venture, Porsche had several advantages. The first was his own reputation as a first-class engineer and in particular, an innovator. As the author has been moved to comment in the past: 'If Doctor Lanchester hadn't invented it by 1900, then Doctor Porsche almost certainly did before 1930' – a truism which nonetheless underlines Porsche's capacity for highly original thought in any area of mechanical engineering. Second, with the advantage of his past contacts, Porsche was able to assemble a team of top-quality specialists. Boards of directors might have found him stubbornly wedded to concepts at odds with their own, but Porsche it seems, also had the ability to make converts to his point of view, and such people invariably remained loyal. As a third factor, the economic problems of the early 1930s meant that

Above: An early (1922) glimpse of the next great Porsche, the Doctor's son Ferdinand "Ferry", the lad to the right of the car, with his father behind him. The car is an Austro-Daimler "Sascha", a light and nimble 1.1-litre racer which won 51 races out of 52 starts. Doctor Porsche was by now General Manager of Austro-Daimler, and (of course) the guiding hand in the design of the car.

Above right: Ferdinand Porsche (on the right) in 1924, with the supercharged 2-litre Mercedes that won the Targa

Florio in the face of formidable opposition. At the wheel of the car is the almost equally legendary Alfred Neubauer, before he realised his greatness in racing team management rather than driving!

Right: Ferdinand Porsche worked for various car manufacturers for years before founding his own company. Here, he pauses during a run over the Katschberg Pass in a Steyr Type 30 – one of his designs – in 1929. His wife Aloisia is seated in the rear of the car.

many small and medium-sized companies were quite willing to save money by contracting-out their design and development to a first-rate consultant, leaving them free to devote their slender resources to the business of series manufacture.

Thus, by the time the 'Dr Ing. h.c. F. Porsche GmbH Konstruktionsbüro für Motoren-, Fahrzeug-, Luftf-ahrzeug-, und Wasserfahrzeugbau', to give it its full

THE PORSCHES – FATHER AND SON

title, had been formally incorporated in Stuttgart in 1931, its staff included a number of men whom Porsche had known both at Daimler-Benz and at Steyr, and who were formidable engineers in their own right. They included Karl Rabe, who became chief engineer under Porsche himself, Erwin Komenda who took charge of body design, Karl Fröhlich, a transmissions specialist, Josef Kales with prime responsibility for engines, Josef Zahradnik, a chassis engineering specialist, and the aerodynamicists Franz Reimspeiss and Josef Mickl (this, be it noted, at a time long before the industry at large took aerodynamics in any way seriously).

To this team Porsche added Adolf Rosenberger as his business manager, and the lawyer Anton Piëch,

who was already his son-in-law, having married Ferry Porsche's elder sister Louisa in 1927. In due course this couple had a son, yet again christened Ferdinand, destined to play a major role in the fortunes of Porsche and of the German motor industry as a whole in later years. And, of course, there was Ferry

Left: A classic 1937 portrait of Doctor Porsche, already aged 62, at last with his own Stuttgart-based engineering consultancy and design office.

Below: The first design to emerge from Porsche's independent consultancy was the Type 7, a conventional 2-litre saloon for Wanderer, a company soon destined to become part of the Auto Union. Types 1 to 6 did not exist – Porsche began with Type 7 to create a better

impression on his early customers!

Right: Far more original was the light rear-engined car designed for Zündapp as the Type 12. Zündapp had previously been motor cycle specialists, and the Type 12 had a rear-mounted air-cooled 3-cylinder radial engine incorporating Zündapp technology, along with a backbone chassis and all-independent suspension. Only three prototypes were built.

Porsche himself, who was already emerging (although only 22 when the company was founded) as an engineering innovator in his father's mould.

The company's first officially designated project was the development of a new mid-range, straight-6 2-litre car for the Wanderer concern – one of the four companies (the others being Audi, DKW and Horch) which were about to merge to form Auto Union. Not wishing to inflict on any customer the possible worry associated with the idea of being his very first customer, Porsche designated this project the Type 7. The Type 8 was a larger, straight-8 3.25-litre Wanderer; Type 9 was a project for a supercharged version of this engine. A commission from Horch led to a study by Porsche for a swing-axle rear suspension, under the designation Type 10. This led Porsche to take out patents on a trailing-arm suspension geometry with torsion-bar springing.

Type 12 was a significant type number, covering the work done by Porsche on a car which would be compact, efficient and relatively cheap. The efficiency and the low cost would be achieved by combining a number of techniques which Porsche had been evolving, including lightweight construction, good aerodynamics and new approaches to engine design. Porsche 'sold' the concept to the Zündapp motorcycle company and by the end of 1932, had evolved a prototype with a rear-mounted 3-cylinder radial engine, a backbone frame, rear wheel location by very substantial single transverse wishbones, and close attention paid to aerodynamics – thus creating a vehicle in which it is possible to see the outline of the Volkswagen. The contract stipulated a four-seat, two-door car which would return a fuel consumption of 8 litres per 100km (35.3mpg) while averaging 60km/h (37mph).

The strange engine, designed at least in part to take up minimum space at the rear of the car, was not as it turned out one of Porsche's better ideas (although it may have been insisted on by Zündapp). According to some sources, the engine was a 5-cylinder radial but the available pictures appear to show a 3-cylinder unit with 120-degree spaced cylinders. It was water-cooled, with a radiator installed above the gearbox and just ahead of the rear axle line, with air drawn through it and the whole engine compartment by what appears

to be a small, rear-mounted version of an aircraft propeller. Whatever the details of the arrangement, the cooling was far from adequate and the engine's poor performance may have been responsible for Zündapp discontinuing its interest in favour of increasing its output of motor cycles. Porsche sought instead to interest NSU in his design. He encountered more solid interest here, for NSU had been a manufacturer both of motor cycles and four-wheeled vehicles until 1928, when it sold off its vehicle operation to Fiat. By 1933, it had become one of the larger motorcycle manufacturers and looked again to diversify into cars.

Porsche accordingly took the Type 12 as a base and used it to develop the Type 32, now with torsion-bar springing and (after a series of investigations including one involving a two-stroke power unit) an air-cooled flat-4 engine of 1,470cc, developing 28bhp. A series of prototypes was built, mainly in 1934, and one of them still survives in, significantly, the Volkswagen Museum. The Type 32 did not proceed, however. According to some sources, NSU was discouraged by its high tooling costs, but it has also been suggested that small print in the NSU/Fiat agreement of 1928

forbade the surviving NSU motorcycle operation from extending its activities to cars (although it did, eventually, in the 1950s).

While this process was being worked through, Porsche became deeply involved with the development of the mid-engined Auto Union Grand Prix cars, initially under the designation Type 22. Reams have been written about the epic struggle between Auto Union and Mercedes on the racing circuits of Europe in the 1930s, but from our point of view the important thing is that the cars served as rolling laboratories in which Ferdinand Porsche could advance and prove

Below: Having failed to convince Zündapp, Porsche took a broadly similar package to NSU as the Type 32, although this time the engine was an air-cooled flat-4. The lessons which would lead to the creation of the Beetle were being learned, although the NSU likewise never made it into production.

Right: Porsche's main claim to public fame during the 1930s came with his creation of the legendary Auto-Union Grand Prix cars. Here he inspects the 16-cylinder power unit of one of these formidable but highly successful racing machines.

THE PORSCHES – FATHER AND SON

his theories in almost every area of car design – in engines and transmissions, aerodynamics, lightweight construction and chassis engineering.

Porsche's enthusiasm not only for high performance, but for high performance achieved through efficiency and ingenuity, was leading him towards the idea of a new generation of sports car. He briefly studied the application of his latest theories to high performance road cars in a new Auto Union study, under the designation Type 52. By this time, though, he was deeply committed to the project, which he had personally 'sold' to Adolf Hitler, for the car which became the Volkswagen (Porsche Type 60). This story deserves a chapter to itself (see Chapter 2).

By this time, the clouds of war were gathering for the second time in Porsche's career. The outbreak of the First World War had seen him as technical director of Austro-Daimler and aged 39; the declaration of WW2 following Germany's invasion of Poland, saw a much wearier Ferdinand Porsche, now aged 64 and combining the responsibilities of his own company with those of overseeing the build-up of Volkswagen production at Wolfsburg. As a citizen of what was by then the Greater Germany – into which Austria had been subsumed in 1938 – his options were in effect as limited as those of his British counterparts. He ran a major engineering company, therefore he was required to work on projects as directed by the authorities.

Until 1945, the Porsche company worked on two main strands of development. The first was the adaptation of the Volkswagen design to a wide variety of military uses; the second was the evolution of heavy armoured vehicles. Porsche worked through a whole series of tank designs, not always successfully. Henschel beat it to the contract for the Tiger tank, for example, the Porsche Type 100 being rejected and existing prototypes being converted to mobile artillery carriers. Only two prototypes of the huge Type 205 tank, the incongruously named Maus, were completed prior to the German surrender. The company's final military projects, at least if the type numbers are taken as chronological, were the Type 293 personnel carrier and the Type 300 jet engine. Subsequent type numbers, issued during 1945 and 1946, relate mainly to agricultural tractor projects. Some time earlier, many of the company's personnel were relocated to the quiet backwater of Gmünd in Austria, away from the constant air raids from which Stuttgart was by then suffering. This, at least, was an advantage of being a technical consultancy rather than a large-scale manufacturing organisation.

There is nothing to suggest that Ferdinand Porsche ever actively supported the Nazi regime, although one may understand if he was relieved that his status meant he was treated with a certain respect by the authorities. Once the war had ended, matters took several turns for the worse. The Porsche family had for the most part returned to the ancestral estate at Zell-am-Zee, in the American Zone of Occupation of Austria. The surviving engineering team in Gmünd was in the British Zone. Communications were difficult – not that there was very much to communicate, since there was no demand for 'native' German engineering services and Gmünd became little more than a repair workshop operating on a hand-to-mouth basis.

Worse was to come. In November 1945, Ferdinand Porsche and Anton Piëch were invited by the French to 'discussions' at Baden-Baden, in the French Zone of Occupation of Germany. They arrived as guests – at least, nominally – and left as prisoners, transferred to an unsavoury jail in Dijon, deep in France. The whole affair seems to have had its roots in politics. Somebody in France had ventured that the transfer of the Porsche design bureau to that country, accompanied by as much Volkswagen-related equipment as could be moved, might make a valuable contribution to post-war reparations. The idea was stamped upon by the surviving French motor industry, led by the Peugeot family, and its allies in the French government, before it could ever really take shape. The arrests followed, with talk of war crimes, although no charges were ever brought. Somebody in France seems then to have decided that even if the original idea had come to nothing, Porsche and his right-hand man were worth something, and bail was set at half a million Francs for each man. Even so, perhaps Ferdinand Porsche should have felt himself lucky that his name was not Louis Renault.

In 1942 the pressures of war, plus Porsche's versatility of thought, created the Volkswagen-based Type 166, the Schwimmwagen, complete with 4WD and amphibious capability, with a rear-mounted hinge-down propeller unit for progress across water, steered by the front wheels.

The business which generated the necessary million Francs to free Porsche and Piëch came from Italy, via a tortuous series of connections which included Carlo Abarth and Rudolf Hruska (who would one day find fame of his own as technical director of the team that designed the Alfasud). The upshot was a contract with Piero Dusio, who at the war's end had founded the Cisitalia concern, initially to build light sports cars with Fiat mechanical components mounted in light, largely hand-crafted tubular steel chassis and bodies. The two vehicle projects covered by the contract were for a Grand Prix car (Porsche Type 360) and an advanced sports car (Type 370). In the event, the sports car was never made but the GP car eventually emerged, with a supercharged (but not intercooled) mid-mounted flat-12 1.5-litre engine teamed with a transaxle whose gearbox – also ahead of the rear axle line – was equipped with Porsche's own synchromesh system. One reason for the gearbox installation, which led to the wheelbase being longer than might otherwise have been the case, was that provision was made for 4-wheel drive, with a propeller shaft running from the front end of the gearbox, beneath the engine's dry sump and thus forward to a further geared drive unit at the front which, among other things, had to raise the drive from the low-set propeller shaft to the wheel centre-line.

Although the Porsche team drew from their pre-war Auto Union GP experience, the new GP car would have been a challenge by any standards and although the Type 360 ran, it never enjoyed any success in the face of the Alfa Romeo, Maserati and Ferrari dominance of the earliest years of post-war GP racing. One is tempted to draw parallels with the saga of the original BRM, designed to compete in the same formula, which likewise sought to achieve the highest level of performance through equally high levels of daring innovation and complication. Lacking the budget for an extensive development testing programme of the kind to which the Auto Unions had been subjected, the Cisitalia never stood any real chance. Even as it was, the cost of the programme is often held to lie at the heart of the financial problems which brought the Cisitalia operation to its knees only a few years later.

However, the agreed fees for carrying through the programme were duly paid, and the income was devoted to paying the fee demanded by the French for the release of Professor Porsche and Anton Piëch. By the time the Professor was able to make his way

One of the projects principally responsible for keeping the immediate post-war Porsche consultancy financially afloat was Piero Dusio's commission to design the Cisitalia Formula 1 car, with mid-mounted flat-12 supercharged engine in unit with one of the first gearboxes to be equipped with Porsche synchromesh. Provision was made for 4WD.

back to Zell-am-Zee and thence to Gmünd, he found that the team led by his son Ferry had learned other lessons from their dealings with Dusio and Cisitalia. Duly impressed by what Dusio and his Italian engineers had achieved with simple but sound engineering and cheap, off-the-shelf mechanical units from Fiat, creating the D42 racing car and the 202 sports coupé, they had turned their attention to doing the same thing with a German accent, so to speak. For Fiat, inevitably, one would read Volkswagen, since the Porsche team was already intimately familiar with the product.

Like the Cisitalia 202, any Porsche product would need to earn money in low-volume production. That meant it more or less had to be a sports car which could justify a high price, leaving some margin over its manufacturing cost, through exceptional performance and attractive looks. Work had accordingly begun on the Type 356, whose long and complex engineering development story forms the subject of Chapter 3.

CHAPTER 2

The Beetle – laying the foundation

As related in Chapter 1, Ferdinand Porsche spent half a lifetime evolving his concept of cars which achieved good performance through efficient and thoughtful design. In essence, the Porsche principle was to improve both by using the latest available technology – or inventing an even better one – and by deleting what was not necessary, rather than adding feature upon feature until performance had been achieved regardless of cost and weight. It seems to have been his confidence that he could make this principle work to produce a very cheap, fairly basic but perfectly satisfactory car that led him to propose, in conversations with Adolf Hitler (whose roots, like Porsche's, were essentially Austrian) the idea of a 'people's car'. This would carry four occupants without complaint at a constant 100km/hour, making it eminently suitable for travel on Germany's planned network of autobahns, while consuming no more than 8 litres of fuel per 100km (35.3mpg). These conversations ultimately led to the programme to develop the Porsche Type 60, which became the Volkswagen.

Undoubtedly Porsche also foresaw that a contract to design and develop such a car would assure the long-term future of his engineering bureau, which experienced some hard times in the early 1930s despite the high quality of its core team. And the Professor already had a good many ideas in mind when it came to the car's configuration. Many of these ideas were not, in the strictest sense of the word, original. In particular, the extent to which Porsche drew on the chassis engineering ideas of his contemporary Hans Ledwinka has long been debated. The likely truth is that they evolved their philosophies in parallel, although certainly the two men knew each other – and each other's work – well, having a strong link through their shared connection with the Steyr concern. However, by the 1930s Porsche was an engineer both of high standing and immense experience, having (as we have seen) already served as technical director of Austro-Daimler and of Mercedes-Benz – and having walked away from both companies when their boards of management tried to constrain his engineering efforts within the bounds of the conventional.

In fact, by the time the Type 60 programme was well underway, Porsche had to balance it with another major commitment, that of being (as we have seen) technical director for the increasingly successful Auto Union GP racing team, and the creation of its series of formidably powerful cars, until his contract came to an end at the conclusion of the 1937 season and of the

750-kilogram formula. By this time Porsche was in the process of fighting his way through a political as much as a technical challenge. The Type 60 was moving through its development process with the emergence of larger batches of prototype and pre-production cars, and was being made ready for production in an all-new factory – against the entrenched opposition of the existing German motor industry, and especially those making cars for the lower end of the market. Undoubtedly there were also those, just as there were among the Allied industrialists invited to run their rule over the Volkswagen when the Second World War was over, who sincerely thought it an outlandish and unpromising design, and a waste of money.

Shaping the Volkswagen-to-be

Porsche's vision for a 'people's car' embraced three main areas – the general configuration and chassis layout, the powertrain and the body. To achieve his ambitions, he needed to break away from convention in all three. The need for lightness had convinced him of the advantages of a rear-mounted engine, so long as it was not too heavy, and as already related he moved in this direction in his creation both of the Type 12 for Zündapp and the Type 32 for NSU. The rear-engine layout had several advantages. It did away with the then-conventional transmission, saving weight and freeing extra space within the cabin. It placed its weight over the driven wheels for good traction. It made the design of the car's front end, especially the suspension and steering, easier and cheaper.

It cannot be said that the alternative of front-wheel drive never entered the equation, because these were the years when Citroën's *Traction Avant* was causing its own sensation. The *Traction* may have emerged slightly too late to influence Porsche's train of thought, but the Professor would surely have rejected the idea in any case, as too expensive. We have to remember he was working under the severest cost constraints, having undertaken that the Type 60 would at least break even for a price of under 1,000

The backbone-and-platform chassis design meant the Beetle could easily be built as a convertible. Here in 1935 Ferry Porsche, with his wife alongside and family friends behind, drives the first known convertible prototype, the car which was designated V2, in the town square of Tubingen.

Reichsmarks, little more than half the price of the cheapest car (an Opel) existing in the German market. A rear-mounted engine it would be, therefore, the only hurdle being that it involved the expense of an independent rear suspension. This was no real challenge. The first swing axle design, by Rumpler, had been patented by Adler as early as 1904, and had been used with success in post-World War I cars, most notably perhaps by the Tatra T11 and its successors from 1921 onwards. The Tatras had been designed by a team led by Hans Ledwinka – and this is where the accusations start to fly, especially since by 1933, Tatra was testing a prototype (the V570) with a rear-mounted, air-cooled flat-twin engine and aerodynamically optimised bodywork.

Opting for the swing-axle

Looked at rationally, it is difficult to see what solution Porsche could have adopted for his low-cost project other than the swing axle, so long as he wanted a rear-mounted engine (the 1920s Tatras had been front-

Doctor Porsche stands beside one of the W30 cars, from the pilot-batch mostly built under contract by Daimler-Benz. The W30 body had been completely redesigned compared with the early prototypes, and the engine too had continued to evolve, although the definitive product was still one stage away.

engined; Ledwinka had adopted independent rear suspension entirely for the sake of the improved ride comfort and roadholding which resulted from the much lower unsprung weight). By the mid-1930s, alternatives such as the de Dion layout (patented in the 1890s!) existed, but they were too expensive, and also too heavy, to be seriously contemplated.

Above all, the swing axle is cheap. All it requires is that the drive shaft to each wheel should be universal-jointed as close as practicable to the output from the final drive. So long as the up-and-down angle of movement of the drive shaft is small, less than 10 degrees or so, a plain Hooke-type joint is sufficient (although most modern designers would automatically opt for a constant-velocity joint). The drive shaft itself acts as one of the locating links for the rear wheel; all that is then required is a trailing arm of reasonable length, to constrain the wheel fore-and-aft without pulling it too far forward towards the extremes of suspension travel. The drive shaft can be of fixed length; there is no need to incorporate a splined connection to allow the length to vary, as is required in alternative layouts. Porsche, by now wedded to the idea of torsion-bar springing, saw advantages in joining the front ends of the two trailing arms via a transverse torsion bar clamped at its centre.

Simple and cheap it may be, but the plain swing axle also comes with a problem. The wheel is always at right angles to the drive shaft, and if the drive shaft droops at a significant angle as the car passes over a hump while cornering, for example, the positive camber angle of the wheel reduces grip and the car will oversteer. This is even more so if power is still being applied to the wheels, since the need to transmit power also reduces the tyre's cornering grip. The answer, eventually applied to the Beetle towards the end of its production life, is to add a second suspension link (thus forming a semi-trailing arm) to locate the wheel sideways as well as fore-and-aft, and to make the drive shaft double-jointed so that it no longer dictates the camber angle. But this is, relatively speaking, a heavier and more expensive solution, and there was no question of its adoption at the time of the Beetle's inception. Indeed, the first use of semi-trailing arms for the rear suspension of a production car seems to have been in the Lancia Aurelia of 1950.

Despite this arguable drawback, the rear suspension choice for the Type 60 fell on simple swing axles, and if Professor Porsche foresaw (as he probably did) the handling problems which would result from their use, or indeed the stability problems which would arise from the tail-heavy weight distribution of the car, they were a penalty which had to be paid for keeping the target cost below 1,000RM.

Porsche also used transverse torsion bars at the front of his car – in this case two of them, each carrying a trailing arm so that the front wheel hubs were carried on pairs of arms, the whole assembly secured to the front end of the chassis platform. Another advantage of mounting the engine at the rear was that the load on the front wheels was reduced, so that the steering could be made 'quick' and yet light, and the installation of the steering column and linkage was easy because there was no engine to find a way past. One may argue that Porsche's chosen layout was illogical compared with, say, a modern strut-type front suspension, but the body design he had in mind was not compatible with the feeding of suspension loads at widely separated points. Also, by confining the

mountings to a small area in the extreme nose of the platform, he limited the opportunity for road noise to enter the cabin. This was actually quite important in a car intended for what was then a high cruising speed. Too much road noise would have made it a misery.

The engine

Porsche studied a whole range of options in his search for a Type 60 power unit which would provide the necessary output with low weight and minimum cost. Since the engine was to be installed aft of the final drive, it had to be both short and light; a conventional in-line unit was out of the question (and the idea of transverse installation had yet to taken seriously by anyone, even the imaginative Porsche). His experience, not least with the Type 12 and the Type 32 but also from his one-time aero-engine background, convinced him that the best engine configuration

A bizarre engine concept carried a long way into the development programme was an arrangement in which two pairs of pistons ran in parallel, thus maintaining piston area while reducing the reciprocating mass and therefore vibration. The engine was indeed compact and powerful; sadly, it was all too ready to overheat and break crankshafts, and was abandoned.

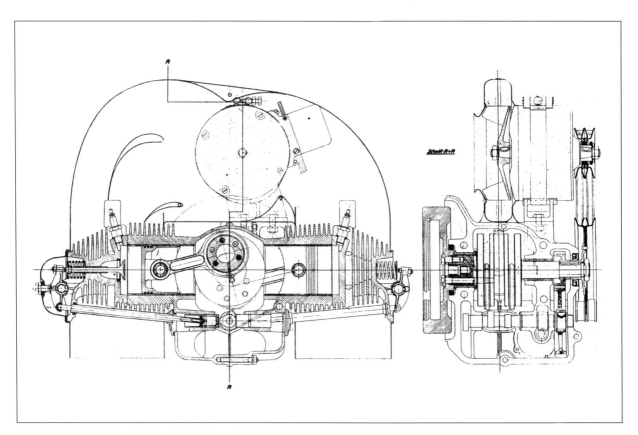

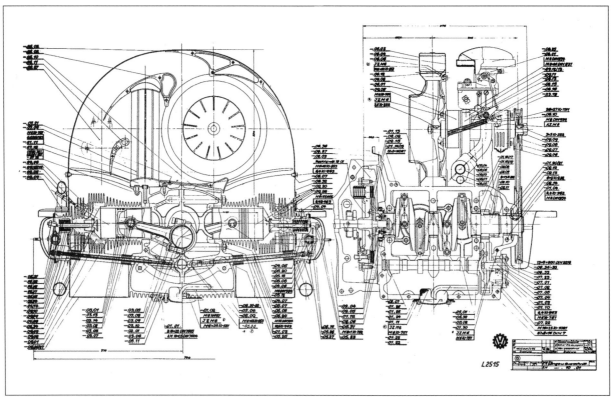

would be horizontally-opposed, either a flat-twin or a flat-4. He was likewise convinced of the virtues of air cooling (which a horizontally opposed engine would make much easier) for the sake of lightness and simplicity. The search for the optimum engine was wide-ranging. A two-stroke was contemplated and rejected; so was a sleeve-valve engine. For a long time, a flat-twin was favoured, until Franz Reimspeiss, a relatively recent Porsche recruit, suggested what we now think of as the classic Beetle engine – a flat-4 with a magnesium crankcase, with cylinders sandwiched between the crankcase and the overhead-valve cylinder heads, and a single camshaft mounted parallel to and below the crankshaft, with just four cam lobes operating the eight valve gear pushrods. Reimspeiss costed his design and proved, remarkably, that it was cheaper than any of the flat-twins.

In retrospect it is perhaps remarkable that the Porsche team did not make the engine even simpler and more compact by adopting a side-valve configuration, at that time probably still the most common layout worldwide. If the minimum Beetle specification had been all Porsche had in mind, he might possibly have gone this way – although Ledwinka at Tatra was in the process of moving to a flat-4 engine (for the Tatra 97) with a single overhead camshaft per cylinder bank. Porsche would have known this. He would also have wanted to look forward rather than back in so basic a matter as valve configuration – and above all, although he quickly determined that the way to achieve high reliability in the Type 60 was to throttle its engine with deliberately small inlet valves so that 100km/hour was also in effect its maximum speed, allowing it to be 'driven flat-out all day long', he seems to have had in mind even then, the far greater potential of an OHV engine to deliver more power for other purposes.

Because of its flat-4 configuration, the engine was of course short from front to rear, barely protruding beyond the extreme aft point of the wheels. Reimspeiss's choice of construction meant it was also light. It was mostly cast light alloy, magnesium or aluminium, except for the cast-iron cylinder liners. Separating the cylinders from the main crankcase (and splitting the crankcase vertically so that it could be assembled around the crankshaft and camshaft) meant that none of the castings was especially large, and therefore called for no great investment by the foundries. Actually assembling the engine was a labour-intensive business, but that was no great consideration at the time, although it became a drawback in the Beetle's much later years.

Above left: Contemplating an ultra-short flat-twin engine rather than a flat-4, Porsche avoided the worst of the twin's yawing out-of-balance by using twin connecting rods on one side, allowing the two pistons to be in-line rather than offset. This was the D-motor, which from the front could almost be mistaken for the definitive flat-4

Left: Eventually Porsche settled for the flat-4 engine configuration, this drawing showing the original 985cc

version. The vertically split crankcase sandwiched the crankshaft and the camshaft beneath. Note that the combustion chambers have become wedge-shaped; the spark plugs can just be discerned.

Above: The early V3 cars had a relatively small slotted aperture serving both rear vision and the needs of cooling airflow. The rear body shape at this point in the programme was not very Beetle-like ...

The definitive Type 60 engine had a single small carburettor and bifurcated inlet manifold feeding the four inlet valves through two 'siamesed' ports, one in the upper face of each cylinder head, while the exhaust pipes emerged below and fed into transverse silencer. Adequate cooling was achieved with an engine-driven fan, blowing into carefully arranged ducting.

The Type 60 transaxle broke no new ground. The transaxle layout itself (engine and gearbox on opposite sides of the final drive, with a link between the two running above the differential) was already well established. The gearbox was a straightforward two-shaft, four-speed, all-indirect unit; three speeds would have been cheaper but, given the need for a high top gear for that unstressed 100km/hour cruising, and a first gear low enough for mountain pass-climbing (you can see Alpine peaks from Stuttgart on a clear day), four was felt to be the acceptable minimum. Certainly cost was saved by excluding synchromesh, a technology in which Porsche was deeply interested, as post-war developments would show; but the Type 60 was not designed down to the minimum possible price. Rather it was the best the Porsche team could achieve within the 990RM target price.

The body

Unitary body construction was familiar enough by the early 1930s (and was adopted by Citroën for the *Traction Avant*) and clearly pointed the way forward for car body structures. Nobody who was confronting the challenge of creating a light, roomy,

modern family car with good performance and economy could afford to accept the weight penalty conferred by the then-conventional twin-rail chassis. Porsche, however, took the unitary concept in a particular direction. Having tried the possible alternative of a 'backbone' chassis in the Types 12 and 32, he elected for the Type 60 to use a self-supporting platform, welded from pressed steel panels, to which the body would then be mounted. In effect, both would be quasi-unitary, self-supporting structures. Although not quite as efficient and therefore light as a one-piece structure, the Porsche concept was well suited to its proposed production system and was probably cheaper than a fully unitary one-piece body. It was also one which, fortuitously or otherwise, meant that the Type 60 platform could be adapted to accept a variety of alternative bodies, from the military *Kubelwagen* of 1940–45 to the varied and once ubiquitous Dune Buggies of the 1960s and 1970s. There appears in the Porsche Type number listing, it should be noted, a Type 160 study, dated 1941, for a completely unitary Beetle body, combining the floorpan and upper shell into a single welded unit. It is far from clear why such a study was undertaken at that time, but the idea might have been to determine the implications – including the

weight savings – of moving to completely integral construction.

Because the streamlined two-door body designed by Erwin Komenda was also virtually self-supporting when it had been assembled, once the platform and body had been combined, the result was a stiff vehicle by the standards of its time. Yet it remained easy to separate the body from the platform, and this was often done for repair purposes. Post-war production Beetles were famous among other things for their sealing, which indicated how careful and close was the body-to-platform fit. It was always easier to close the

Beetle's doors if a window was slightly open, allowing air pressure to escape, and with modest attention to seals and grommets where controls passed through the body shell, a Beetle would float almost indefinitely in smooth water. But the practical benefits of sealing were low aerodynamic noise and good dust-proofing.

Erwin Komenda faced a delicate task with the body design, since there existed some sketches made by Hitler himself (he had, after all, begun adult life as an artist) and the spirit of these had of necessity to be retained while creating an attractive and structurally efficient body shell. Aerodynamic considerations played some part although there is no evidence that the Beetle shape was ever subjected to a major wind tunnel programme during its development. In terms of pure drag coefficient, the Beetle body looks good as far as its B-post but questionable from there aft, with little control over airflow separation lines. In so far as the car's legendary waywardness in sidewinds is concerned, it is clear that any offset airflow created a significant yawing moment around the aft-set centre of gravity – so this was not purely a matter of the 'sail effect' of having the larger proportion of side area forward of the CG. That was not, however, a major concern when viewed against the need to keep the cost down.

Left: Almost from its inception, Porsche's concept of the Volkswagen involved a self-supporting backbone chassis and basic platform, partly dependent on its all torsion-bar springing. In this view, the extreme rearward mounting of the engine is most apparent, as is the relative ease with which the transmission could be extended to 4WD.

Below: In the W30 cars the rear body contours had become more recognisably Beetle-like, but the rear opening had metamorphosed into a remarkably complex set of three slotted sections. The car shown (No 14 in the batch of 30) was the first example to be fitted with bumpers.

A matter of minimum cost

The very low projected cost of the Beetle has to be viewed against an extremely unusual background. It was to be a non-profit project, which is why the existing German motor industry put as many obstacles as possible in its way. If it had succeeded, and if war had not broken out, it would have been sales out of their pockets. To overcome such objections and ensure the project could proceed, it was therefore determined that the Type 60 would be built in a completely new factory financially backed by the German government, as being the only way in which the project could

Above: By the time the Volkswagen had been signed-off for production, the early body schemes featuring dual-purpose rear slots had given way to the original small, "split" rear window for rearward vision, and below it, a set of slots positioned above the engine compartment, to serve the needs of the engine cooling system.

Right: In the late 1930s, the German military authorities became interested in "command car" derivatives of the Volkswagen, attracted as much by its low price as by its all-round virtues of good traction and easy maintenance. Thus as early as 1938, this Type 62 was undergoing trials which would lead to a string of derivatives including the celebrated Kubelwagen.

be brought to fruition. A site was chosen at Fallersleben, between Hanover and Darmstadt, with canal access for the delivery of raw materials. In later years the factory, and the town which grew up around it, became known as Wolfsburg after the castle which overlooked it.

Apart from the zero-profit concept, it was also assumed from the outset that the Beetle would very quickly achieve high economy of scale by being built in very large numbers. It was likewise assumed that suppliers, mindful as they would have been of the identity of the project's ultimate backer, would be willing to contribute to its success by making their components available more or less at cost. Clearly, any product programme based on such an approach would be able to achieve a remarkably low final cost by any normal benchmark.

There was a precedent for this philosophy, and that was found in the success of a programme which yielded a 'people's radio', the VE 301, which sold for a modest 65RM (and enabled the bulk of the German population to listen to Hitler's propaganda speeches). The VE 301 was primitive in many respects and depended for its performance on careful manual trimming and tuning, but it worked and it was cheap – in

fact, around half the price of the next-cheapest set on the market. Millions of Bakelite-cased sets were manufactured during the 1930s, enabling the objective of 'a radio for every German family!' to be fulfilled – and the idea was that the Beetle would apply many of the same commercial principles to ensure that many German families, if not all of them, would be able to own a car. There was, intriguingly, a later project to produce an affordable 'people's television' which would have sold for 625RM. Part of the interest lies in the fact that anyone should contemplate selling a crude TV for two-thirds the cost of a Volkswagen, but really that only indicates the steep learning-curve of electronics technology during the 1930s, a stage which might be equated to the process the motor industry had passed through 30 years previously.

While the Type 60 progressed through its development stages – a process which might be more closely likened to clearing a series of hurdles, since Hitler's approval had to be sought on each occasion – Porsche turned his mind to using the car as a basis for a wider range of models. A whole series of new Type numbers resulted. Type 62 was an open-sided off-road vehicle (making maximum use of the self-supporting nature

of the platform). Type 64 was a sports coupé using Type 60 components – shades of the Type 356 to come. Type 66 was a Beetle with right-hand drive (one wonders why, since exports were not on the agenda at that time). Type 67 was an 'invalid vehicle'. Type 68 was a panel van, although not in the spirit of the eventually ubiquitous Transporter which was a wholly post-war development. Then comes a gap before we encounter the more obviously military derivatives, the Type 82 – the celebrated *Kubelwagen* – and its Type 87 derivative with simple 4-wheel drive, to which the Beetle's mechanical layout readily lent itself through the taking of a second output from the gearbox nose and thence through a propeller shaft to a front differential (both front and rear differentials could be locked to help progress over the worst terrain).

Type 92 was a command car consisting of a near-standard Beetle body on the high-ground-clearance platform of the Type 87. Then comes Type 128, the original design for the amphibious *Schwimmwagen*, a project which progressed through Type 138 before emerging as the definitive and more compact Type 166 with 4-wheel drive and rear-mounted fold-down propeller driven by a geared shaft from the conveniently rear-mounted engine.

These projects were received with differing degrees of enthusiasm by the German Government which was now in effect picking up all the bills for development. The Type 64 in particular was frowned upon as altogether too frivolous. Understandably, as time went on, the Types 82/87 and the Type 166 were greeted very differently, and the newly built Wolfsburg plant built some 55,000 and 15,000 of them respectively before the end of hostilities, plus a relative handful of the Type 92 and of conventional Type 60s in a number of body styles, including a convertible, for 'official' use.

Sporting derivatives

Porsche was not to be defeated, however, by official opposition to his Type 64 project. His alternative approach was to propose a special version of the Type 60 to take part in the road race to end all road races – an event planned to be run on closed roads, just like the Mille Miglia, but all the way from Berlin to Rome. Because success in such a widely promoted event would be excellent publicity for the Type 60, approval was readily given for the preparation of a team of three cars. Nobody at that stage was to know that the

planned date of the race, 3rd September 1939, would be overshadowed by other events which would cause it to be abandoned; Hitler was by then occupied with his invasion of Poland and the consequent British declaration of war.

To avoid any questions which might arise from the creation of a completely new Type number, Porsche designated the project Type 60K10, indicating that it was merely a Type 60 to which one of a series of special body studies (K for *Karosserie*) was mounted. And the vehicle did indeed stand on a standard Type 60 platform: same wheelbase, same track. It differed in two significant details, its engine and its body. For the engine, the Porsche team undid all the restrictions which had been built into the production engine. With larger inlet ports and valves, a separate downdraught carburettor for each pair of cylinders, and a higher compression ratio, the 985cc flat-4 was persuaded to produce 50bhp instead of 24bhp, although various of its parts needed detail redesign to accept the additional stresses.

The body was the real work of art. While retaining some of the visual cues of the standard Type 60, especially in profile, the racing car body was low both in frontal area and drag coefficient. It had not only a better fineness ratio (ratio of length to maximum cross-sectional area) but also smoother overall flow, evidenced by the faired-over wheel arches. Its narrow 'glasshouse' almost suggested a single-seater, but in fact there were two seats, the co-driver seated some way aft of the driver, allowing both seats to be moved towards the centre-line. The stagger also allowed the fuel tank to be extended into the space where the passenger's legs would otherwise have been, while the battery was housed aft of the driver's seat. The sleek nose was just long enough to accommodate two spare wheels, one behind the other, parallel to and above the steering column – which says something about the slender section of wheels in those days.

The combination of higher power and lower drag meant that the Type 60W10 could cruise at 90mph, and maintain that speed for some time thanks to its greater fuel capacity. Yet it was by no means a pure competition car, as was proved during the war period when, their original purpose having been made redundant, senior Porsche staff including the Professor himself used them as personal transport between factories and government ministry meetings. One car of the three was withdrawn from use during the war following an accident; another was reported destroyed by American troops when they overran the Porsche family estate at Zell-am-Zee in 1945. The third miraculously survives to this day, in the Porsche Museum.

The importance of the Type 60W10 was that it enabled Ferdinand Porsche to maintain his interest in, and development of, a light and efficient sports car at a time when he was being discouraged from doing so by any conventional means. It has every right to be regarded as one of the main precursors of the Porsche Type 356, and therefore of everything which came afterwards. In particular, it pointed the way to post-war Porsche engine development, and to the importance of low frontal area and excellent aerodynamics – even if, for a long time, that concern had to be fed by a basic understanding, and the use of cut-and-try, rather than detailed wind-tunnel work. Those things would come, but there was always the Type 60W10 as the original inspiration.

Although Ferdinand Porsche had set the entire Volkswagen project in motion, he had less time to devote to it afterwards, in the relatively few years remaining to him. He retained some responsibility for and interest in the operation of the Fallersleben/ Wolfsburg works, but between 1939 and 1945 (see Chapter 1) he was far more occupied with the technical needs of the German armed forces, as were all German engineers of his standing.

It is recorded that in November 1950, Ferdinand Porsche visited the Wolfsburg factory for the first time since 1945. No doubt he was interested and encouraged to see how it had managed, with some initial assistance from the British Army of Occupation

in whose zone it stood, to overcome all initial difficulties and work up to manufacture of the Beetle in substantial numbers. By that time it would already have been possible to discern the rising trend which would turn it into one of Europe's major car manufacturers, with a range of products all based on Porsche's Type 60 concept. It must have provided a reassuring glimpse of what he had achieved, and of his legacy, but for Porsche it was only a glimpse. A few weeks later he suffered a stroke, and on 30th January 1951 he died, aged 75. His old colleague and fellow-engineer Hans Ledwinka survived him by many years, dying in Munich in 1967. The argument as to whether, and to what extent, the Type 60 had profited from Ledwinka's ideas led in the early post-war period to Volkswagen paying Tatra a modest sum in settlement of any outstanding claims. The argument itself, naturally enough, remains unsettled, although it seems that, as is so often the case, there is nothing to prevent great minds thinking alike, and that the argument more often arises as to which one was first to reach the doors of the patent office.

The upshot of the Volkswagen programme was the building of the huge factory at Wolfsburg (pictured here in 2002), into which fresh life was breathed after the war with the encouragement of the British Army of Occupation and the celebrated Major Ivan Hirst. It is recorded that Doctor Porsche visited the Wolfsburg site only once after 1945, and that was late in 1950, very shortly before his death. (Volkswagen)

CHAPTER 3

The first Porsche-badged car – the 356

The Type 356 raised Porsche's status from that of an engineering consultancy struggling to make its way in early post-war Austria (initially) and then Germany, to being a small but significant and respected car manufacturer.

Old Professor Porsche had always been a sports car enthusiast. He had seen potential in the Volkswagen Beetle in the years up to 1939 but as we have seen, had been discouraged from trying to realise it. Even so, as already pointed out, he evolved the Type 64, which might be described as an aerodynamically superior Beetle with a much more powerful engine, which would have competed in the planned Berlin-to-Rome 'Axis' Rally of 1939, if the event had taken place.

When hostilities ended, the Professor was incarcerated at Dijon – in extremely bad conditions – by the French until his son Ferry had accumulated enough profit from engineering consultancy to bail him out. One of the first things the old man did was to examine a prototype sports car, the 356/1, which Ferry had put together from a collection of Volkswagen (engine and suspension) and hand-crafted components. This car was mid-engined, with the Volkswagen power unit ahead of the rear axle and the gearbox behind. The Professor made the apparently reasonable suggestion that the layout should revert to the original Volkswagen arrangement, with the engine as the rearmost component. In that way, a space could be created above the gearbox for a luggage platform or even for two extremely occasional back seats. Although the Volkswagen engine was a flat-4, it was too tall to be treated in the same way: the engine itself was shallow, but once an induction system and cooling fan and ducting had been added, it took up most of the available depth aft of the front seats.

Suggesting the change would have seemed entirely logical to the man who had developed the original Volkswagen, and who was aware that its air-cooled engine didn't weigh much, and was short enough not to exert too much of a cantilever load at the extreme rear. No doubt he also rightly pointed out (with arguments which would be rehearsed time and time again as the Porsche company's products evolved) that further benefits would include easier access to the engine for maintenance, a simpler and easier gearshift linkage, easier cooling, and lower noise levels inside the car. The result of the redesign was the second prototype, 356/2, whose 2,100mm wheelbase was interestingly was only 50mm (1.9in) shorter than that of the original mid-engined prototype. It was also 290mm (almost a foot) shorter in its wheelbase than the 2,400m

wheelbase of the Volkswagen itself, emphasising that the 356 was by no means built on the Beetle floorpan, even if it used many of its suspension components.

Thus the 356 – so called because at least nominally, it was the 356th project tackled by the company since Ferdinand Porsche first set up his own shop – evolved as an attractive coupé body, designed by Erwin Komenda, built on a folded and welded sheet steel backbone-and-platform chassis, using Volkswagen Beetle suspension (parallel trailing arms and transverse torsion bars at the front, swing axles and torsion bars at the rear), with a modified Volkswagen engine and the existing transmission. The result was so practical and attractive that the decision was taken to build the car in series, initially in very small numbers with hand-crafted external panels in aluminium. In this way Porsche committed itself to the rear-engined layout rather than beginning life as a pioneering manufacturer of mid-engined sports cars.

The story of the 356, from its inception in 1948 until the last cars were delivered in 1966, was one of almost continuous development of the engine and transmission, much of the effort devoted to overcoming the drawbacks of the Volkswagen engine and indeed of the whole principle of air cooling. There were the constraints imposed by the dimensions of the flat-4 Volkswagen crankcase, conceived by Porsche Senior as a compact, minimum-weight power unit of modest output, with its cylinder bore spacing of 102mm and its 37mm offset between banks (thus dictating the dimensions of the crankshaft to a large extent). Likewise there would always be concerns about cooling: about the transfer of heat from the cylinder walls to atmosphere, about the design of the cooling fan and ducting to sweep air through the engine at a sufficiently high rate, and about the oil flow rate, since the oil played such a significant part in transferring heat from the hotter parts of the engine into areas from which it could radiate.

There was also, of course, the chassis. The Volkswagen was hardly the ideal starting point for a sports car in many respects, even though it enjoyed the advantage, rare in the 1940s, of all-independent suspension. Light and compact the engine might be, but with two people in the car the weight distribution was well rearwards, worse than 35:65 front-to-rear. The

A 1950 photograph of Ferdinand Porsche with the "Gmünd Coupé", with Ferry at the wheel. This car was rear-engined, in accordance with Dr. Porsche's suggestion that Ferry's early design for a mid-engined car should be amended to provide more interior space, superior cooling and easier maintenance.

Left: The 356/1 of 1948, the very first car to carry the Porsche name, had been designed by Ferry while his father was still being held to ransom by the French authorities. Of evident aerodynamic quality and also very light (585kg), it bore hardly any external sign that its engine was air-cooled, in effect a Volkswagen flat-4.

Below left: This view of the Gmünd Coupé shows to great effect the narrowness of the wheels and tyres on which the early Porsches ran, with the benefits of lower weight, reduced frontal area and

reduced steering loads – not to mention the likelihood that if control of the tail-heavy car was lost, it would be at lower and more manageable speed.

Below: The first production Porsches were powered by the Type 369 adaptation of the VW flat-4, with new cylinder heads and revised valve gear to enable to valves to be made much bigger, removing the deliberately "strangled" effect of the original. A single downdraught Solex carburettor per bank enhanced the output, which rose from 26bhp to 40bhp! Note the domed, very deep-skirted pistons.

potential problems were compounded by Porsche's retention of the Volkswagen swing-axle layout. Even though it had a lower centre of gravity and arguably better aerodynamics than the Wolfsburg saloon, the Porsche 356 was always going to be a car which would, to put it kindly, call for skilled and sympathetic driving, with an awareness of what happens in the event of clumsy steering and abrupt accelerator operation while cornering. Through the life of the 356 Porsche endeavoured to creep up on these problems but it could never, of course, tackle their fundamental cause without altering the entire character of the car. The trouble was that after a while, the character became the essence.

Type 369 – the first definitive Porsche engine

Even before the war, Porsche had studied various ways of improving the power output of the Volkswagen

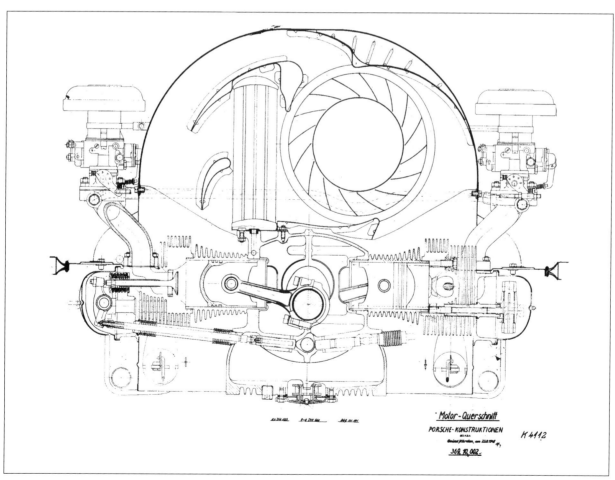

Motor-Querschnitt
PORSCHE-KONSTRUKTIONEN
K 4112

flat-4. In principle this was not difficult, given that the standard engine had been designed with deliberate breathing restrictions. Its inlet and exhaust ports were a miserly 28mm in diameter, so that it was unable to achieve a great enough gas flow to approach its mechanical limits, making it 'unburstable'. The plus side was that the gas speed through the tiny ports was high enough to help achieve adequate torque at low engine speeds, perceived by the average driver as flexibility. But Porsche was not interested in average drivers and it was quite happy to sacrifice some of this flexibility for more top-end power. Those tiny valves were the inescapable bottleneck. Otherwise the company might have looked first at different valve timing with more overlap, and a change to a single Solex downdraught carburettors per cylinder pair – which was part of the package anyway – might in itself have had more immediate effect.

A study (Type 369) was undertaken, seeking the easiest and cheapest way of increasing the valve diameter and so increase the gas flow and the power output. Ease and cheapness were essential, because the initially small and struggling company could afford nothing in the way of major investment in new processes or complex components. The Type 369 had to be a minimum evolution of the Volkswagen engine – an engine which, it should be recalled, had adjacent inlet valves (with siamesed ports) with the exhaust valves at front and rear, so to speak. To increase the valve diameter a new head design was needed, and took the form of an odd-looking but effective layout in which the inlet valves (still adjacent to each other as in the standard VW engine) remained at right angles to the crankshaft, but the exhaust valves were splayed outwards by 32 degrees (fore and aft, as viewed from above). This enabled the inlet valves to be made much bigger, at 38mm diameter, while the exhaust valves went up to 31mm. The most obvious drawback was that a new method of operating the exhaust valves had to be found.

The existing exhaust pushrods were retained but instead of operating the valves through simple rockers, a neat bell-crank mechanism was designed which did the job without taking up too much space – although the valve covers had to be made longer. The cast-alloy heads themselves came from the Karl Schmidt foundry in Neckarsulm, one of the supportive network of suppliers threaded together by the Porsche team. If Porsche was lucky in one respect in its formative years, it was that Germany at this time was full of companies struggling to regain a commercial foothold, and willing to undertake relatively small-volume tasks, which ten years later they might have rejected. With other suitable changes (although the standard Volkswagen camshaft and therefore valve timing was retained) the power output was dramatically increased, from 26bhp to 40bhp, later 44bhp with a higher compression ratio. Mainly because the valve timing remained standard Volkswagen, peak power was still achieved at only 4,200rpm.

Ultimately, a second drawback of the cylinder head design became obvious and proved rather more difficult to solve. The oddly asymmetric cylinder head layout called for likewise asymmetric pistons. This did not greatly matter in the early days when rot-gut petrol was the norm – to the extent that Porsche advised adding up to 40 per cent benzol to increase the octane rating, even with a compression ratio of only 6.5:1 and the domed pistons were symmetrically shaped. But later, when the combustion chamber volume was reduced by building-up the piston opposite the inlet valve in order to increase the compression ratio, the net sideways combustion pressure on the piston loaded it against the inner wall of the cylinder and the asymmetric load on the piston rings consequently increased oil consumption.

Moving body production

To begin with, the bodies were built from hand-beaten aluminium panels. The result was a lightweight 2+2 with commendable performance and economy, enhanced by the low frontal area and good aerodynamics (even though Komenda had worked 'by eye' and the design was never put into a wind tunnel). At first the cars, eventually 52 of them, were assembled one at a time in the establishment – by no stretch of the imagination was it a factory – at Gmünd in Austria, one of the places to which Professor Porsche had dispersed his technical staff in the final days of the war. The cars sold, largely by word of mouth and reputation (it was many years before Porsche ran anything resembling an advertising campaign), at first, largely in Germany and Switzerland. At that time nobody seemed to mind that the rearward weight distribution and swing-axle rear suspension meant the handling was distinctly wayward in hard cornering, especially if the power setting was changed. The performance, and the looks, of the early 356 were charm enough.

The consistent demand, exceeding what Gmünd could hope to produce, made it clear that this was a

product good enough to be built in greater volume. In 1949, Ferry Porsche, with the blessing of his father, took the most important steps in this direction. He moved production to Stuttgart, back to Zuffenhausen where his father's company had operated before and during the war. Initially he had to sub-let the site from the body-building concern Reutter, to whom he also contracted the task of turning the 356 body into a set of steel panels which could be pressed and welded in significant volume. In fact Reutter undertook to deliver complete, painted and trimmed bodies, with Porsche then inserting the powertrain and chassis components. Eventually, in 1964, Porsche bought-out Reutter's Stuttgart operation, but by then, the product story had moved on. The volume production project succeeded to the extent that by the beginning of 1950 cars were beginning to emerge from Zuffenhausen at a rate sufficient to see around 400 completed by the year-end, and by the time the original 356 gave way to the 356A in 1955, some 7,600 units in all had been delivered.

Type 506 – the 1300 engine

By this time, further engine development had already become a priority, as more power was sought to retain the 356s performance advantage. Increasing the compression ratio was an option denied because of poor fuel quality. The adoption of valve timing with more overlap might have helped, but this option was

Porsche's interest in aerodynamics was never simply academic. This is the second car ever built, 356/2, the Coupé counterpart of 356/1 the roadster, complete with taped-on tufting to enable study of which way the air was really flowing close to the bodywork. One hopes the visibly poor fit of the driver's door did not upset the results obtained too much …

perhaps surprisingly put on hold for a while. Instead, first priority went to increasing the capacity.

In fact, Porsche had begun by reducing the capacity of the then-standard Volkswagen engine. It is worth bearing in mind that this 1,131cc engine was a bored-out version (to 75mm) of the original pre-war engine which had dimensions of 70 x 64mm for a capacity of 986cc. The very first 'standard' Porsche Type 369 engine actually reduced the standard Volkswagen bore to 73.5mm, taking the capacity down to 1,086cc, which among other things, enabled the cars to compete in the 1,100cc class in sports car racing. As early as 1951 one of the early aluminium-bodied coupés, the 356-002, had taken a Le Mans win in this class, sadly too late for Professor Porsche to enjoy, since he had died in January, following a stroke, aged 75. The class win provided the company with a further boost to its growing reputation, as did a second one the following year, and it entered a team of some kind in every subsequent 24 Hours event for many years afterwards.

Porsche did not wait for Volkswagen's own engines to grow in size, although eventually they did. The Volkswagen 'architecture' was there, but from the beginning, Porsche went its own way in terms of

engine development. Its interests, after all, were different. Up in Wolfsburg their concern was with durability. In Zuffenhausen it was with performance. Consequently Porsche developed larger-capacity versions of the flat-4 engine before Volkswagen, and did it in a different way. Indeed, it is remarkable to contemplate that no Porsche 356 engine ever had dimensions identical with a Volkswagen engine.

The first move to increase capacity came very early, in 1951, with the appearance of the Type 506 engine. (There is no rational explanation, incidentally, for the jump from 300-series to 500-series type numbers; the complete listing appended to Ludvigsen's monumental study shows only one 400-series number, Type 425, a light diesel tractor!) Seeking extra capacity through the simple expedient of boring-out the existing engine, Porsche took advantage of some work carried out by Mahle, who during the war, had demonstrated the feasibility of running pistons in hard chrome-plated aluminium cylinder bores. This technique enabled the bore to be opened out all the way to 80mm, making the capacity 1,286cc. As a bonus, the chrome-plated all-alloy cylinders were lighter than their partly cast-iron predecessors – the weight saving was 5kg per engine – and cooling was improved. There was no benefit to the power output, but the torque rose from 70Nm to 81Nm, well worth having but with a concomitant snag: such a figure pushed the capacity of the standard Volkswagen 4-speed gearbox to, if not beyond the limit.

Above: In 1951 Porsche took a single 1.1-litre car to Le Mans, driven by the French pairing of Veuillet and Mouche, and took a class win, completing 210 laps compared with the 267 of the race-winning Walker/ Whitehead Jaguar XK 120C. It was no more than a foretaste of what was to come, once the Stuttgart competitions department got into its stride.

Right: Porsche applied its newly defined baulk-ring synchromesh system to a gearbox for Volkswagen, the Type 384, but it was rejected by Wolfsburg. Porsche then developed the unit for its own use, with a weight-saving magnesium casing, as the Type 519. The actual synchromesh system proved to be a significant earner of licence fees for the company, for many years.

Type 519 – the first all-synchromesh gearbox

For this, there was an answer in the works: Porsche had already been working on a synchromesh gearbox for Volkswagen, using the newly devised and very effective (and extremely compact) baulk-ring technology devised by Leopold Schmid. As Laurence Pomeroy observed in a review of technical developments *in The Motor Yearbook* of 1953, the baulk rings 'take up so little space that the fully synchronised set of four speeds can be fitted into the gear case originally designed for the unsynchronised gears. What is more, the effect of these split synchronising rings is so powerful that bottom gear, upon which the 1.1-litre Porsche car will reach nearly 30mph, can be instantly engaged …'

In the end, despite these virtues, Volkswagen did not accept the Porsche design (Type 384) and sought its synchromesh mechanism elsewhere, which was almost certainly a mistake. Porsche for its part had to take the brave decision to produce its own gearbox, evolving the 384 into an extremely light unit using a cast magnesium casing. At first it outsourced the entire gearbox manufacturing project to Getrag, but the latter was more used to heavy-duty truck gearboxes and found it difficult to maintain the required standard of assembly in a unit so much smaller and lighter. In the end, Porsche took final assembly and testing back in-house.

This transmission served well in its original application but its importance for Porsche extended well beyond the 356. Its highly effective synchromesh system quickly became popular within the industry at large, and it eventually earned Porsche substantial

licensing fees for many years. It also served as a timely reminder that although the company was establishing itself as a car manufacturer under the leadership of Ferry Porsche, it would continue its activities as an engineering consultancy. Even in these formative and difficult years, it had been commissioned by Studebaker to assist in the development of what became the Avanti. In 1951 alone, the company filed over 100 patents relating to aspects of vehicle technology.

Type 502/527 – the 1500 engine

If the additional torque of the 1300 engine posed a threat to the integrity of the original Volkswagen transmission, the output of the Type 502 was certainly too much. The object of the Type 502 programme was to combine the bigger bore of the 1300 engine with a longer-throw crankshaft. To achieve this, another hurdle had to be overcome. Within the standard

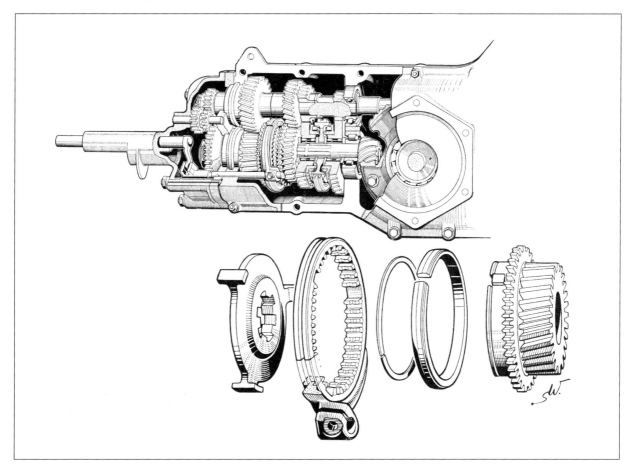

Volkswagen crankcase (vertically split, cast in two halves and bolted together to sandwich the crankshaft with the single central camshaft directly below it) the clearance between the crank and the cam was minimal. More specifically, it was the big-end bolts which were crucial because in the Volkswagen configuration, it was the bolts and their lugs which passed closest to the cams. For a time, it seemed there was no alternative to redesigning the crankcase – at great, and indeed at the time, unacceptable expense – in order to increase the distance between the crankshaft and camshaft centres (or, of course, to adopt some form of twin-camshaft layout, which would have been equally costly).

Yet another Porsche supplier came to the rescue. The Hirth company had some time since developed a technology for building-up crankshafts from their component parts, rather than casting or forging them in one piece for subsequent machining. The joints between webs and journals were radially serrated and pushed together, then locked in place by the insertion of very fine-threaded screws. As an economic method of making crankshafts in large volume it was a nonsense, but it meant the connecting rods could be made in one piece, with 'banjo' big-ends into which roller bearings were inserted. Thus the big-end bolts and their lugs were done away with, and the crankshaft throw radius could safely be increased by 5mm, adding 10mm to the stroke to make the Type 502 engine dimensions 80 x 74mm for a capacity of 1,488cc.

The built-up Hirth crankshaft was paradoxically well suited to the Porsche. If anything is bad for such components, it is to have the engine lugged along at low speed in high gear, close to peak torque. This 'hammers' the joints and eventually induces wear (in the Hirth-type shaft) or gradual circumferential slippage (in shrink-fitted crankshafts of the type used in the Citroën flat-twin engines, for example). But few Porsche owners would lug their engines in this way, even if the engines had invited such treatment, which they did not. Peak torque operation was bad, peak power operation much less so, and the built-up crankshafts proved sufficiently durable that they remained in use, in some engines, until 1957 by which time an alternative way had been devised to manufacture and assemble 'split' connecting rods which needed no greater clearance.

Initially, the power output of the Type 502 engine was quoted at 55bhp. A few more subtle changes, mainly to the carburation, called forth a new project

number, Type 527, and raised the power to 60bhp, with a peak torque of 102Nm. The 1500 engine proved to be something of a breakthrough. With 44bhp, the 1100 and 1300 had been no better than brisk in their performance. With 60bhp and torque to match, the 1500 proved much more attractive to the kind of people who were interested, and from 1952 this version quickly became the best-seller. This appears to have prompted Porsche into two lines of engine development. The first was how the 1300 engine could be evolved to produce the same kind of power, since by 1952 a specific output of 46bhp/litre was no longer extraordinary. The second was how then to apply the same kind of improvement to the 1500, to provide it with even more power and better performance.

Type 528 – the 1500 Super and beyond

In reality, the process was slightly convoluted. The first move was an obvious one – to fit the 1500 engine (Type 527) with a new camshaft with more valve timing overlap. Up to this point the standard Volkswagen camshaft, with nominal timing of 2.5-37.5-37.5-2.5 degrees and valve lift of 8.5 and 8.2mm for inlet and exhaust respectively, had been retained. In the new camshaft, the timing was 19-54-54-19 degrees – hardly excessive by modern standards – and the valve lift was increased to 9.6/9.25mm. The result was the Type 528 engine, with 70bhp at 5,000rpm, for which it was found necessary to use sodium-cooled exhaust valves to achieve good durability. This engine went into the 356 1500S, immediately ratcheting another turn into the spiral of engineering requirements: the significantly improved performance, in a car which was also beginning to put on weight as creature comforts were added, now called for better brakes.

The 1300 was developed in a rather different way. First of all its internal dimensions were juggled. Combining the original narrower 73.5mm cylinder bore with the longer-stroke 74mm crankshaft offered a capacity of 1,256cc. Opening out the bore by just 1mm, to 74.5mm, yielded 1,290cc, nicely within the 1.3-litre limit. Switching to these dimensions for the 1300 meant that a 74mm crankshaft, and matching connecting rods, could be standardised (except for the 1100 which would not long continue).

This in turn encouraged the development of new-type connecting rods so that a forged 74mm crankshaft could be used instead of the built-up Hirth component, with a cost saving. The first approach to the problem was to split the big-end on a diagonal, so that the bolts and their lugs would not protrude directly downwards, but in the end a configuration was devised in which the bolts were housed entirely within the 'banjo' envelope. Possibly through engineering conservatism, the new connecting rods and 74mm forged crankshaft were first used in the 'base' 1500 engine, redesignated Type 546. This appeared for the 1953 model year, alongside the existing 1500S. Late in 1953, the 1300S companion to the 1500S emerged, in effect a small-bore 1500S with all the same engineering features, but delivering 60bhp. Meanwhile serious questions about the braking performance of these higher-performance versions were answered with the fitting of substantially larger brake drums – 280mm instead of 230mm diameter. These were of revised construction and were basically cast alloy with steel-lined friction surfaces.

Porsche delivered its 5,000th car in March 1954, and the development of both powertrain and (to a lesser extent) chassis continued. For the 1955 model year, the engine's basic construction changed (although not its configuration or dimensions).

Porsche had for some time been concerned that any work on the engine involving attention to either the crankshaft or the camshaft required the splitting of the entire crankcase into its two halves – in effect, a major overhaul. So its engineers involved a 'three-piece crankcase' in which most of the main vertically-split crankcase was retained, but the nose section (actually the 'tail', the engine of course being installed flywheel-forward) could be removed separately. This meant the cantilevered fourth crankshaft bearing, and more importantly the timing gears, could be attended to without splitting the whole engine. In other respects the engine remained unchanged, including the bore centres, the offset, the Mahle chrome-lined cylinders, and the cylinder heads. The new crankcase, now cast in high-silicon aluminium alloy rather than magnesium, was adopted for the entire engine range, 1300 and 1500, in standard and 'S' versions, the latter retaining the built-up Hirth crankshaft, as its final

The 356A, identified by its one-piece curved windscreen, was launched at the 1955 Frankfurt Show, for the 1956 model-year. The choice of engine size was reduced to a very basic 1300, and a 1600 – and the 1300 was destined not long to survive. The 356A also saw the introduction of comprehensive chassis modifications to render the handling rather more predictable.

application. The original 1100 engine was thankfully discontinued, so that the 74mm stroke became standard for all 356 engines.

On the chassis front, Helmuth Bott had been examining and devising possible improvements all through the early 1950s. At one stage he examined proposals to replace the Volkswagen front suspension with a strut-type layout – a notion which resurfaced in the 911 – but he did not proceed with it in the 356. Instead, he adopted a front anti-roll bar which increased the tendency initially to understeer (and therefore hopefully delaying the onset of oversteer) while evolving a more comprehensive package for the heavily reworked version, the 356A. This was made ready for announcement at the 1955 Frankfurt Motor Show, for the 1956 model year.

More civilised: 356A

The official production count for the 356 was 7,627 units when the 356A was launched. Outwardly, the new version was little changed, apart from having a

In September 1955, Ferry Porsche drove one of the first examples of the 356A convertible to Wolfsburg, for a celebration which included the unveiling of a bust of his father, old Doctor Porsche.

one-piece curved windscreen, the car having been launched with a two-piece screen, which later metamorphosed into a one-piece component with a central 'fold'. All the significant changes had been made in the engine compartment and in the chassis.

The big decision was effectively to scrap the 1300 and 1500 engines and standardise on a new capacity of 1.6-litres, partly for the sake of a useful increase in torque. The only unit from the old range to survive was, remarkably, the 'base' 1300 engine, still with just 44bhp at 4,200rpm, which soldiered on into 1957 presumably for those more interested in the show of their 356 than in its go. Certainly there seemed to be little point in having two different engines, 1300S and base 1500, both delivering 60bhp. Now the 1500 engine was opened out to 82.5mm bore, for an actual capacity of 1,582cc, to create the new 1600 which would be offered in 'base' and S versions. Regardless of version, they now used both the three-piece crankcase and the 1600 was equipped with a forged crankshaft, although the 1600S retained the built-up Hirth crankshaft until the 1958 model year. The new engines were Type 616, sub-divided into the 616/1 which was the 'base' 1600, the 1600S being the 616/2. Outputs were 60bhp and 75bhp respectively. Both versions now used Porsche-developed valve timing, the base engine with slightly more overlap than the long-serving standard Volkswagen timing, and the 1600S with slightly less overlap than the former S camshaft (17-53-50-14 instead of 19-54-54-19).

The chassis modifications, all in the interests of taming the lift-off oversteer which was now more widely acknowledged to be rather wicked, were considerable. The recently introduced front anti-roll bar was stiffened, still further increasing initial understeer, but the roll-bar attachments were redesigned to reduce friction, making the effect more progressive. In a further fairly dramatic move to make it more difficult for drivers to create clumsy steering inputs, the caster angle was doubled, and in addition, the steering geometry was cleverly rearranged to induce additional understeer when the car leaned during cornering. Unfortunately, these changes meant not only that the steering became heavier, but also that it was more subject to road shocks, requiring the fitting of a steering damper. At the back, the real problem-end of the car, the trailing arms were made longer to reduce the swing-axle effect. The spring rates were softened so that there was less roll stiffness, and thus a lower rate of load transfer at the rear. Finally, the wheel and tyre sizes were changed from 5.00-16 inch on 3.5-inch rims to 5.60-15 inch on 4.5-inch rims which, Bott's team had determined, increased the maximum cornering force which could be maintained.

The 356A was well received, especially the standardisation of the 1600 engine – and given extra spice by the simultaneous announcement of the Carrera, powered by a completely new engine (although still an air-cooled flat-4) with twin overhead camshafts per cylinder bank. Porsche delivered its 10,000th production car in March 1956, only two years after the 5,000th unit had emerged.

Autocar carried out a road test on a 1600 in Germany early in 1956, noting that as tested, the Porsche was more expensive in the UK than the contemporary Jaguar XJ140 Coupé. The 1600 achieved a maximum speed of 102mph (compared with well-nigh 130mph for the Jaguar) and accelerated to 60mph in 15.3 seconds. Such figures seem far from impressive when measured against those of any modern hatchback, but in the mid-1950s European fuel quality was still generally poor, and the 1600's 7.5 compression ratio and, no doubt, its ignition timing reflected that every bit as much as the 70bhp output. To look at things through the eyes of the *Autocar* testers of the time, the 1600 was a match for the Lagonda 3-litre or the BMW 501, both tested in the same year. It took that Jaguar, or the Jensen 541, really to outrun it, and they both returned test fuel consumption far worse than the Porsche's 31mpg. *Autocar* noted that the engine 'was noisy over 4,000rpm (80mph) for cruising' and that 'below 1,500rpm it suffered from reduced response and snatching' so there was clearly, at that time, little scope for resorting to wild valve timing in a quest for greater power output, if one wanted to retain acceptable road-going behaviour.

Rather more surprising is the *Autocar* test's assertion that 'the handling has a less "rear-engined" feel to it' although 'a certain skittishness at the rear, attributable partly to the swing-axle suspension, can be felt … the stability remains very good indeed …' Readers of the day would have known how to interpret these Delphic messages, which could be uttered now that the original 356's behaviour had been partly tamed by the new package of chassis modifications. There was nothing but praise for the brakes and the steering, however. Indeed, there was 'no trace of fade' and maximum braking was achieved with a modest 50lb pedal effort.

Carrera: something else

The Carrera engine was developed, as the Type 547, by a team led by Ernst Fuhrmann. Initially, the chosen dimensions were 85 x 66mm for a capacity of 1,498cc. The completely new aluminium crankcase had 122mm bore centres (instead of 102mm for the standard Volkswagen component, and with 40mm instead of 37mm bank-to-bank offset). Thus the crankshaft – a built-up Hirth type crank, more economical to manufacture in view of the small production volume envisaged – had to be completely new. The 547 engine was longer, but (because of its shorter stroke) little wider than the standard engine – which meant it would fit the 356 body without too much trouble. The combustion chambers were typical high-performance hemispherical, vee-opposed valves angled 39 degrees above and below the horizontal.

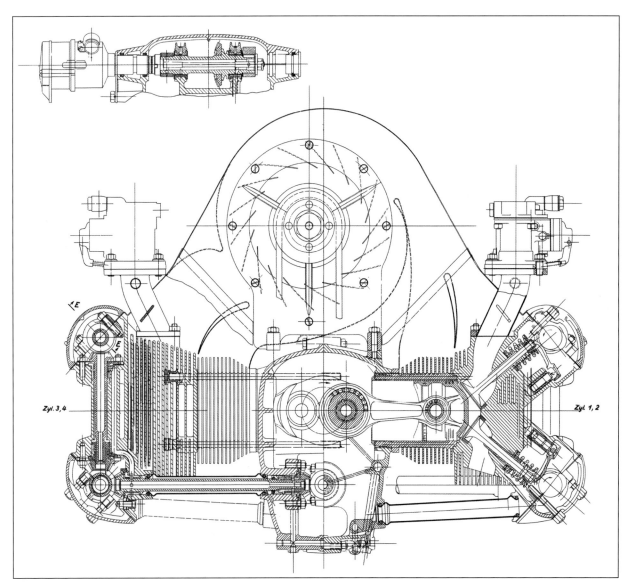

The valves were, naturally, much bigger than in the OHV engine: 48mm inlet, 41mm exhaust. The cylinder heads were also notable for dual ignition, one spark plug positioned – without any apparent regard for service accessibility – 'at each side' between the valves, with dual distributors driven from the ends of the inlet camshafts. The cylinders were chrome-faced alloy and the downdraught twin-choke carburettors were new instruments from Solex. In recognition of the increasing problem Porsche was experiencing with keeping oil from surging into the wrong places in its horizontal pairs of cylinders, Fuhrmann had wisely gone for a dry sump.

However, the real interest of Fuhrmann's engine was its valve gear – the drive to its four camshafts.

Real performance for the 356 came with the development of the Carrera 4-cam engine, designed by Ernst Fuhrmann. This all-new engine, with increased cylinder bore spacing, was fitted with two direct-acting overhead camshafts per bank, with a quite astonishing and ingenious bevel gear and shaft actuation system in which the drive was taken from the exhaust camshaft, across the top of the cylinder head and between the cylinders to the inlet camshaft.

Today, we would expect to find a chain drive or possibly a toothed belt, running in a single stage or in two stages, over a drive sprocket on the crankshaft nose, and four larger sprockets driving the camshafts at half engine speed. But Fuhrmann took a geared drive from

Right: The 4-cam Carrera engine existing in road-going and racing forms. Seen here is a racing unit with four individual exhaust pipes, and distributors for the two plugs per cylinder, driven from the ends of the inlet camshafts. The downdraught carburettors, one per bank, and twin-choke Solex instruments.

Below: A side-on shot of the same racing engine, with the inlet camshaft cover removed and the bevel drive from the exhaust camshaft clearly visible. It is interesting to note that while the inlet cam cover has the Porsche logo cast into it, the cover for the hotter exhaust camshaft is finned to help heat dissipation.

the flywheel end of the crankshaft and from there, ran a jackshaft aft to the geometric centre of the flat-4 engine. Here was a second bevel gear, double-faced and 40mm wide to match the cylinder bank offset, from which further shafts and gears drove the exhaust camshafts between the two cylinders of each bank. From here in turn, mini-shafts and gears ran upwards to drive the inlet camshafts. It was a truly astonishing and extremely expensive arrangement, but it added nothing to the overall length of the engine – and it worked. Initially installed in the tubular ladder-framed Type 550 sports-racing car, it delivered 110bhp at 7,000rpm. For the 356 Carrera, first shown at Frankfurt in 1955 alongside the 356A, this was unwound to 100bhp at 6,200rpm, in which state of tune the Carrera could be driven on the road without difficulty.

Pushrod developments

With the virtual standardisation of the 1600 engine, the pace of power unit development slowed although detail improvements continued. One move, for 1957, was the adoption of pistons with slightly offset gudgeon pins in order to counteract, at least during a vital phase of the compression stroke, the unequal sideways component of pressure distribution on the piston due to its asymmetric shape. For 1958 the cylinders of the 'base' 1600 reverted to cast-iron construction, while the 1600S adopted a forged rather than a Hirth crankshaft and the 1300 engine was finally consigned to oblivion. At the same time Porsche switched from Solex to Zenith carburettors.

More significant in some respects were the ongoing improvements to the transmission. For 1957, the Type 644 gearbox arrived, with a one-piece aluminium alloy casing rather than the vertically split Volkswagen

magnesium alloy type. In 1958, diaphragm-spring clutches were fitted for the first time, reducing operating loads. Then, for the 1959 model year, that transmission in turn gave way to the new Type 716, whose improved synchromesh design, resulting in reduced push-through loads, helped overcome complaints of high loads needed to engage first gear especially. On the chassis side meanwhile, one of the few significant

changes during the life of the 356A was the replacement of the original Volkswagen worm-and-nut steering box with a ZF worm-and-peg box which was directly interchangeable and, through better mechanical efficiency, resulted in lighter yet quicker steering.

Change of character: 356B

For the 1959 model year, the 356 underwent a major and visible metamorphosis. New regulations in the important US market forced a redesign of the body to raise the headlamps. The opportunity was taken to fit more substantial bumpers, and the result was a shape, which from some angles, was almost a halfway house to the 911 (although only in retrospect as the 911 was several years in the future). The new body was designated T-5 and there was a weight penalty.

To begin with, the only important mechanical change was yet another new transmission, the Type 741, with further improved synchromesh. The 1600 and 1600S engines were retained to begin with, and

indeed for some time. Anticipating complaints that greater weight plus identical power output meant lower performance, Porsche had however developed a new 1600 version, the Super 90, which became available during 1960. The Super 90 engine (Type 616/7) delivered 90bhp at 5,500rpm thanks to better breathing on the inlet side, the inlet valves being enlarged from 38mm to 40mm diameter with higher valve lift into the bargain – and the compression ratio raised to a daring 9:1. Fuel quality in Europe was fast improving. Torque output remained a modest 121Nm (89lb ft) at no less than 4,300rpm, suggesting the Super 90 might not be at its best in slow, heavy traffic.

There was a lot more to the Type 616/7 than revised cylinder heads and valve timing, however. The crankshaft was a revised design with large counterweights, the exhaust valves were sodium-cooled, and larger Solex carburettors were fitted to cope with the greater mass flow and maximum power. The original hard-chrome cylinder lining was replaced by a new process, also developed by Mahle and called Ferral which involved flame-spraying a thin coat of molybdenum steel onto the cylinder walls. The connecting rods were strengthened and so was the crankshaft, with larger main bearings increasing the amount of overlap and therefore the stiffness. Even more vital was the installation of an even larger oil pump to improve cooling, just as much as lubrication.

In 1960, just prior to the arrival of the Super 90, *Autocar* conducted a test on a UK-market 1600S ('Super 75' to UK buyers). One suspects this car (80 XMF) was a rather special one, since among other things, it came on Michelin X tyres which Porsche eventually shunned in favour of a radial developed to a company brief by Dunlop. The *Autocar* performance figures were certainly impressive for a 75bhp car weighing 1,932lbs (876kg). The mean maximum speed was 108.8mph, suggesting the raised headlamps had done little harm to the drag coefficient. The car reached 30mph in 3.2sec, 60mph in 11.4sec and 90mph in 28.8sec. Overall fuel consumption was recorded as 29.2mpg.

Apart from commenting that the engine was noisy (mainly induction noise) and that there was no cold-starting device – the accelerator had to be pumped

For the 1959 model year, following a 4-year run for the 356A, there came a change to the 356B with new, raised headlamps and more substantial bumpers. Many of the 356B changes were forced by new US regulations. The overall visual impression, at least in retrospect, is a part-way move towards the 911.

two or three times before the starter was operated – *Autocar* devoted many of its words to chassis behaviour, again coming to what we might now regard as surprising conclusions. The opinion of the testers was that the car '… remains both stable and predictable; it has been said that the new rear-end geometry has made this the first Porsche which could be drifted round a bend … Any oversteer tendency would pass unnoticed in normal use.' It was further noted that 'Over the years, various modifications to the suspension and steering gear have given the car progressively more orthodox handling characteristics.' Most of these changes of course came as part of the 356A package, and the non-standard Michelin Xs certainly made a difference. The between-the-lines message was still that the 356 called for expert and knowledgeable handling: note the '*more* orthodox handling' implying, of the *Autocar*-reading *cognoscenti*, that it was still some way short of being orthodox.

For the rest, the magazine testers were no better than lukewarm about the drum brakes – a distinct downgrading from the lavish praise of the 1956 test. There was also criticism of the lack of cabin ventilation, which meant the windows had to be part-open most of the time.

However, the definitive answers – in so far as there could be one, where the handling was concerned – were on the way. The definitive 'handling package'

appeared with the Super 90, in the form of the rear compensating spring and Porsche's choice of radial-ply tyre, the German-made Dunlop CB59, the size 165R15. The compensating spring worked in the opposite sense from an anti-roll bar: it reduced the rear spring stiffness and therefore the load transfer from the inside to the outside rear tyre when cornering, at the acceptable cost of allowing a higher roll angle. Porsche's way of doing this was to add a transverse leaf spring at the rear, accepting vertical load, but pivoted at its centre so that it contributed nothing to roll stiffness. The existing torsion-bar springs (which were themselves 'packages' of leaves rather than solid bars) could then be softened, so that the vertical spring rate remained the same, but the roll stiffness, and therefore the load transfer effect which could cause such problems with the swing-axles when it really took hold, was reduced.

Final laps

By the early 1960s everyone at Zuffenhausen knew a replacement for the 356 was on the way, but the pace of development of the existing car hardly slackened. For the 1962 model year, the T-6 body was introduced: externally a matter of greater glass area, with a revised and improved cabin interior, but more fundamentally with a completely new 13.2-gallon fuel tank forming the base of the front luggage compartment, replacing the original 'saddle' tank in front of the bulkhead. As a welcome spin-off, an external filler cap was provided, beneath a flap in the front wing. What it did not have was disc brakes.

Porsche had taken its time assessing the implications of a switch to disc brakes and had undertaken its own development, as part of a Type 695 programme, as well as working with potential suppliers. The company had looked at Dunlop technology, then worked with Teves/ATE to develop a system which more closely met its requirements, especially in terms of durability.

There were few changes to the engines at this time, although the 1600S engine – now the middle of a range of three, providing 60, 75 and 90bhp respectively – joined the plain 1600 in having cast-iron cylinders and revised pistons. In this form it became the Type 616/12.

The need for the disc brakes had become dire. The *Autocar* ran a test of a Super 90 in the autumn of 1962 and found it rather disappointing – or rather, as the test commented, '... it would seem that the 1960 Super 75 was particularly super.' The mean maximum speed of 111.3mph was down on what was expected in the light of the near-109mph maximum of the Super 75. Acceleration figures were 3.8sec to 30mph, 11.5sec to 60mph and 26.0sec to 90mph – actually slower at the bottom end (possibly because the higher Super 90 torque peak made it more difficult to achieve a clean 'road test' standing start) and not much of an improvement at higher speeds. Worse yet, overall fuel consumption was down from 29.2mpg to 24.4mpg.

As to the car's handling with the compensation spring fitted, the comment was that 'Porsche handling characteristics have changed progressively over the years, and this Super 90 has practically lost the oversteer, tricky in unfamiliar hands, of most of its predecessors.' That statement contains a double sting: not only the now-it-can-be-told admission of earlier handling problems, but that weasel-word *practically* which rightly suggested this was still not a car for the clumsy or the unwary. The steering, though, was praised as 'very light and precise'. On the other hand, 'In one important aspect Porsche have trailed behind most other European builders of fast touring or sports cars – brakes.' The real complaint was that '... from higher speeds they become cobbly (sic) and rough to such a degree that even the passenger is always aware of them.' The text directly suggested it was high time Porsche switched to discs. This did not actually happen until the final 356C was introduced for the 1964 model year.

With the 911 now imminent, the 356 range was simplified, with just two modified engines, 616/15 and 616/16. These were developed by a team led by Hans Mezger, and reflected his view that much of the emphasis of earlier iterations had been misplaced. The

exhaust valves had remained the same size through generations while the inlet valves had become bigger and bigger. In the interests of better balanced gas flow through the engine, Mezger accordingly reduced the inlet valve diameter from 40mm to 38mm, while increasing the exhaust valve from 31mm to 34mm. The result – accompanied by a half-point increase in compression ratio in each case – was that the output of the of the 1600S engine remained at 75bhp but the torque was marginally increased, while the former Super 90 engine, redesignated 1600SC, now delivered 95bhp with a similar 123.5Nm peak torque. However, the peak power speeds were now slightly higher while the peak torque speeds were slightly lower, suggesting easier driving in normal road conditions.

During 1964, a change was made to Biral cylinder construction, yet another new technology in which cast-iron sleeves were inserted into a mould before the cylinder was cast in aluminium alloy, which was continued into the early-series 911s.

On the chassis side, the front anti-roll bar was stiffened, while the rear torsion bar spring rate was reduced, both changes which tilted the balance further towards understeer and away from terminal roll-induced swing-axle oversteer. Even then, this trend had already upset some of the early-school Porsche purists in making the 356 easier as well as safer to drive, but the car was by now being sold in numbers which guaranteed that not all its drivers would be able to feel their way to the safe limit, or to recover if they transgressed it. By the same token, the disc brakes made things safer for drivers who did not know what fade was until it was too late. In fact, the disc brake system fitted to the 356C was a considerable step forward. Not only did it provide large discs on all four wheels: it also pioneered the idea of providing the rear discs with small integral drums to form an effective parking brake – the lack of which was a frequent criticism of early all-disc systems.

One close look at the 356 in this final form came in a *Motor* road test of the 1600SC in July 1964. Rather like the *Autocar*'s 356B, this car proved slightly disappointing when it came to performance if the *Autocar*'s 1960-vintage Super 75 was taken as the benchmark. The extra 20bhp lifted the maximum speed only to 112.5mph, while the acceleration times were 4.6sec to 30mph, 13.2sec to 60mph and 31.4sec to 90mph, all well down on *Autocar*'s Super 90 and suggesting a sub-standard test car. The road test text is annoyingly silent about this, but the very poor time to 30mph suggests, again, some difficulty in making a clean standing start (and a 1-in-4 hill restart proved impossible). The test does note that while the accelerator-pumping technique provided reliable cold starting, hot starts were 'sometimes chancy'. The heyday of high-quality fuel is recalled by the note that 100-octane fuel was used throughout the test; the days of rot-gut petrol requiring low compression ratios was long gone.

As for the chassis, the *Motor* testers begin by coming straight to the point: 'There was once a bogey about Porsches. Early examples had massive oversteer, making the tail treacherous in the wet and skittish in the dry. Now the ghost has been laid … transverse compensating spring to help keep the back in place on corners by reducing weight transfer at the rear. Skill is still needed, but the behaviour is now predictable.' That was certainly a laying-bare of the early history, but there was still the destructive little aside: to *help* keep the back in place on corners, note – not to *keep* it in place. The only way to approach that would have been to replace the swing axles with something altogether better behaved (and better yet, to find some way of making the car less tail-heavy).

The disc brakes worked, however. 'For high speed stopping, the discs are a success. Pedal forces are rather heavy, but … even the hardest use failed to raise them by more than a few pounds, and recovery was quick. There was never any deviation from a straight line and brakes remained quiet throughout.' As for the handbrake, it would 'easily lock the rear wheels or hold the car on a 1-in-3 slope'.

The *Motor* test more or less summed up the state of the Porsche 356 as it came to the end of its production life. The car had seen continual engine development, although not always in a straight line, so to speak. The engineers had at times been forced into taking the options they could afford rather than the ones they would have preferred. The transmission had likewise been steadily improved but always remained 4-speed. As for the chassis, it was always a case of seeking measures which would alleviate the basic drawbacks of the rearward weight distribution and the swing axles. At no time was Porsche able to contemplate the substantial re-engineering which would have been called for to achieve a major improvement – by devising an alternative to the swing axles, for example. Yet there is the abiding evidence that many enthusiasts preferred the car the way it was. Driving a car which is known to be 'difficult', and not coming to grief, says something about you – and not least to your fellow *aficionados*.

Coming to the end of the model's run: the final-series 356C appeared for the 1964 model year, five years after the 356B. Easily the most important change was under the skin, with the adoption – at last – of disc brakes. A much bigger fuel tank, beneath the luggage compartment floor rather than forward of the bulkhead, was also welcome. This hardtop car does not display the greater window area of the T-6 coupé body.

Carrera postscript

For the most dedicated, the story did not quite conclude with the 356C, since an end also remained to be written to the Carrera's career. Inevitably, this consisted of a search for ever more power, which in turn led to the 'stretching' of the 4-cam engine. As already pointed out, Fuhrmann had designed it with a substantially wider cylinder bore spacing than the standard 356 engine, so boring-out was easy, and there was no reason why the stroke should not be increased as well.

In fact, the strand of Carrera development kicked off in 1957 with the announcement of the Gran Turismo, in which the rated power was increased to 110bhp at 6,400rpm but without making any fundamental changes to the engine. Most of the increase came from a more efficient exhaust system, although

with the penalty that the air/exhaust heat exchange heater was deleted. The GT also came with a larger fuel tank and wider (drum) front brakes.

The following year, 1958, saw the 4-cam engine bored-out to 82.5mm for a capacity of 1,587cc. Along with this, the built-up crankshaft gave way to a forged crank running in conventional journal bearings. The Carrera 1600 engine, carrying the Type 692 designation, delivered 105bhp at 6,500rpm as the 692/2, or 115bhp at 6,500rpm for the 1600GT with a higher compression (9.8 instead of 9.5) and larger-throated Weber carburettors. Two years later, the 692/3 engine became the 692/3a with strengthened crankshaft and connecting rods.

The final iteration in the Carrera development strand was also the most radical. The Carrera 2 appeared in 1962, with an engine designated Type 587, indicating that it had been a long time 'in the works'. In fact, studies for a 2-litre engine had begun very shortly after the original Type 547 4-cam had been laid down. It was bored right out to 92mm, and the crankshaft stroke increased to 74mm, the same as in the standard 356 engine – but this was not, of course, the same crank since the engine's bore centres and offsets were different. The resulting capacity was 1,966cc. Interestingly, no changes were made to the cylinder heads: the combustion chambers, valve sizes and angles remained unchanged. One significant change, and a bit of a give-away as to where the engine was most highly stressed in an overall sense, was that an even bigger oil pump was fitted: more than any

The final word in the 356 story came with the late introduction of a full 2-litre Carrera engine, delivering up to 155bhp depending on version. Here, a Carrera 2.0 roadster exhibits typical 356 chassis behaviour and handling: inside rear wheel well off the ground, and the front wheel angle indicating that the driver – obviously a skilled one – is applying plenty of opposite lock to combat the characteristic oversteer.

previous 356-series power unit, the 587 was crucially dependent on a high oil flow rate for the cooling of some areas.

As always, increased capacity translated into greater torque output, the 2-litre Type 587 delivering 162Nm instead of the 120Nm of the 1.6-litre Type 692 – and what is more, the torque peak came at 4,600rpm instead of an eye-watering 5,000rpm. Power output rose to 130bhp at 6,200rpm. For the final higher-performance versions, Carrera GS and GT, the power was 140bhp and 155bhp respectively. Today, we would not regard 155bhp from a 2-litre engine as anything special, even without taking exhaust emissions into account, but that is a measure of how far engine design has advanced in the interim. At the time, the 4-cam Carrera engine represented one of the peaks of production engine technology, even if that production was in small volume. It could hardly be said to have laid the foundation for what was to come, because Porsche's future lay with six cylinders rather than four, yet in many ways it prepared the enthusiasts for the future.

Porsche 356 engines

Year	Model	Engine	Series	Technical details (all bhp are DIN)
1949	356	1131	–	First Gmünd cars with VW derived engine
		1100	369	73.5 x 64mm = 1,086cc, 40bhp
1950	356	1100	369	Steel-bodied cars from Zuffenhausen
1951	356	1300	506	80 x 64mm = 1,286cc, 44bhp: chromed bores
1951	356	1500	502	80 x 74mm = 1,488cc, 55bhp: as 1300 but with Hirth built-up long-stroke crank, roller big-ends
		1500	527	As Type 502 but revised carburation etc, 60bhp
1952	356	1500	546	As 527 but forged crank, 55bhp
		1500S	528	As 527 with more valve overlap; 70bhp
		1500	546/2	As 546 but three-piece crankcase, for 1953 model year
		1500S	528/1	As 528 but three-piece crankcase, for 1953 model year
1953	356	1300S	589	74.5 x 74mm=1,290cc, built-up crank, valve timing as 1500S, 60bhp
1954	356	1100	369	Discontinued, effectively replaced by 1300A
		1300A	506/1	Dimensions as 1300S but forged crank, original 'mild' valve timing, 44bhp
		1300	506/2	As 506/1 but three-piece crankcase, for 1955 model year
		1300S	589/2	As 589 but three-piece crankcase, for 1955 model-year
1955	356A	1600	616/1	1600 engines standardised, 1300 and 1500 withdrawn. Now 82.5 x 74mm = 1,582cc, three-piece crankcase, forged crank, slightly revised valve timing; 60bhp 'base' engine
		1600S	616/2	As 616/1 but higher valve lift, more valve timing overlap: 75bhp
1961	356B	1600S	616/12	As 616/2 but cast iron cylinders, new pistons; 75bhp
		1600S90	616/7	Super 90 engine with substantially more valve timing overlap, more valve lift and higher compression ratio; 90bhp
1963	356C	1600C	616/15	Final 'base' engine, smaller inlet valves, larger exhaust valves, revised valve timing; 75bhp
		1600SC	616/16	Final 'S' engine, as 616/15 but Super 90 valve timing, 9.5 compression ratio; 95bhp

4-camshaft Carrera engines

Year	Model	Engine	Series	
1955	356A	Carrera	547/1	Original Fuhrmann 4-cam engine, Hirth type crankshaft, 85 x 66mm = 1,498cc, 100bhp
1958	356A	Carrera 1600GS	692	Bored-out to 82.5mm for 1,588cc, forged crankshaft; 105bhp
		Carrera 1600GT	692/3	As 692, higher (9.8) compression ratio, Weber carburettors; 115bhp
1962	356B	Carrera 2	587	Bored and stroked, 92 x 74mm, 1,966cc; 130bhp
		Carrera 2000GS	587/2	As 587, higher (9.8) compression ratio, revised exhaust; 140bhp
		Carrera 2000GT	587/2	155bhp with revised exhaust.

Production volumes:

Period	Type	No. of units
1950–55	356	7,627
1955–59	356A	20,345
1959–63	356B	30,963
1963–65	356C	16,668
1955–59	356A Carrera (1500 and 1600)	700
1960–65	365B Carrera (1600 and 2000)	375
1963–64	365C Carrera 2 (2000GS)	126

CHAPTER 4

1963: birth of an icon – 911 (and briefly, the 912)

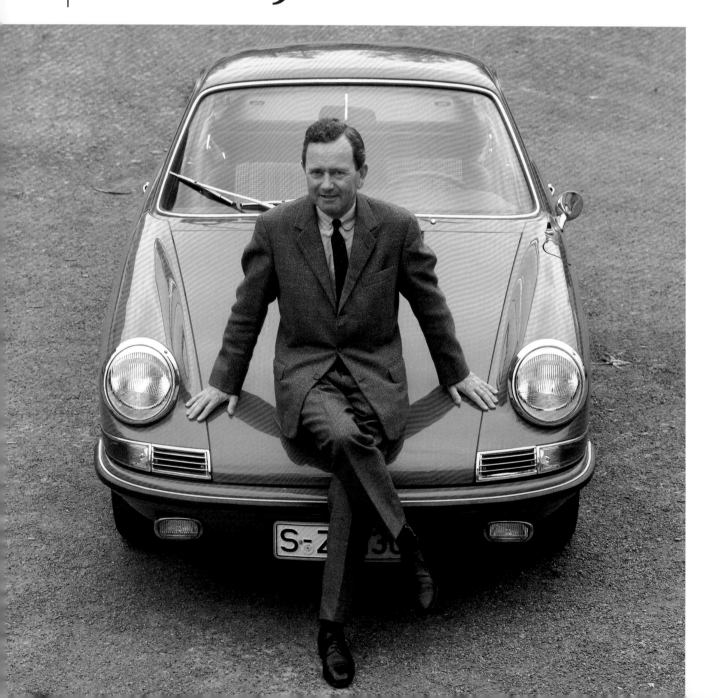

At the 1963 Frankfurt Motor Show, Porsche displayed a brand-new car, not so much a replacement for the 356 as a step up, larger and more powerful, with a flat-6 instead of a flat-4 engine. The new car was shown well in advance of production, and in reality the 356 had two more years of production ahead of it. Among other things, the delay provided the opportunity to change the newcomer's type number from 901 to 911, after Peugeot's lawyers had served a reminder that the French company had registered all the three-figure numbers with a zero in the middle! When the car did eventually emerge from the production line and begin to reach customers, it actually did so in two forms, the 911 and a less powerful 4-cylinder version, the 912. As *The Autocar* explained in its first road test of the 912 in September 1965, '… the 901 (later changed to 911) … was little more than a production prototype to prepare the way for a new range of Porsche models. But despite the early announcement, it is only this year that the previous Type 356 body has been discontinued and right-hand drive versions of the new car are only now beginning to come into this country.'

Books have been written about the 911 and this is no place for another one. Suffice it to say that the 911 in its later incarnations was very much – as people have often said of various Rolls-Royce projects – a triumph of development over design. The 911 being produced at the time of writing bears no more than a superficial resemblance to the car first conceived in the early 1960s as a slightly up-market successor to the 356. That resemblance does crucially include its general and very recognisable shape – even though they have not one panel in common – and its mechanical layout, with the engine overhung, like that of the 356 and of the Volkswagen Beetle, aft of the rear axle line. The shape may be admirable but the mechanical layout certainly is not. By the time the 911 appeared, the Beetle had already proved its susceptibility to front wheel locking under braking, to the onset of sudden oversteer when clumsily driven, and poor straight-line stability in sidewinds, all of these being due mainly to the tail-heavy weight distribution. Good traction was the only real compensation. So far as the 911 is concerned, the rest of the story is concerned with a search for ever improved performance while at the same time doing as much as possible to alleviate the ill effects of the basic layout. It is perhaps part of the apparently eternal

appeal of the 911 that Porsche has never completely succeeded in the latter task.

The tale of 911 evolution is such a long one that even in this book it must be covered in no less than seven chapters. This one looks at the model's earliest days, the basic decisions which led to the car being the way it was and is, and the overcoming – in so far as was possible – of its earliest and most manifest drawbacks. Later, in Chapter 6, I cover the first Turbo derivatives, which are very much a separate technical strand, and finally (starting with Chapter 9) the later naturally aspirated 911s, once they had received the substantially new 3-litre engine in 1978.

The drawbacks of the rear-engined layout did not deter the Porsche team in 1961, when serious work on the 356 replacement began. Before commencing any analysis, it should be emphasised that far from setting out to design one of the longest-lived of all motoring legends – at the time of writing, 41 years and going strong – the designers and engineers at Stuttgart had in mind no more than a larger, prettier and faster replacement for the 356. At the time, Porsche had the outlines of a product plan in mind which might have seen the new car live as long as the 356 – effectively around 15 years, but probably not that long.

The new car's size was determined as much as anything by the decision that it would be

After his father passed away, Ferry Porsche was very much in charge of the company's fortunes. Here he sits on the bonnet (or rather, the front luggage compartment lid) of a very early 911, long before the car established itself as one of the ultimate motoring icons.

rather more of a 2+2 than the 356, whose nominal back seats were not merely for children, but for small children, yet which would remain well short of being a full 4-seater which would have involved direct competition with Mercedes' coupé range, which were little less than restyled two-door saloons. To create the necessary extra space in the back seat, the wheelbase was set at 221cm (if you are sufficiently pedantic, 2,211mm) which was 11cm (4.3in) more than the 356. The styling team was directed by Ferry Porsche's son Ferdinand Alexander ('Butzi'), and the engineering of the body was entrusted to Reutter. Among the interior features was the ability to fold down the backs of the tiny back seats to form a decent rear luggage platform. Despite its shape the body was not given a hatchback, apparently because Reutter was worried that such a feature would be prone to leakage and aerodynamic noise.

1963: BIRTH OF AN ICON – 911 (AND BRIEFLY THE 912)

Left: The original 911 shape was master-minded by Ferry's son Ferdinand Alexander "Butzi" Porsche. Here, Butzi poses not with a 911, but with a 901, which was to have been the type number before trademark registration protests from Peugeot forced the shift to 911. In every important respect, it was only the number that changed, and not the car.

Below left: Side-by-side shot of a late-series 356 and a very early 911 show the considerable changes made by Butzi Porsche to create the new car, even if the spirit of its predecessor was retained. In particular, the windscreen

is much larger in area and the luggage compartment lid sweeps right down to the front bumper, losing in the process the tricky curved shut-line of the 356 panel.

Below: The real essence of the 911 was its all-new flat-6 engine, seen here in cutaway. Points to note include the rocker arm actuation of the opposed valves, the triple-throated downdraught carburettors, the big axial-flow air-cooling fan driven from the crankshaft, and of course the extremely complex exhaust system. Unlike the 356's 4-cylinder engine, packaging the 6-cylinder within the available space would always be a problem.

Flat-6 engine

The new car's larger size implied greater weight, which in turn called for the creation of a new engine to maintain the kind of performance which Porsche customers already expected. The new engine might, just, have been a big flat-4 but there was no easy way in which the Volkswagen power unit of the time could be stretched to the necessary 2-litre capacity. As related in Chapter 3, the 356 Carrera engine had indeed been stretched to 2-litre capacity, but the 4-cam Carrera power unit was non-Volkswagen in its fundamental dimensions (cylinder bore spacing and offset) and was extremely expensive to manufacture. Nor, indeed, did it offer the kind of driving characteristics to appeal to a wide audience, some of it more enthusiast than expert, of the kind Porsche now had in mind. Thus the decision was taken to develop a completely new and more suitable engine. It would inevitably be more expensive because there could be no more use of cheap Volkswagen-sourced components, but on the other hand it meant the engine could be designed with six

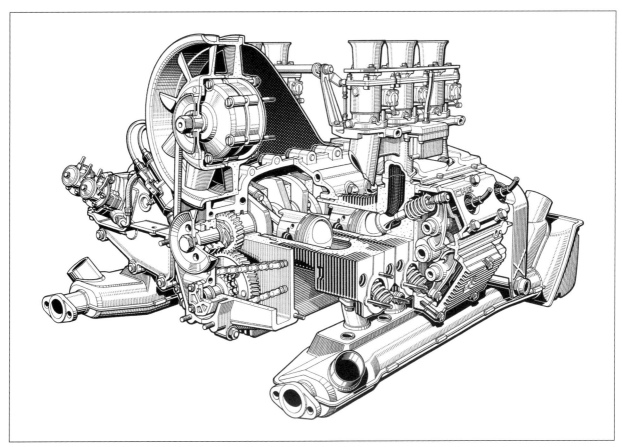

cylinders instead of just four, with the promise of better operating refinement and ultimately (because of greater piston area) more power.

Since it was to be an all-new engine, the choice of configuration was in theory wide open. Today, anyone setting out with the same overall objective in mind might opt for a mid-mounted V6, for example, but Porsche had been the moving spirit in the design and development of the air-cooled, flat-4 Volkswagen engine and there is no indication that management, and the engine design team led by Hans Tomala ever seriously considered anything other than an air-cooled flat-6 – except for one project in which the idea of using engine oil to cool the cylinders was studied. This was by no means a crazy idea since the function of oil in any engine as a means of transferring heat away from engine hot-spots is often overlooked: most people think of oil simply as a lubricant, but actually it is more than that. In the end, though, conventional air-cooling prevailed although decent cooling for a higher-output engine called for a much more efficient fan than the cheap radial-flow device used in the Volkswagen (and the Porsche 356). A new axial-flow fan was therefore developed, and worked well.

The key to the design of the new engine was cylinder head design and valve operation. It was quickly decided to adopt the highly efficient Fuhrmann cross-flow configuration with vee-opposed valves, giving good gas flow into the combustion chamber and out again, into exhaust manifolds beneath the engine; in the definitive design the inlet valves were angled 27 degrees above the horizontal and the exhausts 32 degrees below, for an included angle of 59 degrees. There was no question of carrying-over the complex and expensive valvetrain devised by Fuhrmann for the Carrera engines, but the vee-opposed valves could still be conveniently operated in one of three ways. The first was to install one camshaft above the crankshaft, operating the inlet valves via pushrods, and another below, operating the exhaust valves. In fact, engines with this layout were built and run (Type 745), but with unimpressive results. The inlet valve pushrods made it impossible to fit downdraught carburettors directly above the cylinder head. Instead, the inlet port had to enter from the side, the carburettor outboard of the engine itself. This made the entire power unit assembly uncomfortably wide – apart from which, the 745 turned out to be surprisingly noisy and suffered some durability problems.

The alternative layouts were overhead-camshaft. There could be a single camshaft per head operating all the valves via rockers, or twin camshafts with direct valve operation. The latter was felt to be too expensive, and probably also too bulky. The single shaft arrangement as drawn for the well over-square engine (80mm bore by 66mm stroke, for a capacity of 1,991cc) was agreeably neat and compact, while the carburettors could be mounted directly above the head and the exhaust manifolds directly below, as in the 356 engines but with the complication of needing to serve three cylinders each instead of just two. Thus there was no easy way of ensuring an even distribution of mixture between the cylinders, and carburation was to be something of an ongoing headache for the 911 until fuel injection arrived. For practical purposes there was no alternative to a chain drive to the camshafts (a geartrain would have been too noisy, and toothed belts were in their infancy). Great care was taken, both in the selection of supplier (Reynolds) and in detail design, to make the system quiet and reliable.

A more apparently daring decision was to adopt dry-sump lubrication, but there was really no alternative. One of the problems with any horizontally opposed engine is that of oil surge into the outer cylinder bank under high cornering forces, as Porsche had already discovered in the 356. The new car was one in which the cornering forces would certainly be high. To overcome the problem the sump would need to be extremely deep, but this would reduce ground clearance or force the engine to be mounted higher, reducing the flat-6's inherent advantage of a low centre of gravity. The alternative was to adopt a dry sump, and following trials with a wet-sump engine (Type 827) this was eventually agreed upon.

Porsche had never been afraid of unusual methods of engine construction. The Volkswagen Beetle flat-4, although eventually produced in huge numbers, was anything but conventional. The definitive (Type 901) Porsche flat-6 was built on the same general lines but with even less regard for expense. The aluminium alloy crankcase was split vertically, Volkswagen fashion, and enclosed an extremely complex forged and machined crankshaft. Not only was this fully counterbalanced: it ran in no fewer than eight bearings, one between each crank throw, one at each end, and yet another one supporting the extreme nose. The cylinders and cylinder heads were manufactured individually, the cylinders using the Biral process, first seen in the final-series 356C, in which aluminium alloy cooling fins were cast around a cast-iron core in which the pistons could run without risk of wear.

The cylinder heads were plain aluminium alloy. Each cylinder and cylinder head was secured to the crankcase by long studs, after which the camshaft carrier, again aluminium, was installed on top (or rather at each side, this being a flat engine). Originally, six individual single-choke downdraught Solex carburettors were fitted but in this form the engine suffered a disastrous mid-range flat-spot which could not be completely cured. Before long, the famous triple-choke Weber carburettors replaced them, to excellent effect. The cooling fan, mounted above the front of the engine and belt-driven from the crankshaft nose (hence the extra bearing) housed the alternator in its hub.

The result of all these decisions was an engine which delivered 130bhp (DIN) at 6,100rpm – a specific output of 65.3bhp/litre, by no means bad for a naturally aspirated mid-1960s engine with no nasty snags to spoil its driveability (once the Weber carburettors had arrived). Torque output was 129lb ft (175Nm) at 4,200rpm, rightly suggesting that even so, this was not an engine with strong low-speed urge. However, Porsche engineered an excellent new gearbox which could be either 'standard' 4-speed, or 'optional' 5-speed. A large majority of 911 buyers wisely took the option, and discovered a gearchange gate in which first was the 'odd ratio out', to the left and aft, opposite reverse, while most other 5-speed boxes – not that there were many of them in those days – tacked fifth onto a conventional 4-speed gate, betraying its overdrive nature. The Porsche gearbox was of course all-indirect and formed part of a transaxle. The gearshift linkage, as in the 356 and indeed the Volkswagen Beetle, felt long and loose by some standards but was by no means bad (the shift quality in the later mid-engined 914 was another matter). With the first major reworking of the transmission, Porsche reverted to the more familiar gate pattern, with fifth opposite reverse, to the right.

To smooth the transition between the 356 and the new car – which, being both larger and more powerful, was clearly going to be substantially more expensive – Porsche also made provision to install the 90bhp 1.6-litre OHV 4-cylinder engine from the final-series 356C, teamed either with a 4-speed gearbox or (at extra cost) with the new 5-speed unit, to create an 'entry level' version which would sell for substantially less. Clearly there was no difficulty installing the more compact engine, and the resulting car, designated 912, was both lighter and less tail-heavy, with the promise that it might be more nimble and easier to drive, to compensate for its lack of ultimate performance.

New body, new chassis

The new body was rather better aerodynamically than the late-series 356C, and still commendably compact; in fact, it was two inches narrower than its predecessor, although inevitably longer, overall as well as in its wheelbase. It was also far more scientifically designed than that of the 356. It was a fully unitary structure of considerable stiffness, with particularly strong sill sections and front bulkhead area. A further substantial cross-member ran between the rear wheel arches, with a yawning chasm behind it where the engine would go.

The nose structure was designed with great care so that the fuel tank and the spare wheel, fitting together almost like two pieces of a three-dimensional jigsaw puzzle, left a large, flat floor to a luggage space which could at least – unlike the 356 – accommodate one decent-sized suitcase plus a number of small, soft bags. 'Unlike the 356 which had only a trough about 10 x 10in under the front hatch between the spare wheel and the fuel tank', noted The Autocar, 'the 912 has a large, flat front luggage compartment beneath what amounts to a full-width lid.' Although they were not to know at the time, the body designers in this respect created a considerable problem as later 911 generations grew wider and wider tyres. Not for nothing was the 911 one of the first cars to offer a slender 'space-saver' spare tyre. Today, the 165R15 tyres fitted to the first 911 would themselves most likely be considered to be of no more than space-saver dimensions.

In view of the criticisms which had been levelled against the stability and handling of the 356 – usually looking back to a previous version after improvements had been introduced, but motoring journalism fifty years ago was like that – the suspension of the new car was substantially changed, hopefully for the better. At the front, the Volkswagen-derived double trailing-arm suspension gave way to a strut-type layout, unusual in that the springs were not coiled around the damper, as is more or less customary, but consisted of longitudinal torsion bars anchored to the main body structure. A clever and space-saving feature was that the torsion bars ran forward through the hollow base members of the wishbones.

A cross-member joined the rear mounting points of the wishbones, and to this the rack of the rack-and-pinion steering was mounted. Thus one important feature of the new car was a change of steering system, from the 356's worm-and-peg arrangement, together with elimination of the 356's spear-like steering column which would certainly not be countenanced by any modern safety engineer. Instead, the 911 steering column came in three sections, jointed together so that they would fold on impact. This also enabled the column – there being no engine in the way – to run sideways as well as forwards from the steering wheel, to reach the pinion in the very centre of the rack. A front anti-roll bar ran across the car aft of the rack.

There was nothing unusual about the torsion-bar springing medium, which had been used in cars as diverse as the Citroën *Traction Avant*, the Riley RME and the Morris Minor; it was more unusual to find it in combination with a MacPherson strut, but the geometry of the strut allows for any kind of spring so long as a way can be found to connect it. (In later years, for example, Fiat installed struts at the rear of the 128 and attached their lower ends to the extremities of a transverse leaf spring.) In the 911, deleting the coil spring meant that the strut could be kept very slim, creating more luggage space beneath the 'bonnet'.

From a handling point of view, the most important new feature was the back end, where the swing-axles had given way to semi-trailing arms, formed by blade-type trailing arms (as in the 356) plus substantial semi-trailing members, the two bolted together at their wheel ends to form the complete member. The 'roots' of the trailing arms were attached to the ends of a transverse torsion bar within a tube running across the car, more or less beneath the back seats. The dampers were conventional telescopic hydraulic units.

The new rear suspension layout at least mitigated the problems caused by the positive camber-change if the back end of the car lifted while cornering but they did not altogether overcome them. So long as the arms are merely semi-trailing rather than trailing, there remains a positive camber change to create the same reaction as with a swing-axle, except that to a degree, depending on the angle of semi-trail, the camber change is less. On the other hand, the semi-trailing angle also creates a toe-out wheel angle which will tend to increase the rate of turn. In a sufficiently powerful car this combination of effects creates its own handling problems, if rather more subtle than those of the plain swing-axle.

Porsche was not alone in discovering this, witness some of the accusations levelled at the first of the 'new generation' BMW saloons. But any more effective rear suspension layout such as double wishbones was, in effect, ruled out because the wide, low-mounted engine was in the way. A possible alternative might have been to use strut-type suspension at the back as well as the front, but that either did not occur to the chassis team, or was dismissed as an unknown which might bring problems of its own. (The brilliant example of the Lotus Elan emerged just too late to exert any influence, and other examples like the Datsun 240Z were still some way in the future).

All that should be said at this stage is that Porsche believed the swing-axle would tame the sometimes vicious oversteering reaction of the 356, which had only ever been addressed by setting up the chassis with more initial understeer, and eventually by fitting the compensating spring to reduce the rear roll stiffness. A factor working against the 911's handling was that the 6-cylinder engine, which being longer, inevitably moved the power unit centre of gravity further after of the rear axle line, increasing the rearward weight bias. This in turn meant that the twin dangers of locking the lightly laden front wheels if the brakes were harshly applied (Volkswagen Beetle fashion, one might say) and of initial understeer, especially at higher speeds, had to be carefully guarded against.

The 912: a brief, but strange career

Before proceeding on the long, long story of the 911 it is worth getting the 912 out of the way. The 4-cylinder car enjoyed only a brief life before being effectively replaced by the new, mid-engined, lower-priced 914 family (Chapter 5). It was certainly no ball of fire, although its good aerodynamics and sensible gearing meant it had a reasonable maximum speed. In *The Autocar* test already referred to, the 912 managed a maximum speed of 119mph but took 11.9sec to reach 60mph from rest, not surprisingly on a par with the old Type 356 1600SC. Overall fuel consumption was a rather disappointing 23.6mpg.

Perhaps inevitably, great praise was heaped on the stability and handling. 'We found the car hung on to the chosen line through bends beyond all reasonable limits … until finally the tail swung out gently and progressively, and then came straight again immediately correction was applied,' said the testers, adding that 'There is none of the wandering usually associated with rear-engined cars. On gusty days the car seems to wobble slightly on its tyres …' Well, this was the 912 with less weight in its tail and less power to

Spot the difference: the biggest giveaway is the number plate! The 912 was in effect a 911 but powered by a carried-over 1.6-litre 4-cylinder engine, for those who valued the looks but didn't want the performance of the 911. The 912 ran only from 1966 to 1969, to be replaced by the ugly but cheaper VW-Porsche 914. Porsche needed all the production capacity it had to turn out the "proper" 911.

encourage the tail to depart sideways, but with the benefit of hindsight it sounds astonishingly kind-hearted. There was great praise for the feel and the choice of ratios in the (5-speed) gearbox, and no adverse comment on the fact that 125lb pedal pressure was needed for a maximum-rate stop with the servo-less all-disc brake system.

In any event, the car was never going to enjoy a long life. Effectively launched for the 1966 model year, it ran for three years before the 914 range supplanted it. However, the 912 had the last laugh. The eventual withdrawal of the 914 in 1974 meant that Porsche would lack an 'entry level' model in its important US

market prior to the arrival of the 914's spiritual replacement the 924 (Chapter 7). Accordingly, for one year only, the 912 designation was resurrected, and applied to a version of the 911 in which the flat-6 engine was replaced by the fuel-injected 2-litre flat-4 Volkswagen engine from the 411LE – essentially the same engine which powered the final-series 914. Some American enthusiasts (the 912E was never sold in Europe) rate the 912E as a better car than the 'original' 912 in many respects – not only for its greater torque output but also for its lower replacement parts costs and its partly galvanised body construction, a development process which had begun during the 914's career. Despite this final brief fling, the 912 was never more than a short side-alley off the main path of 911 development, which as already pointed out, was essentially concerned with two things only. One was the achievement of much better performance, while the other might be described as a running battle to achieve and maintain acceptable standards of handling despite the demands created by so much extra power.

Stretching the flat-6

As originally announced, the flat-6 engine delivered 130bhp, which at the time was a reasonable specific power output for a 2-litre SOHC power unit. Two development paths were open to the Porsche engineers: to tune it, and to stretch it. As time went on, they did both, although the greater emphasis was eventually on the stretching. The flat-6 had been designed with a degree of stretch in mind – in fact, Ferry Porsche is reported to have said that if it has been appreciated the degree to which it could be bored and stroked for greater capacity, it would have been designed smaller and lighter in the first place! Before the stretching began, however, Porsche created a range of three engines, one more powerful and sporting in nature and the other less powerful, but with a lower torque peak and fatter curve, therefore easier to drive. These two sat on either side of the standard engine, so that the range became the 110bhp 911T, 130bhp 911L, and 160bhp 911S.

The 911S was actually the first of these derivatives to appear, in 1967. The extra power was achieved through straightforward tuning techniques, including a higher compression ratio (9.8:1 instead of 9:1), valve diameters increased by 3mm, revised inlet valve timing with more overlap (opening earlier, closing later), a revised exhaust system (with smoother flow through the cabin-heating heat exchanger) and suitably revised Weber carburettors with higher maximum fuel flow rate. To make sure the extra stresses were contained, the pistons were forged rather than cast, the connecting rods were nitrided and the little-end bearings strengthened. The distinctly sporting nature of this first 911S can be seen in the fact that peak power was developed at 6,600rpm instead of 6,100rpm, with peak torque coming at 5,200rpm. This was certainly not an engine for the lazy driver, and it is interesting to see how quickly Porsche, with its customer base broadening to include many more who were less than expert, or who simply didn't want to indulge in so much gear shifting, moved to develop the engine in the opposite direction, to produce the 911T.

By the time the 911T appeared, the 911 itself had already passed through its original O-series phase and had moved on to the A-series, introduced for the 1968 model year. The process by which the 911T was derived was equally logical. The compression ratio was reduced instead of increased (to 8.6:1), and both the inlet and exhaust valve timing was 'unwound' to

reduce overlap. As a result, peak power was produced at only 5,800rpm and although the torque peak was still 4,200rpm, the torque curve was fatter and the engine would respond well at lower speeds, which was the whole idea. The lower power output and lower operating speeds also allowed the engine to be made cheaper, with plain cast-iron instead of Biral cylinders, and a crankshaft without the complete counter-weighting of the 911L – as the mid-range car had now become – and the 911S.

One more major tuning feature was added before the stretching process began. For the 1969 model year, the A-series 911 gave way to the B-series, and both of the more powerful engine versions were switched from carburettors to Bosch mechanical fuel injection. As a result, the 911E (E for *Einspritz*, injection), formerly the 911L, now produced 140bhp, and the 911S 170bhp. Peak power speeds increased slightly (the 911S peaking at 6,800rpm, no less), but there was less of the unwillingness and plug-fouling previously experienced if the 911S was driven slowly and gently for any length of time, and fuel consumption at steady high speeds was improved. Conventional ignition gave way to a capacitative-discharge system, and the 911S was fitted with an oil cooler to ensure that oil temperatures remained within bounds under continuous high loads. At the other end of the scale, the 911T engine was left essentially unchanged, continuing with carburettors and still producing 110bhp. All three engines, however, switched from a die-cast aluminium crankcase to a pressure-cast magnesium one, for a weight saving of 10kg (22lb) aft of the rear axle line. It was a useful move towards taming the still-skittish behaviour of the early 911s, although the chassis changes also introduced with the B-series cars (see below) had a more significant effect.

The scene was now set for the first stage of engine enlargement – a simple boring-out from the original 80mm to 84mm, making the capacity 2,195cc. There was no problem with this opening-out: in fact, Paul Frère points out that competition 911s had been bored-out to 87.5mm for a capacity of 2,381cc. All three engine variants were enlarged and fitted to the C-series cars which emerged for the 1970 model year. Now, all three versions were fitted with very similar cylinder heads, the valve sizes being the same in all three cases, and the performance differences were determined mainly by compression ratio and valve timing (and fuel system; the 2.2-litre 911T was still carburettor equipped). But power output rose usefully, to 125bhp at 5,800rpm for the 911T, 155bhp at 6,200rpm for the 911E, and 180bhp at 6,500rpm for the 911S. Because of the greater swept volume, torque was also significantly increased and brought with it the need for a larger-diameter clutch.

The next rational development step was to increase the stroke. The 2.2-litre engine had a substantially over-square bore-to-stroke ratio of 1.27, and this led to a combustion chamber shape which was much too flat for highest efficiency, especially in the high-compression 911S, with an over-large ratio of surface area to volume. The maximum stroke increase which could be achieved with no more than minor alterations to the crankcase was from 66mm to 70.4mm, which combined with the 2.2-litre's bore of 84mm yielded a capacity of 2,341cc, always misleadingly referred to as 2.4-litres nominal, from the time it was introduced for the 1972 model year. Externally, the engine remained almost identical: the crankshaft throw being increased by 4.4mm, the connecting rods were shortened by 2.2mm (from 130mm to 127.8mm) so that the block height (or more accurately, width) remained the same. A fully counterweighted crankshaft was made standard: with the longer stroke, the 'cheap' 911T crankshaft no longer sufficed. Positive piston cooling was introduced, with a system of oil jets spraying on the piston undersides above a certain engine speed – one of

the earliest applications of a technique which has since become widespread.

Remarkably, or so it seemed at the time, Porsche simultaneously reduced the compression ratios of all three versions – to 7.5:1, 8.0:1 and 8.5:1 respectively. In the early 1970s, it should be recalled, American emissions regulations were beginning to call for control of NOx (oxides of nitrogen), while the European authorities were beginning to fret about the amount of lead additive in high-octane petrol. Through their drastic reduction of compression ratio, Porsche both reduced the 911's NOx emissions and enabled the car to run on 91RON regular-grade petrol ('2-star' petrol in the UK). What is more, they did so without damaging the performance. All three versions of the 2.4-litre engine delivered more power, and substantially more torque than their predecessors (enough torque, indeed, to call for an all-new, stronger gearbox). Power outputs rose to 130bhp at 5,600rpm, 165bhp at 6,200rpm, and 190bhp at 6,500rpm respectively, but fuel consumption suffered because the lower compression reduced the engine's thermal efficiency. The author has especially fond memories of the 911E 2.4 for which he wrote the *Autocar* road test; the car would consistently accelerate to 60mph in 7.5sec, proving very easy to get off the line with just

The triple-throat carburettors have given way to short, straight inlet ducts, with petrol feed from an early Bosch mechanical fuel injection system. This was used for all except the "base" 911T. This is a 2-litre 911S engine, delivering 170bhp. Unseen but important, the crankcase was no longer aluminium, but lighter magnesium. The 911S came with a standard oil cooler, which was destined to get bigger and bigger.

enough wheelspin to keep the engine 'on the cam'. It went on to 100mph in 19.5sec, and a maximum of 137mph. Its overall fuel consumption, however, was only 18.0mpg (15.7 litres/100km), and this at a time when European fuel prices were about to rise steeply.

Even yet, we are still only part-way through the engine development story. Having started with a 2-litre engine, bored it out to 2.2-litre capacity and then lengthened the stroke to bring it to '2.4 litres', the next logical step was to bore it out again. If there is space, boring-out is always easier than increasing the stroke, calling at a bare minimum only for larger-diameter pistons, while a stroke increase means a new crankshaft and connecting rods – much more expensive. Consequently the Porsche engineers looked to increase the bore of the flat-6 all the way from 84mm to 90mm, which would result in a capacity of 2,687cc (2.7 litres nominal). The only problem was that there wasn't room: it seemed the engine had finally run out of stretch. At least, it would have, had Porsche not

Changes aplenty as compared with the previous engine: this is the 2.7-litre unit used in the 1976 911S, with Bosch K-Jetronic injection. Boring-out to 90mm for the 2.7-litre capacity was made possible by doing away with cylinder liners and adopting the Nikasil silicon-etching process, which enabled aluminium pistons to run directly in aluminium bores.

gained experience of a new technology, originally developed for the internal surfaces of Wankel rotary engines, in the flat-12 engine of the fearsome 917 racing car. This Nikasil technology allowed aluminium pistons to be run directly in aluminium bores – but bores coated with an extremely thin layer of nickel and silicon carbide which was then etched, leaving a very smooth surface of extremely hard silicon carbide crystals, and between them 'valleys' which very conveniently retained a good supply of lubricating oil. Freed from the need to maintain sufficient wall thickness to apply the Biral process – a cast-iron liner surrounded by a cast-in-place finned alloy exterior – the engineers were able to open the engine to the required 90mm bore, to create the 2.7-litre engine.

At first, the 2.7-litre was built only in small numbers and fitted to a supplementary 911 version, the Carrera, resurrecting the name formerly applied to the 4-cam versions of the Type 356. This became available when the F-series 911 was introduced for the 1973 model year, the first concern being to build 1,000 units to a lightweight specification so that the model could be homologated for competition. In the event, this was not a problem, because demand for the Carrera easily exceeded that target. With hardly any changes from 911S specification other than those needed to achieve the capacity increase, the Carrera engine developed 210bhp at 6,300rpm. This, it should be borne in mind, was an engine which would still run happily on 91RON 'regular grade' petrol. For competition purposes, as the RSR, the engine proved reliably capable of delivering 300bhp.

For the 1976 model year, by which time the 911 had reached I-series, the 2.7-litre capacity was made standard. The structure of the range was changed, the previous T and E designations vanishing so that the 'base' version was the plain 911, while the 911S remained and the increasingly popular Carrera became top of the range. The engines, still with low compression, were power-differentiated almost entirely by valve timing and exhaust configuration, and a different fuel injection system for the Carrera (a significant, almost historic change for this series was the final disappearance of carburettors: the 911 and 911S had Bosch K-Jetronic injection, and the Carrera a plunger-type system).

After a short time, the 911 and 911S engines abandoned Nikasil cylinders in favour of yet another new technology in which the cylinders were cast in a high-silicon aluminium alloy (Alusil), while the pistons were coated with iron in a new process developed by

Mahle. This was a cheaper and more convenient alternative to Nikasil, although the latter was retained for the Carrera engine, and was also eventually adopted for the V8 engine in the 928 (Chapter 8). The respective power outputs were 150bhp at 5,700rpm, and 175bhp at 5,800rpm, indicating that the lower-powered engines had in effect been detuned, making them even more flexible and easier to drive, at some small sacrifice in maximum speed.

During 1974, the 911 Turbo made its appearance (Chapter 6), bringing with it a further enlargement of the flat-6 engine, to a full 3-litre capacity (actually a further boring-out to 95mm, combining with the existing 70.4mm stroke to yield 2,994cc). Competition experience, soon confirmed by the early Turbos, proved there was no reason not to take the naturally-aspirated standard production 911 engine to a 95mm bore, and this was done by stages which reflected the arrival of the 2.7: first the Carrera, which became the Carrera 3.0 for the 1976 (K-series) model year, and then a year later for the entire range, launched for the 1977 model year as the L-series. This, however, takes us to a point where much else had been happening at Zuffenhausen, and the arrival of the standard 3-litre engine marks a convenient break, both to catch up with those other events and to prevent this chapter becoming too long, before looking at the later stages of the naturally aspirated 911 story (Chapter 9).

Sportomatic: a strange diversion

Remarkably early in the career of the 911, because of trends in the increasingly important US market, the question of automatic transmission arose. There was at that time no question of the car being offered with a conventional automatic. It would have weighed too much, and would have sapped performance to an unacceptable extent. This was a time, remember, when existing automatics were mostly 3-speed, and before modern developments like torque converter lock-up had arrived to make automatics more efficient and their reactions more sprightly.

There was an alternative, however. The mid-1960s was a period when there was great interest in the idea of 'semi-automatic' transmission, the idea being to do away with the clutch pedal while leaving the driver in full control of gear selection. A torque converter

replaced the clutch for starting from rest, but instead of a fully automatic gearbox, a manual box was retained together with a separate servo clutch, operated by a sensor in the transmission selector, to disengage drive while the driver shifted between ratios. The concept appeared as an option in a strange assortment of cars, and it was made standard on the NSU Ro80. It was usually reckoned that the multiplication effect of the torque converter meant that fewer forward gears were needed, and most of the semi-automatics including the Ro80 had only three speeds. Porsche decided the idea was worth pursuing to satisfy a segment of the potential US market, and engineered a 4-speed semi-automatic which it designated Sportomatic, which was offered from 1968. This used a Fichtel and Sachs torque converter, a vacuum servo clutch, and microswitch sensors in the base of the transmission selector, to disengage the clutch almost as soon as the selector was moved (the Ro80 sensors were inside the gear selector knob).

The Sportomatic enjoyed what some might regard as a remarkably long life, to the extent of being upgraded for additional torque capacity with the arrival of the 2.4-litre engines, and substantially reworked, with only three forward speeds, in 1977 to match it to the first of the naturally aspirated 3-litre engines. From time to time the rationale of which 911 versions would be offered in Sportomatic form, and in which markets, was changed. It was usually assumed that 911S and Carrera buyers would be less interested in driving clutchless. However, the last Sportomatics were built in 1979 (but possibly sold in 1980), after which, so far as two-pedal 911 driving was concerned, it became a question of waiting for Tiptronic, which was mechanically a completely different concept.

Keeping up: chassis development

As previously pointed out, Porsche adopted a new approach to chassis design for the 911, by comparison with the 911. Both the front and rear suspension layouts were different, in the hope that the misbehaviour, or the 'exciting' handling of the 356 depending on your point of view, would be substantially tamed despite the retention of the tail-heavy, rear-engine layout – and of an engine whose own centre of mass was further behind the rear axle line. In the earliest cars, the O and A-series, this was really not the case.

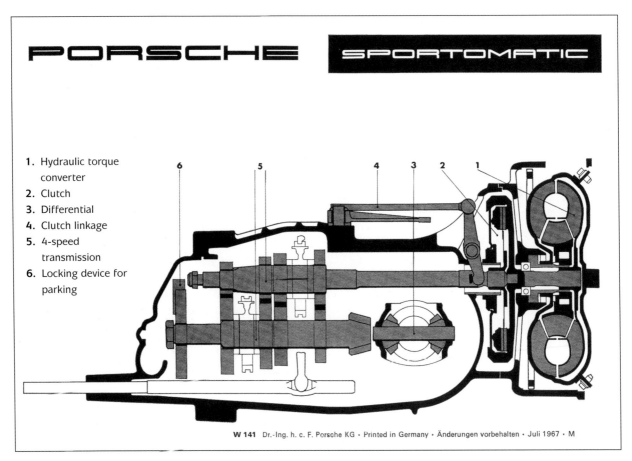

PORSCHE **SPORTOMATIC**

1. Hydraulic torque converter
2. Clutch
3. Differential
4. Clutch linkage
5. 4-speed transmission
6. Locking device for parking

W 141 Dr.-Ing. h. c. F. Porsche KG · Printed in Germany · Änderungen vorbehalten · Juli 1967 · M

There ensued a long series of modifications to try and improve matters, taking into account both the suspension itself and the aerodynamics.

The first substantial move was simple and vital. Adjustment was provided at the upper ends of the front suspension struts after it was discovered that the earliest production cars, manufactured with tolerances which had not been present in the prototypes, were extremely sensitive to minor variations in camber and castor angle. It was also realised that the production line was not initially provided with any means for checking that the torsion-bar settings were properly balanced, with the result, as Paul Frère puts it in his classic Porsche 911 book (Haynes), that 'a car (could) be perfectly horizontal, when viewed from the front, with two diagonally-opposed springs wound up very tight and the other two carrying only very little of the car's weight.' The result, in such a case, was a car which behaved very differently according to whether it was turning left or right, the ratio of front to rear roll stiffness being different.

Once these measures had been taken, the 911's behaviour became consistent but not, in many eyes,

The need of the American market for an automatic (or at least, two-pedal) version of the 911 was first answered with the development of the Sportomatic, seen here in section. It combined a torque converter as its "launch device", plus a servo-operated "automatic" clutch and a 4-speed gearbox whose ratios had still to be manually selected. The option survived from 1968 until 1979.

consistently good. It eventually emerged (revealed in Paul Frère's book) that when early customers complained of twitchy handling, the dealers were ready with a 'suspension adjustment' which consisted of two 11kg (24lb) blocks of metal hidden one inside each end of the flush-fitting front bumper! It was discovered, for reasons which are still not obvious but may have something to do with inertia around the roll axis, that two separate blocks were better than one single one in the extreme nose. For the A-series cars, the 'reinforced bumpers' were made the production standard. Some benefit was also derived from increasing the wheel rim width from the original 4.5in to 5.5in, even though the tyre section remained the same (165R15). The improvement in handling was perceptible but this was hardly an engineering solution worthy of Porsche, who then proceeded to devise for the rear suspension a package of revisions, overseen by the young Dipl. Ing. Ferdinand Piëch, which was far neater and had the benefit of not adding nearly half a hundredweight to the 911's kerb weight.

The change consisted essentially of lengthening the wheelbase by 57mm (2.24in), to 2,268mm (89.3in). In effect, the rear wheels were moved that much aft and the geometry of the rear suspension members altered to match, reducing the semi-trailing angle of the suspension arms. No lengthening of the body was involved: the engine and transmission remained in the same place and to bridge the gap, the drive shafts ran at a slightly 'swept back' angle when viewed in plan. This meant both the inner and outer drive shaft joints ran at a constant small angle, and to eliminate any possible effect on refinement the inner joint (which also accommodated drive shaft plunge) was changed to a constant-velocity type. The new layout actually had two distinct benefits. The handling was improved because of the change in the semi-trailing angle, and the weight distribution became slightly less tail-heavy, sufficiently so to improve both stability and handling. In addition, the benefit of the 'reinforced bumpers' was retained, yet without weight penalty, by replacing the original, big 12V battery on the centre-line with two smaller 6V batteries, wired in series and installed one in each front wing, as close to the corner as practicable (which made them pigs to access for service, but it seemed to be a price worth paying).

Once this modified rear suspension had been introduced in the B-series cars for the 1969 model year, mechanical changes were mainly confined to the fitting and the stiffness of the anti-roll bars, the rim and tyre sizes, and the damper specification. The most logical way to balance the handling of a tail-heavy car is to fit larger (or at least wider) tyres at the rear than at the front, perfectly exemplified by modern Formula 1 cars. It was a long while before Porsche moved in this direction, since some of its important markets required the carrying of spare wheels to replace any road wheel: hence different-size wheels front and rear call for the carriage of two spare wheels of similar sizes, clearly an impossible constraint. It was really only when space-saver spare tyres gained approval and became available that different sizes were adopted, at least to the extent of fitting wider but lower-profile tyres on wider rims at the rear, as first seen in the original Carrera RS which had 185/70VR15 tyres on 6-inch rims at the front, and

215/60VR16 tyres on 7-inch rims at the rear. Thus the front and rear tyre rolling radii were virtually identical but the cornering power of the rear tyres was greater, matching the greater load they carry.

The real 'heavyweight' evolution of 911 wheels and tyres really came with the 3-litre (and above) versions, although it is worth noting that the standard wheel and tyre size quite quickly widened to 185/70VR15 covers on 6-inch rims. Equally, it should be borne in mind that wider rims invariably increase both the track (which is usually good) and the offset (with far more debatable effects), while increasing the loads on the wheel hubs and hub carriers – which manufacturers like Porsche can take into account, unlike those who fit exaggerated components from the aftermarket. Wider wheels naturally demand wider wheel arches, with a visible effect on body shape and (usually) an adverse effect on aerodynamics; and wider front wheels increase turning circle, because of the greater restrictions on their angular movement. Wider is not always better. Certainly there comes a time in the life of any long-lived, high-performance car when engineers decide that if they had ever intended to fit tyres that wide, they would have designed the body differently. That is a technical undertone that lies beneath many of the subtle later evolutions of the 911 shape, right through to the 997.

The other side of chassis development is aerodynamics. Vehicle aerodynamics were still in their infancy when the 911 was taking shape. Engineers were interested in drag coefficient, but much less so in lift or in the yawing moment, the key to sidewind stability. Thus the 911 was designed with an agreeably low drag coefficient (by the standards of its day), comfortably better than the final-series 356C, but far less attention was paid to those aspects of aerodynamics which affected handling and stability – the chassis-related aspects. The deficiency was quickly recognised, and alongside the chassis improvements described above, measures were studied to improve the aerodynamics. The first anxiety was to find ways of reducing the lift to which the body was evidently subject at high speeds.

Aerodynamic lift essentially results from pressure above being lower than pressure beneath. In the 911, the smooth, drooping nose shape appeared to promise downforce, if anything. However, air passing over the smooth lid of the luggage compartment was speeded up, and consequently its pressure was reduced, while beneath the car the flow was slowed, and the pressure if anything increased, by everything that was there to

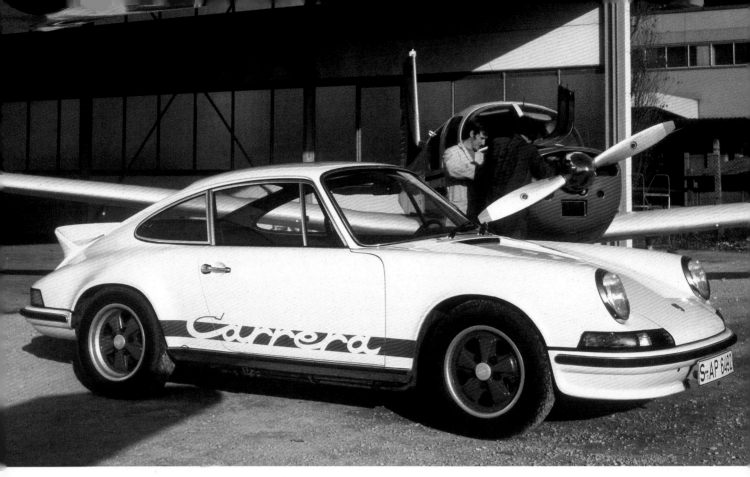

get in its way. The same thing was happening at the back, where the elegant and gradual taper of the rear body, while being good for drag, meant there were large areas (especially at the extreme tail) where the airflow remained nicely attached to the surface and where pressure was consequently low. To put figures on it, measurements taken in the University of Stuttgart wind tunnel revealed that at the 143mph maximum speed of the 911S, the standard body was subjected to a front lift of 183lb and a rear lift of 255lb. Things became even worse in the presence of a sidewind component. At the same time, it was determined that the car's centre of aerodynamic pressure was well forward of its centre of gravity. Taking the centre of the line joining the mid-points of the front and rear axle lines as a reference point, the centre of pressure was in fact nearly 32in forward of it while the centre of gravity (the car being tail-heavy) was several inches aft. This was a certain recipe for instability in gusting sidewinds.

First priority was given to reducing front end lift, since complaints of the steering 'going light' and of increased understeer through high-speed bends. Competition experience had already pointed to the effectiveness of chin-type spoilers and air dams. There are clear practical limits to how deep such a spoiler can be in a road-going car, but even a shallow dam can

The 911 Carrera RS (RennSport) was quickly established as the ultimate high-performance road-going 911. This is a 1973 model-year RS 2.7, clearly no shrinking violet when it came to appearance, not only because of the side decals but also due to the "beard" front spoiler and the rear duck-tail, which really did reduce aerodynamic lift. The RS was the first 911 to have wider rear wheels and tyres than those at the front.

prevent a surprising amount of air from passing beneath the car, reducing the pressure and therefore the lift acting on the nose. The air dam which was quickly introduced for the 911S, and made standard across the range with the arrival of the B-series, was shown to reduce maximum-speed lift to a more modest 103lb. Rear-end lift on the other hand was virtually unaffected, at 252lb. This was quite enough (especially with improved front-end grip) to encourage oversteer through high-speed bends, the more so in windy conditions. The next step was therefore to conquer the rear-end lift also, even though this could only be done by spoiling that smooth rear-deck line.

The first method to be tried was to add a so-called duck-tail spoiler to the rear deck aft of the engine air intake (the grille aft of the rear window). This proved extremely effective, not only in reducing rear-end lift to around a third of its former value, but also increasing pressure around the air intake and therefore the flow through the engine compartment. As a bonus, 'spill' from the sides of the spoiler kept the rear lamp clusters cleaner in dirty weather. There was only one problem: some authorities (including those in Porsche's German home market) considered the duck-tail potentially dangerous to pedestrians and would not homologate it. Porsche returned to the drawing-board and invented an even more effective alternative, the 'tray' spoiler with flexible edges, and actually incorporating the engine air intake which is therefore raised higher and into a more efficient position. A near-perfect aerodynamic balance was then achieved by deepening the front air dam, again with an elastomer rim so that slight contacts with the road and the bottom of steep ramps are not too embarrassing. As a result the total front-plus-rear lift, which would be nearly 400lb at 150mph, is reduced to less than 40lb. It is still not positive downforce, but for a road-going car it is perhaps better to have handling characteristics which remain entirely consistent regardless of speed.

That classic body

The one thread running through the whole history of the 911, from 1963 to 2007, is the immediately recognisable shape of the body. We need only to note the skills which have kept it so, despite all the pressures to make it change. We have already seen how the need to reduce its aerodynamic lift led to the introduction of front and rear spoilers, yet it has always seemed possible to 'see through' the appendages to the original shape beneath. Safety requirements played their part in trying to spoil things, most notably the US requirement for energy-absorbing bumpers fitted from the 1974 model year onwards, yet failed significantly to disturb the picture. Eventually a neater collapsible bumper design became standard even in Europe, and the casual onlooker was probably never aware of the change no matter how familiar the 911 shape had become. Other passive safety features, such as door beams to protect against side impact, have added weight, but done nothing to disturb the shape.

Other less visible concerns also fell within the remit of the body engineering department. These included body construction out of steel which had been galvanised on both sides – now widely used throughout the industry, but of which Porsche was very much a pioneer. Improvements to the heating

system were also a fairly urgent matter. Having an air-cooled engine, the 911 was more or less condemned to using a 356-type (indeed, Volkswagen Beetle-type) system in which heat was gathered from an exchanger built around the exhaust system. In its crude form, this was really unsatisfactory, because its output varied with speed and engine output (it was also a constraint on exhaust system design, but short of installing a dedicated fuel-burning heater, which was indeed offered for some early-series export versions, there was little that could be done about that). Eventually the system was improved to work on the airmix principle, the hot air being blended with cool fresh air and automatically controlled to maintain a stable temperature, but the definitive solution to the problem had to wait for the advent of partly water-cooled engines. Less forgivably, 911 owners had to wait almost as long for decent fresh-air ventilation when cruising with the windows closed.

I have gone right through this chapter without discussing variations in body style. In fact during the pre-3-litre period there was only one alternative, the 911 Targa. Today, no doubt, many youngsters talk about 'targa bars' without realising that Porsche devised the layout in which a roofless but not-quite-convertible body sported a wide and stiff hoop which provided protection during a rollover accident. This also served as the midway support for a two-section roof – a rigid or semi-rigid panel inserted between hoop and windscreen header, and a fold-away rear section with a rear window, to complete the enclosure of the cabin in bad weather. The Targa was remarkably early on the 911 scene, appearing for the 1967 model year. At first it could prove leaky and noisy, as the body designers came fully to grips with the problems created by chopping away the roof and rear pillars of the body within which Erwin Komenda had so carefully distributed the stresses, while remaining faithful to Butzi Porsche's design drawings. But customers were enthusiastic, demand remained high and the company persisted, until the Targa became a thoroughly satisfactory product which was offered as an alternative body style throughout the first decades of the 911's life. The fully decapitated cabriolet came much later, since Porsche like its rivals, believed through the early 1970s that US safety regulations would outlaw any design without positive rollover protection. By the time it was realised this would not happen, time had moved into the territory covered by Chapter 9 … and the Porsche 911 was still less than halfway through its career.

CHAPTER 5

1969–1975: VW-Porsche 914 and 914/6

Almost as soon as the 911/912 was in production, Porsche turned its attentions to a completely new car, this time working directly with Volkswagen. The essential idea was to create a compact and relatively cheap sports car which would open a wider market to Porsche, enabling it to replace the 912 and leave the 911 standing alone as the up-market model. At the same time it would expand the Volkswagen range into a new sector, at that time mainly occupied by the then-surviving British manufacturers. The lower price necessary for this purpose would be achieved partly by burrowing into the Volkswagen parts bin, partly through the economy of scale implicit in building in the kind of volume Volkswagen expected to achieve, and partly through simplifying the structure to make it easier and cheaper to produce. Work went ahead under the Porsche designation 914.

The question was, what kind of car should it be? A two-seater, so much was obvious. The more difficult question was whether to retain the already classic Volkswagen and Porsche mechanical layout with the engine overhung aft of the rear axle line, or to switch to a front engine and rear-wheel drive, which at that time was still the conventional layout for the existing (mainly British) sports cars with which the new model would compete, especially in the important US market. However, there was a third alternative, and that was the mid-engine. This, remember, was an era when the now-familiar layout for single-seater racing cars had only recently been universally accepted – the engine behind the driver but ahead of the driven back wheels. Nor was it just a layout for racing cars. The world of the motoring enthusiasts was awash with tales of coming road cars using the mid-engined layout. The Italians, darlings of

At first sight identical, but in fact not: the difference is betrayed by the smaller bulk of the 4-cylinder Volkswagen engine with its associated gearbox and exhaust system, compared with that of the Porsche-engined 914/6, the latter with its six distinctive downdraught trumpets. Perhaps the most remarkable thing is that the Porsche power unit seems to be little more of a squeeze than the Volkswagen unit.

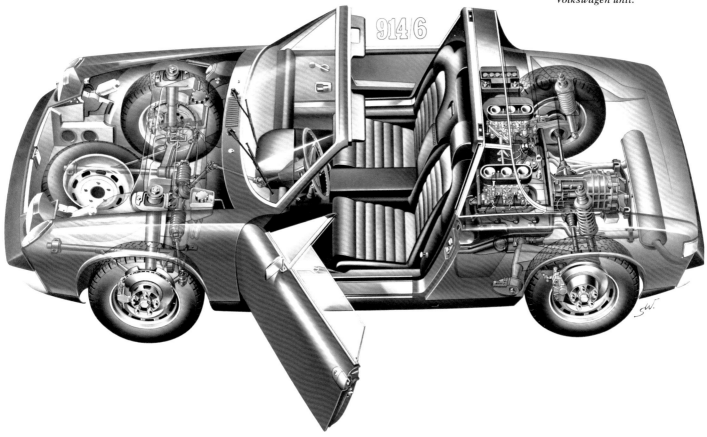

the sports car world at that time, were on the way to using mid-engines in everything from the Lamborghini Miura, through the Ferrari Dino to the relatively humble Fiat X1/9. Lotus was working on the Europa, Matra on the M530, and MG on the stillborn ADO21. The major motoring magazines, those arbiters of fashion, were becoming positively rude about 'old fashioned' sports cars with the engine in front.

There were (and are) at least three sound engineering reasons for the mid-engine layout, although they are sounder in the case of outright racing cars than they are of road cars. First of all, putting the engine in the middle of the car makes for an even front-to-rear weight distribution, which is good for sports-type handling and also for reasonable stability, certainly when compared with a tail-heavy layout. Second, placing the engine's considerable mass close to the centre of gravity reduces the polar moment of inertia – it takes less force to make the car change direction (strictly speaking, to change its yaw rate) which makes it feel more responsive. Third, mid-engined cars can be made more compact, lighter and more aerodynamic than their front-engined rivals, because with the occupants and all the main mechanical components within the wheelbase, the designer is free to do more or less what he likes with the nose and tail.

Porsche – and Volkswagen – took little convincing that they could benefit from two of these three considerations. They already knew that the tail-heavy weight distribution that comes with an engine cantilevered aft of the final drive was a big minus when it came to stability and handling. The German autobahns were liberally supplied with windsocks and 'beware side wind' warnings, mainly for the benefit of Volkswagen Beetle drivers. Mid-engined would be better. The low polar moment of inertia would make the car more nimble – surely desirable in any sports car. The real challenge came with the packaging of the product, of which more later.

Making the engine fit was not too much of a challenge. The air-cooled flat-4 Volkswagen engine, and Porsche's own flat-6, were compact enough to sit immediately aft of a rear bulkhead tight up against the seat backs, and drive the rear wheels through a transaxle. In crude terms, it could be thought of as what the Volkswagen Beetle might have become with its entire driveline the other way round, with the gearbox instead of the engine aft of the final drive. The main challenge would then be to duct enough air to the engine to keep it cool – more difficult with a mid-position than with the engine hung out in the tail

– but with clever ducting and a big fan this wasn't insoluble.

Of course, turning the engine round in this way couldn't be done in a Beetle, or in its larger successors the 1500 and 411, without either borrowing a lot of space from the back seat, or lengthening the wheelbase. For the sports car, there was no objection to having a fairly long wheelbase: the engineers selected a dimension of exactly 2,400mm (94.5in), which was 130mm more than the contemporary Porsche 911 and 90mm longer than the MGB. This created a chassis with a 'wheel at each corner' with its own promise of better stability and handling. It is worth bearing in mind that Volkswagen in the mid-1960s was happy to entertain the mid-engined concept, because at the time, it was seriously working on a Beetle replacement (code-named EA266) with a mid-mounted water-cooled engine mounted beneath the back seat. In the event, the EA266 died a death for excellent practical reasons and the replacement eventually emerged as the transverse, front-engined, front-driven Golf – but the mid-engined sports car did not have to be so practical, and having only two seats eased many of the design problems.

It only eased them, however. Where a practical road-going car is concerned, the mid-engine layout creates three considerable difficulties. The first of these is the provision of decent luggage space. Essentially, the large rear luggage compartment of the conventional front-engined car has to be split, part of the space going to the nose, while the rest of it sits in the extreme rear, above the gearbox. That was what the VW-Porsche designers did, arguing that the total space was quite reasonable. This was true enough – unless you had an item of luggage which would have fitted happily into the luggage compartment of (say) an MGB, but which would not go into either end of the 914. Too bad …

The second packaging problem was internal cabin space. In laying out a mid-engined car, there is an engineering temptation to shift the rear bulkhead as far forward as possible. The VW-Porsche designers were sufficiently sensible not to squeeze the cabin lengthwise to the point where it became intolerable for drivers above average height – but in the 914 as it emerged, there was virtually no space to slip anything behind the seat backs. In fact with a passenger aboard, there was precious little space inside the cabin to stow anything larger than a *Guide Michelin* and a Leica camera: anything bigger had to be nursed, or stowed in nose or tail. The final drawback was access to the engine for anything more than the most routine maintenance (and even that, some would say).

Strangely, given that the 1960s was a period when the automotive stylist really became established as a power in the industry, nobody seems to lay claim to the overall styling direction for the VW-Porsche 914. Its appearance certainly did not evoke the admiration which was lavished on the 911, for example, and that is a matter of fact. It is not for an engineering book to suggest why it should have been so, except to note that

all car design is subject to engineering constraints. From a styling point of view, a mid-engined 2-seater creates fewer constraints than most, and you might have expected the 914 to be beautiful. It wasn't, and the main reasons seem to have been that 'wheel at each corner' layout which made beauty difficult to achieve without adding length at both ends, and also perhaps the feeling that this was a car whose appearance would emphasise its practical nature and moderate price.

In addition, as already mentioned, its body structure was actually designed down to a price, with a minimum of graceful curves which would have been expensive to press and difficult to assemble accurately and neatly. Hence the 914 had a snub nose and tail (despite which, its aerodynamics were by no means bad) and many of its panels looked what they were – cheap and easy to press and assemble. A few concept-car attempts were made to improve the 914's appearance including, in 1970, a 914/6 Tapiro study by

The simple structure of the 914, designed with an eye to low manufacturing costs, seems almost visibly to lurk beneath the rather slab-sided styling, the bluff and simple bumpers and even the pop-up headlamps, that design fad of the early 1970s. One strong appeal of the car was supposed to be its easily removed and installed "Targa" top, but even that led to awkwardly shaped rear pillars ahead of the flat aft deck.

Italdesign, but they seemed only to confirm that the 914 resisted conventional beautification.

In purely engineering terms, given the chosen mechanical layout, the body shell created for the 914 was of necessity completely new. Nothing could be carried over from previous Porsche or Volkswagen models except, of course, the main mechanical units. Because this was to be a volume-production car it was engineered conventionally, in spot-welded pressed steel. Its most innovative feature was the use of a fixed 'Targa' hoop and a moulded, removable plastic roof panel to bridge the gap between that and the windscreen arch. This created the usual problems of a convertible (the roof panel being unstressed) when it came to achieving adequate torsional stiffness, which was sought through the adoption of a substantial centre tunnel and sill sections.

The need to be able to stow the roof panel in the rear luggage compartment determined the latter's shape to a considerable extent, and meant that the 62-litre fuel tank had to be installed ahead of the cabin and above the footwells. The car also featured pop-up headlamps, but these were very much the flavour of the period and in the case of the 914, at least they worked as intended. The steel body was no better corrosion protected than most of its contemporaries, and in subsequent years various weak spots emerged including the sill panels, the areas around the jacking points, and the battery tray which is prone to acid-spill. The problems are no worse than in many cars conceived in the 1960s (and no worse than early 911s), but as is so often the case, they can be expensive to make good.

The chassis used front MacPherson struts, already familiar to the Porsche engineers from their successful use in the 911 and adopted for the same reasons, not least to leave the front luggage space unobstructed. At the rear there were semi-trailing arms. The MacPherson struts followed the unusual (but by this time proven) 911 principle of saving further space through the use of longitudinal torsion bars which actually ran through the tube that formed the base of the lower control arm, rather than coil springs concentric with the damper, so that the strut itself consisted of the damper alone. The rear mounting points of the control arms were themselves joined by a substantial transverse tube, behind which the steering rack was mounted. The rear springs were conventional coils, concentric with the telescopic dampers.

Today, the 914 rear semi-trailing arms look crude, but at least things had moved on from the swing axle

and in practice the arrangement worked well enough, given the car's low centre of gravity and limited suspension travel. To some extent the layout was dictated by the need to leave space for the short but wide engine, a flat-4 (Volkswagen) or a flat-6 (Porsche). The brake specification was impressive for the time, with ventilated front discs and plain rear discs, of 11-inch or more diameter (the 914/6 had slightly larger diameter discs). An excellent job was done on brake balance and proportioning, and the 914 never seems to have suffered from the front wheel locking problems of some mid-engined contemporaries, notoriously including the Lancia Monte Carlo. A peculiar braking system feature was the fitting of an outboard-mounted 'lay-down' parking brake handle, which had to be lifted, and its button held in to release it. Apparently, no good ergonomic position could be found for a handbrake in the centre of the car, and the 'lay-down' arrangement was adopted for ease of access.

The engines would be the main differentiator between the volume-market version to be marketed by Volkswagen as the VW-Porsche 914, and the more expensive and refined VW-Porsche 914/6 which would be sold by the Porsche network. Other differences would concern things like the tyres sizes (originally 155SR-15 on 4.5-inch rims for the 914, and 165HR-15 on 5.5-inch rims for the 914/6), the fitting or otherwise of front and rear anti-roll bars, and the actual manufacturing process. The 914 would be put together entirely by Karmann, a specialist which already had strong links with both VW and Porsche including production of the Beetle-derived Karmann Ghia. For the 914/6, on the other hand, Karmann-built body shells would be taken to the Porsche factory at Zuffenhausen for the installation of the drivetrain and final assembly.

By the mid-1960s the original VW air-cooled flat-4 had hit the physical limit beyond which its capacity could no longer be increased. Volkswagen had therefore embarked on the design of a largely new engine of similar layout, the W80. This engine, with its capacity of 1,679cc (90mm bore by 66mm stroke), was intended principally for the VW 411, that rather disastrous final extrapolation of the rear-engined, air-cooled Beetle theme. The W80's capacity made it a logical choice for the 914 but in its original carburettor equipped form, delivering a paltry 68bhp, it had been poorly received and would have done the sporting 914 no favours at all. Fortunately, a programme was rushed through to equip the 1.7-litre with Bosch

Rear three-quarter shot, this time of a 914/6, again with the Targa top removed, rightly suggests that the car was more attractive from some angles than others. Even the slight bulge over the rear wheel arch is more evident in this view than in others. The flat rear lid covered a luggage space with useful volume, but the wrong shape to accept a substantial suitcase.

D-Jetronic fuel injection, which helped raise the power output to a more acceptable 80bhp for the 411LE, and this was the unit with which the 914 was fitted for the early years of its life. In parallel, the 914/6 was powered by the familiar Porsche 2-litre flat-6, lifted straight out of the 911, breathing through Weber carburettors and delivering 110bhp. The danger of possible conflict with the 911 was effectively removed by increasing the latter's engine size to 2.2-litres at the same Frankfurt Motor Show at which the 914 family was launched, in September 1969.

In both cases, the 914 engine drove through a Porsche-developed 5-speed gearbox, with an alternative 3-speed Sportronic semi-automatic (Porsche) alternative. The manual 914 exposed another mid-engined drawback in that the gearshift mechanism to a rear-mounted gearbox is inevitably long and prone to problems. As *CAR* magazine reported after testing the 914/6 in 1970: 'In neutral the lever is very sloppy, having three or four inches of play in every direction. To find first it has to be pulled to the left, overcoming a very strong spring, then pulled backwards hard. Sometimes it was reluctant to engage at all, so that it was necessary to go back into neutral, dab the clutch and try again … not up to the standard of other Porsches.' Eventually things would improve, although it was only in 1972 that a revised gearbox, designated 914/12, replaced the original 914/11 type. To be fair, the real problem lay not so much in the gearbox as with the proper and decent location of all parts of the tortuous linkage between it and the gear lever.

Reaction to the 914 series was mixed. The chassis was generally admired. Handling, particularly close to the limit and when applying power from the apex of a corner – especially a corner entered too fast – was far more forgiving than that of the 911. Braking performance was generally held to be excellent. The only possible snag was the one that came with the low polar moment of inertia. On wet surfaces this could result in the car being easily spun, if the driver overdid the steering input and thus the yaw rate, and was then either too slow to catch the divergent reaction, or over-corrected and was punished by the secondary swing. Certainly, the *Autocar* magazine road test team (of which the author was a member, 1969–73) managed inadvertently to spin 914/6s on more than one occasion, although naturally, it was more easily done on the test track than on the road. There was nothing wrong with the rack-and-pinion steering, unpowered (naturally) and geared at three turns lock to lock, but when pressing-on in adverse conditions any mid-engined car can begin yawing faster than the driver anticipates. Yet another mid-engine problem referred to in some tests is that of noise, with the engine separated from the cabin only by a single fire-wall bulkhead. In the 914, it seemed that much of the noise was actually generated by the big, fast-running fan which drew air through the cooling system, rather than by the engine itself.

Performance was another matter. In its most basic 4-cylinder form the 914 weighed 900kg – not very much in today's terms, but with only 80bhp and 98Nm of torque it was still distinctly slow, and condemned as such in early US magazine tests. The road test results showed a considerable spread but a good average 0–60mph time for the 4-cylinder 1.7 is 12 seconds, with a maximum speed just short of 110mph. The 914/6 was naturally much quicker, reaching 60mph in just under 9 seconds, with a 120mph maximum. Both versions had the same final drive ratio, but the Porsche 6-cylinder engine inevitably had the higher red line. In the UK, the redoubtable family Aldington which at that time ran the Porsche concession through their company AFN, would not allow the 4-cylinder car into the hands of press testers, although they were happy to loan the 914/6 to the right hands – or rather the left hands, since no 914s were ever factory-built with right-hand drive, and British customers had to drive kerb-side, or take the already expensive 914/6 to Crayford, who would convert it, making it even more expensive in the process.

The recorded performance figures make it clear that the Porsche-assembled 914/6 was the version to have, given that there was no doubting the ability of the chassis to match the output. Yet perhaps astonishingly, with the benefit of hindsight, the record shows that only 3,333 914/6s were ever built, with 2,760 of

these coming off the line in 1970, the first full year of production. The last 914/6s were built in 1972. This contrasts with 115,626 examples of the 4-cylinder version, production of which continued through to 1975, with the peak year of 1973 showing 28,457 cars coming off the line.

Why, then, the rapid demise of the 914/6? The reasons were far more to do with marketing than with engineering. Porsche found that demand for the more expensive, and more profitable 911 continued to grow, and the factory in the largely built-up Stuttgart suburb of Zuffenhausen could not be easily expanded. Given the choice between reserving space for continued final assembly of the 914/6 and using it instead for expanding 911 production, the decision was obvious. In any case, it seems clear that customers who wanted a 'proper' Porsche – which is what the 914/6, as opposed to the 914 was supposed to be – had no objection to paying more money for the much prettier 911 which even then had established the foundations of what eventually became a formidable reputation.

The 4-cylinder 914 meanwhile carried on, its engine size increased in 1972 to a full 2-litre capacity (94 x 71.1mm, 1,971cc). This engine, delivering 100bhp in European form and 95bhp (later 88bhp) in emission-controlled form for the USA, ran in parallel with the 1.7 for a while. Eventually, when the Volkswagen 411 was 'up-gunned' to become the 412 with its engine bored-out to 93 x 66mm, for a capacity of 1,795cc, this 1.8-litre flat-4 replaced the 1.7 in the 914 also. Eventually however, the 2-litre engine was standardised for the final months of production, which ended in 1975.

It does not sound like a distinguished career: launched 1969, killed in 1975 after a production run of less than 120,000 over the (effectively) six years. This relative failure was not, however, due to any deficiency of the chassis which, as already pointed out, was well able to handle the power and torque output of the 6-cylinder. In fact, in 1969 two cars were prepared, under the designation 914/8, powered by the 3-litre flat-8 engine from the 908 sports-racing car which won the 1969 World Championship, complete with the 908 5-speed gearbox. The original idea seems to have been to determine just how much output the 914 chassis could accept without significant modifications (beyond the inevitable wider wheels and tyres, around which the front wings had to be flared).

With Bosch mechanical fuel injection the 3-litre engine delivered 300PS and was said to have been capable of 250km/h. It spent its life mainly as

The "proper" 916, a very rare beast indeed, was powered either by a 2.4-litre flat-6 or by the "full house" 2.7-litre Carrera power unit. Only eleven were built in all, and five of them went in the first instance to Porsche family members. Distinguishing features included a welded steel roof, for much improved stiffness, and heavily flared arches to provide sufficient room for the considerably wider wheels and tyres.

Ferdinand Piëch's personal car. The second 914/8 was more extensively modified, in particular with a fixed steel roof which must have contributed significantly to torsional and bending stiffness. It was also provided with a fuel filler flap to avoid the need to open the bonnet to gain access to the filler. In this car the fuel injection was replaced by Weber carburettors, reducing the output to a reported 260PS. Finished in typical Porsche silver, and strictly road-legal (there were some doubts as to the status of the first prototype) this car was never a test vehicle, but instead, was prepared as a 60th birthday present for Ferry Porsche. He drive it for around 10,000km before handing it over to the Porsche museum for safe keeping, where it can still be seen.

There was no further going to 8-cylinder extremes with the 914, but the scope for increasing the size of the 6-cylinder Porsche engine was obvious. In 1972, a pilot-series of 11 cars was prepared, under the designation 916 (presumably to distinguish it from the 914/6) with the larger engines (and matching gearbox) by then being fitted to the 911. The first three cars had the nominally 2.4-litre – actually 2,341cc – engine delivering 190PS with fuel injection; the final eight examples were powered by the 2.7-litre, 210PS Carrera engine. The 916 had a number of clear distinguishing features including the same fixed, welded steel roof as in the second of the 914/8 prototypes, bold and chunky wheel arch extensions over the 185/70-15 tyres on 7-inch rims, and body-coloured rather than black bumpers. The 2.4-litre 916 was reported as having a 0–60mph time of less than 7 seconds and a maximum speed of 145mph.

As time passed, the 916 became recognised as one of the rarest and most elusive Porsches of all. No less than five of the 11 were at one time owned by members of the Porsche or Piëch families. All else aside, they stand as proof of what the 914 might have become, if the decision had not been taken to abandon it. However, it was not the end of the idea of a 'People's Porsche', which would soon take a new, better looking and more practical form with the emergence of the 924 and its successors (Chapter 7).

CHAPTER 6

1974: birth of the Turbo

Ernst Fuhrmann, the mastermind of the 4-cam 356 Carrera engine, had left Porsche in 1961 but, after a spell in the engine components sector, returned in 1972 as chief executive. This time, he was the moving spirit behind the project which took the turbocharging technology which had already been deployed in Porsche's competitions programme, and applied it to the 911. Whether his motivation was at one fell swoop to turn the 911 into a true 'supercar' in the same class as the Ferrari Boxer and Lamborghini Miura, or simply to accept the technical challenge of broadening the Porsche range (which at the time still included the 914/6), is a moot point. Challenge it certainly was, despite the experience gained in competition. In any case, Karl Ludvigsen insists, the evolution of the road-going Turbo and that of the turbocharged racing programme proceeded 'along an entirely separate path', not only because the requirement was different but because completely different fuel systems were involved. It is certainly true, however, that in the early 1970s, turbocharging was the only quick and easy way to give the 911 a substantial power boost. The alternative would have been an all-new engine, probably mounted in a different place, and the end result would have been a completely different car, not a 911.

Turbocharging at that time was still in its relative infancy where road cars were concerned. Chevrolet had tried turbo technology in the Corvair Monza as early as 1965, but like the car itself, that proved a dead-end. By the early 1970s, BMW was preparing its 2002 Turbo which sold in limited numbers for genuine road use. The Saab 99 Turbo, which many credit with really sparking the turbo boom, did not appear until late in 1977. Yet at the Geneva Motor Show in 1974 the author, then technical editor of *Autocar*, and his Editor Ray Hutton were quietly conducted outside from the Porsche stand and, in a quiet corner, were introduced to the Turbo and invited to drive it for an hour or so. We might have felt a little more nervous had we known that this was one of only seven pre-series Turbos made during 1974, all of them dedicated to demonstration and press testing. We were warned, however, that this car lacked the definitive (4-speed) gearbox, and would therefore be pushed to withstand the stresses imposed by a press-style standing start test (3,000+rpm, foot sideways off the clutch pedal and hope the wheels spin sufficiently to keep the engine 'on the cam').

Officially, it was not the 911 Turbo, simply the Turbo. The differentiation was further emphasised by the adoption of the factory designation Type 930. This new beast was not, in fact, to be considered as a 911 at all. Yet it is rather surprising, looking back at the words Ray Hutton filed at the time, to find him implying some disappointment that it looked very much like any other Porsche 911. 'Only the wider rear track, the black-finished wheel centres, the funnel-shaped headlamp washers and the discreet "turbo" badge beneath the rubber-edged rear spoiler provide the clues,' wrote Ray, having pointed out that in the UK at least, the Turbo would sell for around 50 per cent more than the then-current 911 Carrera (and 17 had already been ordered). To the author, wearing his engineer's hat, the rear track and the rear spoiler both looked huge. Even so, the real interest lay beneath the engine cover.

To begin with, the engine was a full 3-litre unit. This, remember, was at a time when the standard 911 had only just moved up from 2.4 to 2.7 litres, before even the 911 Carrera had moved up to this size. The Turbo, which in the Porsche book was the Type 930 and not a 911 at all, was the first production car in which the flat-6 engine – then a mere decade old – was bored-out by a further 5mm, creating a well over-square unit of 95x70.4mm for a capacity of 2,994cc. Was this the ultimate stretch of the original 2-litre 911 engine, or was it something more than that? This is discussed in more detail in Chapter 9, which continues the story of the naturally aspirated 911 once it had reached the full 3 litres. Suffice it so say that the only parts of the Turbo engine common with the 2.7-litre engine were, astonishingly, the crankshaft and connecting rods, and the cylinder head covers. Everything else was new, including of course the KKK turbocharger and all its associated ducting and pipework.

Always notable for its significantly wider rear wheels and tyres, and a massive rear spoiler playing an active role in overall airflow management within the engine compartment as well as over the rear of the car – the hallmarks of any early Porsche Turbo, when compared with its naturally aspirated equivalent. This particular specimen is a 3.3-litre, the first to benefit from an intercooler.

To put raw figures on it, the original Turbo delivered 260bhp at 5,500rpm, compared with 210bhp at 5,900rpm for the contemporary 2.7-litre Carrera. Even more impressively, though logically for a turbo, its torque peak was 253lb ft at 4,000rpm, compared with the Carrera's 188lb ft at 5,100rpm. What was more, because of the turbo's characteristics, we were told that over 250lb ft was available all the way from

3,000rpm to 5,000rpm. Maximum boost pressure was set at 0.8 bar, around 11psi. The 3-litre capacity (the boring-out had already been engineered for race engines) was chosen, it was said, to provide crisp pick-up even when the turbo was not boosting. Since the compression ratio had been pulled all the way down to 6.5:1 to steer well clear of any danger of detonation on full boost, the lack of low-speed torque and response might have been noticeable if the engine had been left at 2.7, let alone 2.4 litre capacity. Even as it was, the cylinder head ports had been narrowed to increase gas speed and assist the low-speed torque.

Different though its development path may have been, the turbocharging system clearly reflected all the lessons learned with the racing programme. It was however radically different from the race cars. For a start, it had been engineered to make it compatible with the Bosch K-Jetronic continuous-flow mechanical fuel injection system which was at that time Porsche's fuel system of choice. In an attempt to overcome the problem of turbocharger lag which was already known to make life difficult, even for experienced racing drivers trying to optimise circuit times, Porsche engineered an installation which included not only a conventional waste-gate, but also a vacuum-controlled, spring-loaded 'dump valve'. If the driver lifted off for a short time, this dumped boost back into the duct from the exhaust to the turbine, and so maintained the turbocharger's rotor speed rather than allowing it to slow, and thus create the impression of lag when the driver put his foot down again.

You cannot create substantial extra power without rejecting an equally substantial amount of extra heat, and so the Turbo's cylinders were more deeply and heavily finned. Additional oil cooling was also provided, for both engine and transmission, underlining yet again the vital importance of oil in helping to control internal temperatures in a nominally air-cooled engine. One might expect so much heat rejection to be bad for fuel economy, yet when *Autocar* eventually tested a right-hand drive Turbo, some 18 months after that first drive, the car returned 18.5mpg overall (15.3 litres/100km) which was certainly not bad for a car with this kind of performance. The key performance figures from that test were 60mph reached in 6.1sec, 100mph in 14.5sec and 130mph in 28.7sec. Maximum speed, measured in near-ideal conditions in Germany, was 153mph (246km/h), already 400rpm beyond peak power in top.

Autocar mentioned that the Turbo was difficult to blast cleanly off the standing-start line. Its 0–30mph time was 2.8sec, while the Carrera 2.7 had managed 2.1sec. That deficit clearly shows in the 0–60mph time. The huge, grippy rear tyres and the lower torque until the turbo begins to deliver, were the main culprits, although the 4-speed gearbox may also have had something to do with it. There were no complaints, however, about the response in each gear once the car was properly on the move.

It now seems odd in the extreme to offer an expensive 150mph car with only a 4-speed manual gearbox, but today we live in a world where everything has forward five speeds and many cars have six. Porsche's rationale was that given not only the high torque but the huge spread of the curve, four gears were plenty. The red line speeds, again from the *Autocar* test but actually calculated rather than measured, were 52mph in first, 89mph in second and 130mph in third, at 6,800rpm. The test car was of course fitted with the 'proper' transaxle developed to accept the Turbo's full punch, with features including a set of four differential pinions (rather than just two) to increase the torque capacity. Porsche toyed with the idea of a twin-disc clutch but settled for a single-disc unit of greater diameter, which proved entirely suitable.

Just as there was anxiety to ensure the transmission would be man enough for the task of handling the extra power and torque, the sense of worry was increased by the engine's extra weight; another 70lb all added to the mass aft of the rear axle line. The decision really could not be avoided: the rear wheels would have to be larger than the fronts, whatever problems that created in terms of a suitable spare wheel (cars were supplied with a slender spare wheel shod with a Goodyear Spacesaver tyre, which had to be inflated with the compressor supplied, before being fitted). To begin with, the tyre sizes were 185/70VR15 on 7-inch rims at the front, and 215/60VR15 on 8-inch rims at the rear, which is why the rear wings had to be so dramatically flared. Before long the specification switched from the original Dunlop tyres to the then-new Pirelli P7, the widths increasing (and the sections lowering) to 205/60VR15 at the front, and 225/50VR15 at the rear. The entire rear suspension was strengthened, the geometries were considered in detail with some anti-dive built into the front for the first time, and the front and rear anti-roll bars were stiffened. In its test, *Autocar* commented that the overwhelming handling characteristic was understeer, and that 'in a corner, to accelerate is to understeer, *pro rata.*' The test team also commented that if a driver needed to shed speed quickly after entering a corner much too fast, 'the car does not lose grip disastrously at the back … it is a lot easier to hold than the Carrera was.'

That initial version of the Turbo certainly proved its worth in the eyes of enthusiastic customers. Originally it had been hoped to sell the 200 which would allow competition homologation. Then the

Right: This was the original 3-litre Turbo engine, at a time when the naturally aspirated cars were only 2.7-litre. The extra capacity (from a 5mm bore enlargement) was supposed to ensure that there was enough low-end torque to match the output when the turbo boost came on stream. Compression ratio was only 6.5:1, to avoid any danger of full-boost detonation.

Below: The Type 930 Turbo in its original 3-litre form, still visibly a 911 derivative even though the company tried to present it as a distinct companion model. The wider rear wheels, under those bulging arches, were a response not only to the extra power and torque that had to be transmitted to the road, but also to the extra weight of the Turbo engine sitting aft of the back wheels.

sights were raised to 500, and by May 1976, scarcely two years since the handful of top journalists were slipped behind the wheel of a pre-production car in Geneva, the thousandth Turbo emerged from Zuffenhausen. Another 300 had been added by the end of the 1976 model year, and the USA had proved to be one of the largest markets despite its nation-wide 55mph speed limit. And the car was not cheap: despite some initial misgivings about the price that would be needed to cover the cost of a full luxury specification, including air conditioning in some markets, the decision was taken to equip the Turbo as the top car in the range. As a result, the asking price for a 1977 model-year car was nearly 68,000 DMarks, which was truly folding money in those days, as was the $28,000 asked in the USA.

For that 1977 model year, the Turbo inherited all the beneficial changes made to all 'J-body' 911s, including a brake servo. The 1977 cars were also equipped with 16-inch rather than 15-inch wheels, the extra half-inch of ride height enabling it to meet US bumper height standards with less difficulty. The big change, however, came the following year with the enlargement of the engine. Both the bore and stroke were increased, the former by 2mm to 97mm, the latter by 4mm to 74.4mm. The result was a swept volume of 3,299cc, a 10 per cent increase which would itself have been enough to raise both power and torque. But the engineers introduced one other very desirable feature, an intercooler which reduced the compressed air emerging from the turbo compressor by something like 50°C, increasing its density before it entered the engine. This had the additional benefit of allowing the compression ratio to be increased, without danger of detonation, to 7:1 from 6.5:1, a useful lift which increased thermal efficiency, although it also called for the use of premium fuel, which was to have implications in some export markets. The result was that peak power rose from 260PS to 300PS (221kW) at 5,500rpm, an improve-ment of over 15 per cent, while peak torque shot up from 350Nm to no less than 412Nm at 4,000rpm, an increase of nearly 18 per cent.

This 3.3-litre Turbo was to remain effectively the same for a remarkably long time. It was finally phased-

The 3.3-litre Turbo in cutaway, showing the engine and transmission installation in relation to that vast slatted grille above the rear spoiler, but also the state of Porsche chassis and suspension thinking in the mid-1970s. For the Turbo, many detail changes were made, and initial understeer was considerably increased.

1974: BIRTH OF THE TURBO

out with the 1989 model year, which meant its career extended over a remarkable 11 years in all. During that time, some customers were able to further increase its performance with 'Sport Kit' modifications from the factory, including a bigger turbo and intercooler, revised higher-lift camshafts and a revised exhaust system. The result was a further 10 per cent power increase, to 330PS at 5,750rpm, with 470Nm of torque at 4,500rpm. This, however, was one side of the coin, and a very expensive one which also carried some slight penalty in terms of low-speed driveability, which probably worried owners very little.

The other side of the coin was the engine as tuned for the US and Japanese markets with their far tighter exhaust emission limits. For a time indeed, the Turbo was not exported to the USA at all. From January 1980 the tightened US emission limits could only be met with the use of a catalytic converter. Given the state of converter technology at that time, plus the fact that the unleaded fuel then available in the USA was almost entirely 91RON, Porsche estimated that the 3.3 Turbo's output would be reduced to 240PS, and that, it was felt, would reduce the appeal, and sales, to an uneconomic level. This state of affairs continued until the 1986 model year, when the readier availability of 94RON fuel, plus advances in converter technology, made it possible to offer the Turbo in Federal-compliant form with 282PS and 390Nm of torque – still well down on the European figures, but no longer derisory.

With the return to North America, Turbo production lifted from the hundreds to the thousands. In the calendar year 1988, 2,061 units emerged from Zuffenhausen. Yet at the same time, the writing was on the wall for the Turbo, temporarily at least. Soon it would be the case that European-market cars too would need to be catalyst-equipped, and it was felt that European enthusiasts would not put up with American levels of performance. By this time the naturally aspirated 964 was well along its development road, and alongside it there existed a plan for a companion Turbo with twin turbochargers and 959-style 4-valve cylinder heads, allied with a 3.5-litre capacity. Alas, this scheme came to naught, and there was a hiatus in the Turbo's history, not just in the USA, but world-wide.

Naturally enough, the Turbo was not simply about engine development. There was a constant concern to ensure the transmission and chassis were up to the job. The 4-speed gearbox remained all the way through to 1989, with some juggling of ratios when

the 3.3-litre engine arrived. Having only four speeds meant the unit was shorter, and made room for a larger clutch with a centre designed to absorb crankshaft vibration without passing it on to the transmission. The 3.3-litre car also received a further strengthened final drive. In 1989, the Turbo finally acquired its fifth speed when a suitably strong gearbox became available with the introduction of the (naturally aspirated) Type 964. Where the suspension was concerned, remarkably little was done other than to re-rate the dampers, the torsion bar springs and the anti-roll bars as appropriate. The brakes were another matter altogether, because the combined extra weight and performance of the Turbo meant there were situations in which there would be an awful lot more kinetic energy to kill. For the 3.3-litre, Porsche actually carried over technology from the racing 917, with

An interesting comparison with the 3-litre engine, this is the 3.3-litre, larger in bore and stroke, and with the great benefit of an intercooler, sitting above the engine and directly beneath the enlarged grille set into the spoiler. The revised plumbing meant a completely different, and simpler-looking exhaust arrangement. Intercooling meant the compression ratio could be raised, hence a reliable 300bhp for the first time.

This is the final iteration of the air-cooled Turbo engine, opened out to 3.6-litre capacity, in effect a single-plug adaptation of the Type 964 unit with the single turbocharger and associated plumbing carried over from the 3.3-litre. Power output was 360PS, with 520Nm of torque to stress the transmission to the utmost.

The 1981 Frankfurt Show saw a concept four-wheel drive (4WD) Turbo Cabriolet exhibited on the Porsche stand: the 4WD went into the 959 rather than the 930, at least to begin with and in a far more highly developed form. The Cabriolet, and an equivalent Targa, were added to the Turbo range for the 1987 model year.

There were no 1990 model-year Turbos. Production of the long-running Type 930 ceased with the Zuffenhausen works summer break in 1989. No replacement appeared until late in 1990, for the 1991 model-year. This new Turbo was not the advanced 24-valve, water-cooled twin-turbo, the stillborn Type 965, but rather a standard Type 964 with the body modified to give it a 'Turbo look', and powered by a further evolution of the previous 3.3-litre air-cooled single-turbo engine. To justify its status, the new model would need more power than its predecessor, despite now being equipped with a catalytic converter to comply with the new EC exhaust emission limits. The starting point was the old 'Sport Kit' engine standard, which had delivered 330PS in non-catalyst form. Suitably developed, with a much larger intercooler and a cunning new exhaust system from one of whose apparently dual tailpipes the exhaust proper emerged, while the other pipe served as the exit from the turbo wastegate, the air-cooled 3.3-litre engine was persuaded to yield 320PS (235kW) at 5,750rpm, and 450Nm of torque at 4,500rpm. The compression ratio was still 7:1, the maximum boost pressure 0.7 bar, and 95RON fuel was required.

This not very new engine went into a 964 body modified principally to allow widening of the front and rear tracks, and the fitting of wider wheels. The basic suspension geometry remained the same, though its mountings and members were of course altered to match the wider tracks. The 17-inch wheels had 7-inch front rims, with 9-inch rims at the rear, the tyres sizes being 205/50-17 and 255/40-17. To begin with, Bridgestone supplied the standard tyre, although alternatives were offered later. Power steering was fitted to the Turbo for the first time, and came with hydraulic rather than vacuum brake boost, and a cunning ZF limited-slip differential the effect of which was much less under acceleration than under braking. This was to avoid the danger of excessive slip limitation leading to gross understeer when pressing on. The brakes were an odd but effective combination, the fronts identical with those of the heavy 928, while the rears were in effect the 944 Turbo front brakes. Cost and development time was thus saved,

cross-drilled brake discs and four-pot calipers. For a long time, the Turbo was the benchmark high-performance tyre application, fought over by the major tyre companies. Indeed, it still is.

Opinions as to the driving quality of the early-series Turbos, as expressed in the enthusiast motoring press, varied considerably. Some testers mentioned upsetting wheel hop when making full-bore standing starts; this seems to have been a function of tyre, track surface and meteorology, because others had no trouble. There was general agreement that the car was very good-natured when driven gently, this at a time when plug oiling, and other bad manners, still afflicted some high performance cars. When pressing on, things remained calm until the limit was approached. Reading between the lines of some of the Turbo tests published both in Europe and the USA, it is clear that the car remained easy to handle up to perhaps 80 per cent of its limit (and its limit, bear in mind, was very high) but that extracting the last 20 per cent called for intense concentration and a deal of hard work, especially at the unpowered steering.

All through the 1980s, if one ignores the engine department's head-scratching over evolving exhaust emission regulations, the Turbo simply cruised along.

the braking capacity was quite sufficient and the balance was good.

There was one final stretch left in the air-cooled Turbo. Its basis was simple. The naturally aspirated 964 engine had been enlarged to a full 3.6-litre capacity by boring-out from 97mm to 100mm (with suitable changes to the crankcase and other features; see Chapter 12). Could this engine be turbocharged, or would its cylinder walls be too thin to take the strain? Racing experience suggested the engine would survive and that durability would be satisfactory, and so it was done. The 3.6-litre Turbo was in its most basic terms the 964 engine, but with one spark plug per cylinder instead of two, fitted with the turbocharger and plumbing from the 3.3-litre. The compression ratio went up to 7.5:1, and the maximum boost pressure to a slightly alarming 0.9 bar.

The result of this work, carried through with great speed, was the highest output yet seen in a road-going Porsche: 360PS (265kW) at 5,500rpm, and 520Nm of torque at 4,200rpm. Retaining the original turbocharger for the larger engine actually gave better response over most of the speed range; a larger turbo would have delivered even more power, but at the expense of response and driveability, especially at lower speeds. Detail changes were made to the chassis, by far the most visible one being the adoption of even wider wheels and tyres, 225/40-18 at the front and 265/35-18 at the back, with rim widths of 8in and 10in respectively. The rear suspension used the 'solid' trailing arm of the Carrera RS rather than the 'compliant' one of the standard 964, and while brake disc sizes remained the same, brake pad area was increased.

Even though it set new standards, this full 964-based Turbo was destined for a short life. It saw only one full calendar year of production, in 1993. Like the basic 964, it was something of a stop-gap, further hampered through being developed during some of Porsche's darkest days, as the 1980s turned into the 1990s and a world-wide economic slump reduced sales to a life-threatening ebb. So far as the Turbo was concerned, there would now be another short hiatus in its life before an even more capable new model, based on the Type 993, which was about to replace the 964, came to market.

A comparative rarity, the 3.6-litre Turbo, with 964-based body, was in full production for one year only, 1993. It replaced the "Turbo look" 964 of 1991, which was powered by the final iteration of the 3.3-litre unit. Wheels became 18-inch for the first time, and tyres even wider. There were detail suspension changes too, and larger brake pads.

CHAPTER 7

1976: 924 and its development series

The mauling suffered by the VW-Porsche 914 at the hands of its critics (even though, in the end, the model sold reasonably well, especially in the USA) meant that almost as soon as it had been announced, the joint company set up to oversee the programme (the Ludwigsberg-based VW-Porsche Vertreibsgesellschaft) began looking earnestly at a replacement. The design of this new car would be governed by two principles. First, it would correct the deficiencies of the 914, especially its lack of interior stowage space, its sometimes over-sharp handling and its interior noise levels. Second, it would do rather better in terms of using standard 'off-the-shelf' VW Group parts, since, apart from the engine and steering, the 914 had actually achieved less in that respect than originally contemplated.

By this time, the contents of the parts bin had become much more varied and in many ways more suitable. The VW Group had grown larger and had significantly changed shape compared with the way it had been in the mid-1960s when the outline of the 914 had been laid down. It had fought its way through a traumatic period during which its over-dependence on the Beetle, and its inability to devise a worthy successor, threatened for a time to almost bring the company down. In a sense, the Beetle had succeeded despite its inadequacies, through a happy combination of timing, price, market growth and shrewd concentration on product quality. Attempts to expand Volkswagen into a comprehensive range, using Beetle-type technology (rear-mounted, flat-4 air-cooled engine) magnified the inadequacies rather than overcoming them, and failed miserably. The culminating 411/412 series, the last of the rear-engined, air-cooled cars, was ill-received. Consequently, VW – under the leadership of a succession of relatively short-lived CEOs who sought to step into Professor Nordhoff's shoes – evolved a new strategy which would employ water-cooled engines and (after a little dithering) front-mounted, with front-wheel drive. In this, Volkswagen was encouraged by its acquisition of Audi in 1964. Porsche, in its consultant role, played its part in the evolution of the new-generation Volkswagens (Chapter 11) and by 1970 it was unthinkable that any new VW-Porsche sports model would retain a Beetle-type engine.

Commercially, the idea was that the new car would be a Volkswagen rather than a Porsche, a replacement as it were for the 914 rather than the 914/6, and that it would form part of the programme for expending and diversifying the Volkswagen range beyond the Beetle straitjacket. Thus the project was formally launched with a Volkswagen development series number, EA 425, with Porsche undertaking the development programme in line with its long-standing position as product engineering consultancy to Wolfsburg. In the early 1970s it was Porsche's intention, so far as its own range was concerned, to diversify upwards and sideways rather than downwards. Thus the programme to develop the big 928 actually began before a start was made on the EA 425/924.

The entire commercial background changed early in 1975, when VW's new managing director, Toni Schmücker (lured away from Ford to replace Rudolf Leiding), found himself facing a formidable set of problems including the lingering aftermath of the 1973 energy crisis, and a cash flow challenge arising from the fact that money had been spent on developing new front-driven models (the Passat, Scirocco and Golf) which had yet to deliver any financial return; in 1974, Volkswagen had lost a record amount of money. Accordingly, Schmücker cancelled the entire EA 425 programme at a time when development was virtually complete. It was just one drain too many on resources. Porsche however took a completely different view. It had put the 928 programme on the back burner when the 1973 energy crisis almost killed the market for powerful and expensive cars. The 924 seemed a more promising alternative to a company which needed to expand its product range and production volume, not least because it was in the process of transforming itself from a Porsche family-controlled enterprise into a listed private company.

The only remaining question was where and how to build the 924, since there was no room at Zuffenhausen. Thus, when Porsche reached an agreement with VW to buy back the EA 425, it also struck a deal that VW would actually assemble the car at the former NSU plant in Neckarsulm. This plant, whose last and most celebrated NSU product was the Wankel-engined Ro80, had been integrated into VW's Audi arm and had begun to function as a kind of extension of the main Audi plant at Ingolstadt, concentrating on the assembly of Audi's more specialised and low-volume models and derivatives.

Last fling of the 968 dice was the Turbo S, with a 3-litre engine delivering no less than 305PS. Note here the final headlamp configuration. This was a car which reached 60mph in under 5sec, and had a maximum speed of 175mph: but it still had only four cylinders, and it found no significant market despite its dynamic virtues.

This early 924 cutaway shows the basic layout, which might almost be conventional but for the rear-mounted gearbox. Front footroom benefited, but the tunnel over the fat central torque tube joining engine to final drive displaced the handbrake outboard, so it had to be "drop-down". Unlike the 914, there was room for two small back seats and a reasonably capacious boot.

Neckarsulm had the capacity to produce the Porsche 924, with the added advantage that mechanically, the 924 was part Audi to begin with.

Front engine, rear-drive, water cooling

Possibly the first Porsche tradition to be ditched during the evolution of what became the 924 was the air-cooled engine. Air cooling was going out of fashion. VW itself was about to abandon it, except in those outposts where the Beetle would linger in production for years to come. Porsche engineers were already aware that their flat-6 had become an air-cooled engine with substantial oil-cooling assistance. Water-cooled engines were cheaper to make, more compact, and imposed far fewer engineering constraints in terms of fan design and airflow through the engine compartment. In any case, the choice for a designer looking through the VW Group 'parts bin' now lay between antiquated air-cooled engines and modern water-cooled engines with overhead camshafts, and it was really a case of no contest.

Because it was felt that a 2-litre engine would be needed to provide acceptable sports car performance by mid-1970s standards, the search for the best power unit concentrated on the Audi engine range. Audi had re-emerged from history as a rechristening of the former DKW concern, control of which had been acquired by Mercedes in 1958, only to be sold on to VW in 1964. The short period of Mercedes control had left DKW with one considerable asset, a brand-new series of Heron-headed (bowl-in-piston) 4-cylinder OHV four-stroke engines with capacities up to 1.7 litres, which achieved high output and efficiency through high swirl and what was for the time, a remarkably high compression ratio. The original plan was for this engine to replace the old two-stroke engine in the otherwise attractive DKW F102, to create the F103. This car metamorphosed into the first post-war Audi after the VW takeover, and the engine was certainly good enough to attract the EA 425 development team, although as things stood, it did not deliver enough urge.

More urge was on the way, however, since under VW Group project number EA 831 the engine was not only to be enlarged to a full (nominal) 2-litre capacity, but also converted to have a single-toothed belt-driven overhead camshaft rather than the original chain-driven side camshaft. Remarkably, this project had first been instigated as the power unit for the new VW Transporter van, the planned successor to the original, celebrated (but now outdated) VW Microbus, but it was admirably suited – with adaptation – to the EA 425, as well as to later-series Audi models.

The capacity stretch of the EA 831 engine was achieved by boring-out the block from the 84mm of the first (OHV) Audi 100 engine to 86.5mm, leaving the bore unchanged at 84.4mm, for a capacity of 1,984cc. An arguable drawback was that even this slight increase in bore meant there was no room for water passages between the cylinder bores, which were thus 'siamesed'. Against this, it left the engine agreeably compact, although this was something which pleased Audi (who had to install it in-line and ahead of the front axle in their cars) more than it did Porsche. Within the engine, the only significant change was that the main bearings were increased from 60mm to 65mm diameter, not as one might imagine, to help withstand higher bottom-end speeds and loads but rather to make sure the cast (rather than forged) crankshafts used in some lower-cost versions of the engine would be strong enough. The overhead camshaft conversion was straightforward, the shaft operating the in-line valves directly via bucket tappets, and the distributor was driven off the back end of the camshaft. A new crescent-type oil pump was inserted between the front main bearing and the drive sprocket for the toothed belt.

This, then, was the engine which would, with suitable adaptation, power the EA 425. There remained the question of how exactly it was to be installed. Early studies indicated that a front-driven layout, using a complete Audi front-drive powertrain, would be the cheapest option. This might have pleased VW (so long as it did not pitch the new car too close to the Golf-derived Scirocco), but the Porsche engineers opposed the idea vehemently, and made their case stick. They would only countenance a car with rear-wheel drive, allowing the driver to exercise control with both steering and accelerator, without the two being in any way interdependent. That more or less forced the adoption of a front engine and rear-wheel drive. A rear engine was out of the question, and a mid-engined layout risked repeating all the drawbacks of the 914, even if an in-line 4-cylinder engine was installed transversely as in the Fiat X1/9, for example.

At some point in the process it occurred to the team that even if the engine was front-mounted, the gearbox need not be. There were already several examples of front-engined, rear-driven cars with their gearboxes mounted at the rear, in unit with the final drive. The most outstanding such design was the Lancia Aurelia of 1950, and its successor the Flaminia.

In 1972, with the new VW-Porsche still on the drawing-board, Alfa Romeo adopted a rear gearbox layout for the new Alfetta. The principle was well proven, and for Porsche it had the advantage of shifting a significant amount of weight onto the rear wheels, enabling a front-engined car to have more even weight distribution and better traction. As an additional advantage, splitting the powertrain mass increased the car's polar moment of inertia, making it

"Rear wheel drive – Front engine – Rear transaxle" says the headline in this promotional shot of the early 924, the basic mechanicals laid bare and a couple of seats (and their occupants) set in place. The rear transaxle was not a new idea – even the Ferrari Daytona had one – but it did make for better static balance and made a lot of space available within the body.

less responsive to steering inputs (to the chagrin of the mid-engine lobby), but also much less 'twitchy', thus overcoming one of the perceived drawbacks of the 914. It also meant that the Audi transaxle (gearbox and final drive) could also be used complete, although at the other end of the car.

The variety of available Audi hardware meant the 924 could eventually be offered with 'standard' 4-speed gearbox or a 3-speed automatic. By contrast, the 5-speed manual gearbox, offered from 1978, was a Porsche-designed unit in which the gearbox sat ahead of the final drive rather than behind it as in the Audi-derived transaxle; this in turn pushed the final drive output rearwards and meant the drive shafts had to run at a constant forward-inclined angle, in a manner reminiscent of the 911 ever since its early wheelbase stretch.

Also part of the equation was the fact that the team developing the substantially larger and heavier 928, upon which (as already pointed out) work had begun prior to the EA 425, only to be halted in 1973/74, had also arrived at a front engine, rear transmission configuration, following a very similar train of thought. At the time, it was possible to see Porsche's future built around a range of cars with this unusual but carefully considered configuration, with front-mounted, water-cooled engines. The sheer survival quality of the 911 layout despite its evident drawbacks had not yet become evident: at the time, after all, the 911 itself was barely a decade old.

One fundamental choice consequent upon the decision to use a rear-mounted gearbox was whether to leave the clutch in unit with the engine, or to transfer it to the rear and install it as part of the rear-mounted transaxle. The Alfa Romeo Alfetta – which the EA 425 team studied closely – had a rear-mounted clutch, which meant that the propeller shaft was permanently attached to the engine, forming part of its rotating inertia and running at engine speed regardless of

There were few real plaudits for the 924's styling, yet it was pleasant enough and efficiently aerodynamic. The pop-up headlamps were still a popular styling feature. Because (unlike the 914) there was no Targa roof, the body could be made adequately stiff without adding too much weight in the floor, sill and scuttle areas. Wheel arches were generous, leaving space to accommodate the expansion that followed.

circumstance. The Porsche team decided it preferred a front-mounted clutch, even though this meant – the other side of the engineering coin, so to speak – that the propeller shaft would instead be permanently connected to the input side of the gearbox and that its inertia might affect the quality of the gearchange.

None of this meant quite as much as it would in a rear-driven car with a conventional front-mounted gearbox, however. Since it has no need to transmit the engine's torque multiplied by the first gear ratio, the propeller shaft associated with a rear-mounted transaxle can be made much slimmer and lighter. In what became the Porsche 924, it was only 20mm in diameter and was carried within a tube 85mm in outer diameter, with 4mm thick walls, linking the bell-housing on the rear of the engine and the (essentially redundant) housing at the front of the transmission. Within this tube, the propeller shaft was supported by four carefully positioned, sealed-for-life bearings. The tube also provided a firm foundation for a stiff, short-throw gear linkage. Less satisfactorily, it meant that clutch replacement was a major operation involving removal either of the engine, or of the tube – calling for major dismantling of the rear suspension! As explained in the original 924 technical description: 'To change the clutch, it is only necessary to unbolt the tube at the front end, disconnect the drive shafts and transaxle mountings, and the whole unit can then be moved rearwards by 3½in. This allows enough clearance for the clutch housing to be removed.' Simple, really …

The chassis itself involved much less original thinking than the drivetrain, and much evidence of the desire to borrow mechanical parts from VW. There were MacPherson struts at the front, this time with conventional concentric coil springs and substantial lower wishbones, all these units being taken (along with the rack and pinion steering installation) from the VW Scirocco. This meant the 924 inherited the outboard scrub-radius geometry pioneered by Audi, which was supposed to deliver a self-correcting steering effect when braking on a 'split-mu' surface, and in other asymmetric conditions. At the back, the suspension came from the last-series VW Beetle, with semi-trailing – in fact, more or less trailing – arms with a transverse torsion bar spring contained within a chassis tube which ran beneath the one that housed the propeller shaft, and immediately in front of the transaxle.

At first, this cross-tube was a single unit, although in later versions of the car it was in two halves, joined at the centre to make some major servicing tasks easier. Only the dampers intruded vertically into the very substantial platform above the gearbox, and which provided one of the things the 914 had so conspicuously lacked – the space for a decent amount of luggage, including really large suitcases. To complete the VW parts-bin picture, even the drive shafts came from the VW 181 4WD vehicle, while the braking system – discs front, drums rear – was inherited from the VW (née NSU) K70.

It took a fair amount of ingenuity and fine-tuning to blend this strange collection of chassis parts into a cohesive platform, let alone one in which Porsche engineers could feel their standards had been maintained. But it was done, and the remaining task was to clothe the car in a body of which the team could feel equally proud. In this case there was no stinting. Everyone was aware that another of the market's objections to the 914 was that the car looked undistinguished at best, and to some eyes, ugly. While nobody has ever 'owned up' to being the lead designer for the 914, there is no dispute that the 924 was shaped by Harm Lagaay, a young Dutchman who was destined many years later (and following spells with other manufacturers) to become Porsche design chief from 1989 until he retired in 2004.

The two most distinguishing features of Lagaay's 924 concept were its use of electrically operated pop-up headlamps – at the time a popular idea – and a rear hatch which consisted almost entirely of a massive, double-curved (and very expensive) rear window. The overall line was acknowledged to be smooth and well balanced, and the finalised production design (overseen by Dick Soderberg) made provision for things like the different bumpers which would be needed to meet US market regulations. Inside, the cabin was 2+2, and the upper halves of the back seats could be folded forward to extend the luggage platform for two-seat grand touring. The oddest feature, forced by the presence of the central transmission tube and gearshift, was the positioning of the handbrake outboard of the driver's seat, with a 'flop-down' handle.

In part, the body shape depended on a low bonnet line which was achieved by tilting the engine at 40 degrees to the right, as part of its adaptation to Porsche's needs. A cast aluminium alloy sump was added, and it was decided from the outset to use fuel injection in the form of Bosch's then-popular K-Jetronic system, which was not electronic but worked on a mechanical-balance principle. One side of the balance was loaded by the air mass-flow, and the other by the fuel delivery pressure so that the greater the mass flow, the greater the amount of fuel delivered. The fuel injection system lived on the 'upper' side of the canted engine which meant the sparking plugs were on its 'underside', despite which, they were not too difficult to reach.

As part of the development programme, Porsche also investigated alternatives to the Heron-type bowl-in-piston combustion chamber, but decided in the end to retain it, not least because it delivered lower NOx emissions, a consideration which was beginning to have some significance in the US market. With the relatively high compression ratio of 9.3:1 (remember the engine had begun life as a high-swirl, high-efficiency unit) and the fuel injection, the engine delivered 125bhp at 5,800rpm, making an interesting comparison (as Ludvigsen points out) with the 130bhp at 6,100rpm of the original 2-litre 911 flat-6. For the US market, the compression ratio had to be dropped right back to 8:1 to enable operation on 91RON gasoline, and the power output was consequently a far more modest 95bhp (SAE net). This was not enough to keep the customers happy, and an urgent development programme, including a compression ratio increase to 8.5:1 and revised valve timing, took the power of the US version to 110bhp for the 1978 model-year, still well behind the European output, but at least sufficient to avoid the car being condemned as downright slow.

Production and further development

Once negotiations between VW and Porsche has been concluded, the 924 was announced in 1975 as a 1976 model. The car was presented very much as 'a Porsche for people who can't (yet) afford a 911'. This time there was no VW version to cloud the marketing presentation, but it remained to be seen whether the 924 would be accepted as such when its engines came from the VW works at Salzgitter and final assembly took place at the Audi works in Neckarsulm. The short answer, it appears, was yes: by the time the 924/944/968 series had run its course, production had reached 325,231 units, far in excess of what was achieved with the 914, and this with a car which was larger, heavier and more expensive (although still much less expensive than any 911).

Initial reactions were certainly favourable. The author, writing as technical editor of *Autocar* in

December 1975, gave his first driving impressions following a press presentation exercise in the south of France. After noting that, even at 6ft 2in (188cm) tall, I drove with the seat two notches forward of fully aft, and that the pedals were better spaced and positioned than in the 911, I gave my assessment of the handling: 'It is not a case of which end goes first. In the end it all goes together, but unlike the 911 it may be retrieved simply by releasing the accelerator pedal (a recipe for instant disaster in the rear-engined car). The 924 simply stops its sideways skitter and slows without drama … There is no trace of the change of heart experienced with some mid-engined cars, understeering through long, fast bends but tail-happy through hairpins.' I praised the steering and the straight-line stability, but placed question marks against the low-speed ride ('lumpy and harsh'), the overall noise level ('road noise and bump-thump, combined with engine noise over 5,000rpm to make high-speed progress more wearing than it ought to be'), and a driveline which was 'not the world's most forgiving; ham-footed driving means jerky progress, more so than in many cars'.

Those press preview cars were pilot production, so there remained scope to counter some of the criticisms (which were by no means unique to the author) through detail changes to engine mountings – the whole engine and transmission assembly sat on just two mountings at each end – and suspension bushings, as well as tyre choice. About a year later I had a much better chance to assess the 924 when I became keeper of *Autocar*'s long-term test vehicle (SLG 360R), one of the first 20 924s made with right-hand drive (with 4-speed gearbox), which arrived with 35 miles on its clock, was run-in, served as the road test car and then remained 'on strength' until it had completed 13,500 miles. It was observed at the time of the road test that the car still felt relatively stiff and performance was likely to improve, and so it turned out. Its 'end of term' performance figures showed that while the mean maximum speed was little changed (it gained 1mph, from 126 to 127mph) the 0–60mph time had come down from 9.7sec to 8.9sec, and the 0–100mph time from 30.4sec to 29.8sec. In top gear, 40–60mph had been reduced from 10.8 to 9.4sec. The overall fuel consumption, which had been 27.8mpg for the road test period, had settled to 27.2mpg long-term.

Porsche quality was evident even in this early car, which developed no fault more serious than the failure of a handle to the (always stiff) bonnet release cable. As technical editor, in true engineering fashion,

I took to carrying a pair of pliers in the glovebox rather than taking time out to have it mended. An odd, one-off fault, was a massive water leak into the interior after the car had stood covered in snow for a week: the ingress never could be traced, despite serious efforts with a hose. A rumbling noise, which felt like tyre fouling, in extreme driving conditions, was eventually traced to the inlet manifold fouling the bonnet side rail. Brake dust from the front pads had made a mess of the alloy wheels, which needed professional restoration.

Reliable though that early car was, Porsche was as ever eager to address any problems that arose, but it was disappointing to find that the long-term car suffered almost as badly from road noise as did the early press preview car. It was fitted with Uniroyal tyres which, from measurements taken over the test period, clearly had a low wear rate by way of compensation. Porsche suggested Pirelli CN36s as a quieter alternative and had 'some improvements in the pipeline in the suspension itself to try and better things.'

One thing which was evident to any engineering test driver of an early 924 was that the chassis, no matter how much it had been contrived as a 'bits and pieces' exercise out of the VW parts bin, had plenty of potential. The standard tyre size on the basic 924 was 185R14, with the option of 185/70R14 for any owner who wanted to tip the balance towards handing rather than comfort. Yet it seemed patently clear that with wider tyres, the car would be capable of handling a lot more power. That fitted well with the direction in which Porsche wanted to develop the model. Through the late 1970s the main planks of the company's future were seen as the 928 and the 924: the 911 was viewed as a sideline operation which would eventually peter out. Given the size, power and price of the 928 once that project was resumed (Chapter 8), there was plenty of scope to move the 924 upscale, increasing its value-added and making it more profitable without

The early 924 Turbo was something of a beast, yet hard to distinguish visibly from the standard car, except for the additional intakes (NACA in the bonnet, slots along the upper nose) *needed to feed extra air for the induction system and to keep the engine compartment cool despite the high temperatures reached by the turbocharger casing.*

any significant increase in production volume. So far as power was concerned, there were three possible avenues of development: to tune the existing Audi-based engine, to turbocharge, or to develop a completely new and more powerful unit.

It was felt that the Audi engine could not be significantly developed in naturally aspirated form. Remember it already had 'siamesed' bores, so any further stretch was out of the question: a longer stroke would have made the engine taller (or, with shorter connecting rods, rougher than Porsche was prepared to contemplate) so that it would no longer fit beneath the 924 bonnet. It was already fuel-injected and, in European form, had a pretty high compression ratio. The only thing which would have made a big difference would have been a 4-valve head, and in the mid-1970s that was a move too exotic even for Porsche to contemplate. Besides, a number of 'private venture' turbocharged 924s began to enter the aftermarket, showing the logical way to go. Porsche elected in the short term to produce a 924 Turbo alongside the basic car, while for the longer term they studied the idea of developing their own compact, 4-cylinder in-line engine, encouraged by the fact that the VW Group was already moving on from the 2-litre Audi unit and would not guarantee to keep it in production at Salzgitter. Indeed, later-production 924s were fitted with engines produced and stored before the power unit line was finally shut down. All these developments would move the 924 up-market into more expensive territory, but that was seen as entirely positive by Porsche which saw it as moving the company back towards more familiar territory, building high-quality cars in relatively limited volume.

924 Turbo

The 924 Turbo was merely the first step along the way, although a significant one. The new version, which actually carried the Porsche Type Number 931 for left-hand drive cars and 932 for right-hand drive (and therefore followed on from Type 930, the original 911 Turbo of 1974), began to be built late in 1978 and was thus in effect a 1979 model-year announcement. The changes to the engine were mainly concentrated in an all-new cylinder head, made from a stronger aluminium alloy to withstand the higher stresses, with shallow bowls topping-out the combustion chambers rather than the completely flat head of the naturally aspirated engine, with the sparking plugs

moved to the 'top' of the engine and bigger exhaust valves. The bulk of the combustion volume at top dead centre was still contained within a bowl in the piston crown, whose flat periphery created a strong squish effect during the compression stroke. The bottom end of the engine remained essentially unchanged, a tribute to its strength. With a compression ratio of only 7.5:1 and up to 12psi boost pressure from the KKK turbocharger (originally developed for commercial vehicle applications) the 924 Turbo delivered 170bhp at 5,500rpm and 175lb ft of torque at 3,500rpm – modest figures by today's standards, but these were the days before sophisticated electronic protection against detonation, and a margin had to be left in all circumstances. Indeed, for the US market the maximum boost pressure was held down to just 6psi and peak power was only 143bhp, with 147lb ft of torque. The new powertrain aside, the 924 Turbo was externally distinguished by additional front-end air intakes and 15-inch wheels, while the 5-speed gearbox was made standard, together with a larger-diameter propeller shaft.

The 924 Turbo power output of 170PS (in Europe) was sufficiently close to the 180bhp of the contemporary 'base' 911SC (180PS) that it seems likely Porsche wanted to see if the 924 would be accepted as a 911SC substitute. It was, after all, a more practical car in many ways, with superior stability and handling and very similar performance. It was priced – in Germany, at least – less than 10 per cent below the 911. Clearly it would have suited Porsche at that time to switch customers to the newer car, but the customers simply would not be switched. As the 1980s progressed the 911 remained firmly in place, the 924 and its later derivatives remained strong and, to the distress of some of Porsche's managers, it was the 928 which found itself less and less loved.

As it transpired, the early 924 Turbo was not without its problems. These were still early days for turbocharged cars. The Saab 99 Turbo, often regarded as the originator of turbocharged production cars (although it was by no means the first to use the technology) had been announced at the Frankfurt Show only one year previously, in 1977. The 924 Turbo found itself on a similarly steep learning curve so far as the early problems of such cars were concerned, with turbo lag and the 'cooking' of oil in the turbocharger after the engine was switched off among the challenges, together with the effect of extreme heat on some under-bonnet components. As a result, Porsche evolved what amounted to a second-series 924 Turbo which replaced the original in 1981. These cars had a new, smaller, lower-inertia KKK turbocharger – the GA – plus a new fully computerised ignition system whose 'mapped' memory allowed the compression ratio to be raised to 8.5:1, resulting in notably improved efficiency. Thus while the maximum power rose slightly to 177bhp for Europe (150bhp for the USA) fuel consumption – often a sore point in the earliest turbo-cars – was improved. The oil 'cooking' problem, which generated a high volume of warranty claims, was solved by arranging that oil continued to circulate through the turbocharger after switch-off, for long enough to ensure the turbine temperature was brought back within bounds.

Part of the appeal of the 924 Turbo (indeed, of any turbo model) was that by increasing the boost pressure – and acknowledging the way it would shorten engine life – a great deal more power could be extracted for competition purposes. Further power could be gained, without too much threat to engine integrity, by fitting an intercooler, something now taken almost for granted but in the early 1980s, very advanced thinking. Because the sports car regulations of the day mostly stipulated homologation as a road car, Porsche evolved this strand of thinking into a complete high-performance programme and distinguished it by adding the Carrera name and distinct Type Numbers: 937 for left-hand-drive cars and 938 for their right-hand-drive counterparts. There were three Carrera versions in all, built very much as limited editions and sold to customers who appreciated exactly what they were taking on. The original Carrera GT (406 examples built) delivered 210bhp, while the Carrera GTS (59 examples) increased this to 245bhp. The ultimate version in this series was the full-race Carrera GTR, of which only 17 were built, with no less than 375bhp.

1982: From 924 to 944 (and 924S)

Production of the 924 Turbo ceased in 1983, by which time the basic 924 was itself most of the way through a career which saw no more than modest but useful improvements, including the adoption of an Audi 5-speed transaxle as soon as one became available, in 1980. The main reason was that late in 1981 Porsche had launched the 944 as a 1982 model-year product. The 944 was in essence a flared-arch 924 body on the

wider-tracked chassis, beefed-up wherever necessary and powered by a brand-new 2.5-litre 4-cylinder engine of the company's own design. Just to confuse things, the new engine also went into a new and visually almost unchanged version of the 924, designated 924S, which eventually came on stream to replace the 2-litre 924 when the latter ended production before the 1985 works summer break.

This new engine was all-alloy, with an open-deck, linerless block. In this it closely resembled the V8 engine in the 928, and in fact, the original proposal had been that the 944 would use 'half the V8' although in practice it didn't work out quite like that. It differed in every respect from the 924's Audi-derived engine, save that it had four cylinders. It was physically bigger, with 122mm cylinder bore centre spacing (as in the 928's V8) allowing a full 100mm bore, and thus large valves for strong breathing, the inlet and exhaust valves being 45mm and 40mm in diameter respectively, while still leaving space for coolant passages between the bores. Again as in the V8, the valves were inclined 20 degrees from the cylinder centre-line, helping to make the unit lower still. The stroke was 78.9mm, making the engine very substantially over-square, with a bore:stroke ratio of 1.27, so although the engine was distinctly longer it was not too tall, and when leaned over at an angle of 30 degrees it was still able to fit comfortably beneath the 924 bonnet.

Gone was the flat-faced Heron head and the bowl-in-piston combustion chambers of the 924: now the piston crowns were flat except for valve-clearance cut-outs, and the combustion chambers were wedge-shaped, with the spark plugs installed in the 'short' sides opposite the in-line valves. The valves themselves were in-line, and operated by the single belt-driven overhead camshaft via bucket tappets.

One of the most intriguing features of the 944 engine, however, was its use of twin balancer shafts running at camshaft speed, one on either side of the block, a feature which had only recently been adopted by Mitsubishi. The idea was to balance out all the secondary forces to which a 4-cylinder in-line engine is otherwise subject. These forces tend to increase with engine size, and any 4-cylinder engine of more than 2-litre capacity is a candidate for auxiliary balancing, as so many modern units show. It was felt that the 944's 2.5-litre certainly needed it, if it was to deliver acceptable refinement in a car which would cost significantly more than the 924 – which had itself been criticised for feeling rather rough at high engine speeds.

The principle of auxiliary shaft balancing was by no means new, having been spelt out by Doctor Lanchester at the end of the 1800s, but it had lain ignored until engine designers began to worry about the operating refinement of large, 4-cylinder engines. As an added refinement of the Lanchester principle, the Porsche (and Mitsubishi) balancer shafts were installed at slightly different levels, thus also – or so it was claimed – counteracting the asymmetric combustion pressure distribution within the cylinder, leading to sideways piston pressure on the cylinder wall. After a good deal of agonising, Porsche paid Mitsubishi a licence fee to use their system, after devising an alternative which circumvented the patent, but was felt to be too expensive to develop and manufacture.

Although the 944 combustion chamber design was completely different from that of the 924, it shared the underlying principle of high turbulence leading to efficient and reliable combustion, allowing the use of a 10.6:1 compression ratio. Thus the engine was able to deliver 120kW (163PS) at 5,800rpm, with

maximum torque of 205Nm at 3,000rpm, with a commendably flat curve promising good driveability. Fuel consumption was good; better in some test cycles than the 924. There was a 3-speed automatic option, but like any 3-speed it sapped both performance and economy, and proved deeply unpopular except in the USA.

To match the capability of the bigger engine, the 944 took the wider front and rear tracks of the 924 Carrera GT, stiffer anti-roll bars, 15-inch alloy wheels with 7-inch rims, and ventilated disc brakes all round. When the engine was announced, the press was told it would be fitted both as a bigger alternative unit in the 924, in parallel with the 2-litre, and in 'a new model based on the 924 Carrera GT'. In practice, as soon as the 944 became available, sales of the 924 began to dwindle. Too few customers wanted a 'base' model with fairly average performance when the quicker, more powerful and more muscular-looking 944 sat in the same showrooms. Soon, the only remaining significant markets were those, like Italy and France, in which cars with engines larger than 2-litres were heavily penalised by higher annual tax rates.

The improvements came, but slowly. For the 1984 model year, the 944 was given the option of power-assisted steering, which was speed-sensitive and higher-geared than the original manual system (3.2 instead of 3.8 turns of the wheel from lock to lock). The market response was such that PAS became standard a year later. To 21st century readers, the idea that a long-nosed, front-engined, wide-tyred high-performance car could have been offered with manual steering in the first place may seem incredible, but it was a different world. In fact reaction to the 944, from both the specialist press and from customers, was overwhelmingly positive. Here was a car that was a proper Porsche, without anything borrowed from Audi, and with much more Porsche-like performance, yet (all things considered) at a reasonable price. Demand for the 944 was such that there was no surplus engine capacity to feed the 924S, which is why this version only entered production in the late summer of 1985. At that time its power output was slightly reduced, to 110kW (150PS) by the simple expedient of lowering its compression ratio to 9.7:1. Cynics said this was to ensure the 924S, with its lower frontal area and slightly lower Cd, would not outrun the more expensive 944; but there was a payoff in the ability to use regular-grade petrol, and the economy was slightly better too. For the 1988 model year, the difference ceased to be, since for the sake of economy Porsche

standardised on one engine, now delivering 118kW (160PS) at 5,900rpm, with 210Nm of torque at 4,500rpm. Then, for the 1989 model year, the 924S was dropped altogether, and the range became all-944.

1985: 944 Turbo

For the 1986 model year, Porsche revealed a new top-range version in the form of the 944 Turbo. There had been a 924 Turbo, ergo there had to be a 944 Turbo, the more so because the Porsche-developed engine was probably a more suitable basis. The engine it its

Left: Cutaway of the 944 engine, an all-new unit which was in many respects half of the 928's V8 and likewise all-alloy. Although it was longer than the original Audi-based unit, there was enough room beneath the bonnet to accept it. However, it had to be inclined at 30 degrees to keep its top end beneath the existing bonnet line. This was one of the earlier 4-cylinder engines to be fitted with twin balancer shafts.

Below: A good many changes are evident in this cutaway of the 944 Turbo, prepared (one presumes) using the earlier cutaway drawing as a starting point. In particular the nose is much deeper, flares have been added to the sill panels, a soft "duck tail" spoiler has been added at the rear, and the wheels and tyres are wider. Beneath the bonnet, an all-new engine, turbocharged and with an intercooler housed in the upper nose.

definitive form was force-fed by a KKK K26 turbocharger with a maximum boost pressure of 0.75 bar, the compressor output passing through an intercooler mounted high and immediately in front of the engine. Compression ratio was lowered to 8:1, and output was 162kW (220PS) at 5,800rpm, while maximum torque was 330Nm at 3,500rpm, a typically high 'turbo' figure achieved at a modest speed. The increased stresses and thermal loadings persuaded Porsche to cast the cylinder block slightly larger, adding 1mm all round, while the valves and valve seats were made from more exotic heat-resistant alloys. A ceramic liner in each exhaust port prevented too much heat from being rejected into the head, and it also helped with faster catalytic converter warm-up.

Speaking of which, the 944 Turbo ushered in three significant new features. First, a catalytic converter was made standard, since it had been decided this powertrain would undergo 'universal homologation', meaning it could be sold in any market in standard form. Second, a new Motronic engine management system made provision for knock protection, retarding the ignition upon receiving warning signals from knock sensors (accelerometers) in the cylinder head. Third, the thorny question of oil 'cooking' in turbochargers – of the oil actually in the turbo unit being cooked to cinders if the engine was switched off immediately

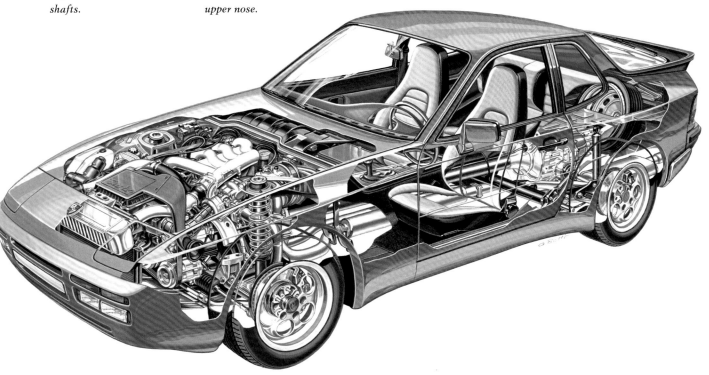

after a fast run – was solved by switching to a water-cooled turbo, with a small pump which carried on circulating water for a while after the ignition was switched off, to carry away excess heat.

Once again, the chassis came in for attention: most noticeably by far, standard 16in wheels were fitted, and the rear rims were wider than the fronts (8in rear, 7in front) even in this front-engined car with a nicely even static weight distribution. The dampers and anti-roll bars were stiffened, while the ventilated discs were again thicker as well as larger in diameter.

It was easy enough to see that, just as the 170PS 924 Turbo had been set up as a potential competitor for the then-current 180PS 911SC, so the 220PS 944 Turbo might be a rival for the 230PS 911 Carrera. Yet again, despite the arguable advantages of the 944, the customers didn't agree. Turbos were still seen as something separate, different, and the comparison was simply not made at customer level. In any case, the customers had something else to think about in the 944 range, with the introduction of the 944S.

The 944S, launched as a 1987 model year car, was equipped with a 16-valve cylinder head which closely resembled that already fitted to the 928S4. That is to say, it used a toothed-belt drive to the exhaust camshaft, from the centre of which a short, single chain drive crossed over to drive the inlet camshaft. As in the 928, the valve and combustion chamber layout was compact, with an angle of less than 30 degrees between the inlet and exhaust valves. On the face of it, the 944S seems to have been something of a development challenge, since the target was naturally to deliver an engine with usefully more power than the 8-valve unit. To achieve 190PS (140kW) at 6,000rpm, the valve lift had to be increased beyond that of the 928, the compression ratio was raised to 10.9:1, and even the fuel injection pressure was increased to improve fuel atomisation. As in the Turbo, a knock sensor function was included. Torque output was 230Nm at 4,300rpm, compared with 205Nm at only 3,000rpm for the standard 8-valve. The greater output and high-revving nature of the engine meant it was not compatible with the 944's 3-speed automatic.

The reaction to the 944S was not favourable. In common with a number of 16-valve engines of the 1980s, it seemed to have lost at the bottom end at least as much as it had gained at the top. Certainly it was quicker, but only if the driver was willing to change down whenever the revs dropped much below 4,000rpm. Eventually, answers would be found and the 16-valve engine would become almost the European and Japanese norm, but in 1987 that day was still to come, and the 944S, pitched precisely as the intermediate version between the 160PS 8-valve and the 220PS Turbo, struggled to achieve acceptance.

There was an easy answer to the lack of low-end torque: make the engine bigger. This, however, is where the 944 story becomes complicated. By the 1987 model year there were three 2.5-litre engines, the 8-valve, the 16-valve and the 8-valve Turbo. A larger swept volume could be applied to any of them, and there was the further possibility of a 16-valve Turbo to top things off. The first stage was to bore-out the 944 engine from 100mm to 104mm, giving a capacity of 2,681cc; simple, but how effective? No boring-out was possible beyond 104mm, so the alternative was to increase the block height so that the stroke could be lengthened to 88mm, which with the 104mm bore, resulted in a swept volume of 2,990cc.

For the 1988 model year the 944 was given first the 2.7-litre engine, whose output of 120kW (163PS) at 5,800rpm, and torque of 225Nm at 4,200rpm, were disappointing advances on the 2.5-litre. Making the engine even more over-square than it already was, was not the cleverest response to a lack of low-end torque. Consequently and in very short order, while the 8-valve 2.7-litre was retained for the base 944, the 16-valve 944S was increased to 3-litre capacity and installed in the revised 944S2, with a much more impressive 155kW (211PS) at 5,800rpm, and 280Nm of torque at 4,000rpm. The 944S2 also gained the bluffer, moulded polyurethane nose section which had hitherto been reserved for the Turbo. By common consent of contemporary road testers, the 2.7 944 was lack-lustre, but the 944S2 was impressive. Meanwhile the differential between the naturally aspirated 16-valve and the turbo was maintained, even though the Turbo remained a 2.5-litre, by a series of improvements (including a larger K26 turbocharger) which increased power output to 184kW (250PS) at 6,000rpm, with 350Nm of torque at 4,000rpm. In this form, complete with comprehensively stiffened chassis with the rear wheel rim width increased to 9in, the Turbo became more of a specialist's car and indeed, for the 1988 model year it was offered as a special series Turbo S (finished in metallic pale pink!). For the 1989 model year, the 250PS specification became standard, as did a moulded plastic rear spoiler, but the 944 Turbo then languished until it was withdrawn in 1991.

The final evolution of the 4-cylinder range had to await the resolution of some trials and tribulations around 1990, which included the transfer of 944 production from the Audi factory at Neckarsulm back to Zuffenhausen (with bodies supplied by Karmann) and the preparation of a 944 Cabriolet, entrusted to ASC (the American Sunroof Company) which took over a small but long-established coachworks in Germany to fulfil the contract, but encountered problems which delayed the launch. Porsche was also in the throes of an 'environmental' programme which would see it among the first car companies to eliminate asbestos and cadmium from its products, and to change over to water-based paints free from volatile solvents. By 1991, Porsche had also become the first German manufacturer to fit all its left-hand-drive models with driver and front passenger airbags as standard. Such moves were valuable and paid later dividends, especially as the environmental lobby became more powerful, but at the time they also diverted effort from actual product development.

Around 1990, a good deal of effort was also devoted to the idea of replacing the 4-cylinder engine, whose relative lack of refinement even with balancer shafts resulted from the 'big banger' characteristics inevitable with 750cc per cylinder, with a smoother 6-cylinder. Both V6 and in-line 6-cylinder solutions were studied, and Porsche is said to have come close to doing a deal with Volvo to use the in-line 6-cylinder unit developed for the Swedish company in Weissach, but in the end the economic solution was to seek further improvements to the 4-cylinder.

The original idea was to carry through a comprehensive package of improvements for the 944S2, which would then become the 944S3. Principal among these improvements was the adoption of the VarioCam system for varying the inlet valve timing through a range of 15 (crankshaft) degrees, and a much improved inlet manifold which, by providing alternative air paths of different lengths, smoothed the torque curve. This move was accompanied by a host of other engine improvements, some of them minor, but including a change from cast to forged connecting rods. Peak outputs rose to 176kW (240PS) at 6,200rpm, and 305Nm at 4,100rpm. Just as important, the revised car gained a new 6-speed manual gearbox, jointly developed with Audi, and a 4-speed Tiptronic automatic option, developed with ZF

Yet another cutaway to compare. This is the 944S2, in which the 16-valve 944S engine was enlarged to full 3-litre capacity, for an output of 211PS. Note that the nose shape is very much that of the *944 Turbo, but the tail "lip" had further evolved into a proper rear spoiler. Beneath it all the original 924 sheet metal remains almost unchanged – the added features are mostly plastic*

using the internal mechanisms of the latter's 4HP18 automatic.

The changes were so comprehensive that the decision was taken, on marketing grounds, to redesignate the 944S3 as the 968. The change of number fooled nobody, for the 968 was visibly almost identical with the 944S2. The changes were worthwhile, however, and the road testers thoroughly enjoyed the 968, in particular its handling balance. In that respect, they said almost universally, it had become one of the best production cars in the world. And when it came to the delivery of power and torque the VarioCam, without being in any way obtrusive, improved the low-end response of the 16-valve engine and with the revised induction, ensured more punch all the way through the rev range. Meanwhile, the 944 Cabriolet metamorphosed into the 968 Cabriolet to complete the range – the Turbo having by now vanished.

Alas, it was not enough. Sales began to languish, and in an attempt to inject more interest, a 968 Club Sport was introduced for the 1993 model year, with the now well-established weight-saving measures although not carried to the extremes of the equivalent 911s. The appeal of the 968 is well summed up in *Autocar*'s 1993 road test of the UK-market Club Sport: 'You lose the back seats, electric windows and mirrors, central locking and a sizeable chunk of sound-deadening. But drivers gain more than they lose. Pukka racing seats and 17-inch alloy wheels from the 911 Turbo are man-sized replacements for largely trivial deletions. Otherwise the rest is stock 968. The three-litre, twin-cam, four-pot engine still develops 240bhp, the six gear ratios are unchanged; as is the suspension, bar a 20mm drop in ride height. You can have 911 Turbo brakes, rock-solid suspension and a limited slip differential if you must, but the package

Left: The 944 Cabriolet, whose development and production was undertaken by the American Sunroof Company (ASC) took a long time to arrive in the marketplace but was well received when it did. There were Cabriolet versions of most of the 944 variants: this is a 944 Turbo.

Above: A comprehensive series of improvements increased the output of the 3-litre 4-cylinder engine to 240PS. Among the changes was the adoption of Porsche's Variocam system which could change inlet valve timing by altering the configuration of the camshaft drive chain loop. This engine came with a 6-speed gearbox.

litre Turbo S, which delivered no less than 225kW (305PS) at 5,400rpm, and 500Nm of torque at only 3,000rpm. With a suitably modified chassis, running 235/40-18in tyres at the front and 265/35-18in tyres at the back, the 968 Turbo S was claimed to reach 100km/h in under 5sec, and have a maximum speed of 202km/h (175mph). But only a handful of them were built, for it had become clear that customers spending that much money did not want 4-cylinder engines. They went, increasingly, to the sporting derivatives of BMW's 3-series instead. Thus Porsche was forced into the decision to bring the 4-cylinder era to an end, in 1995. This at least had the merit of concentrating engineering and production efforts more clearly on the 911, although the next 'poor man's Porsche' – all things being relative, of course – was by then progressing through development in Weissach, to emerge as the Boxster.

costs £1,300 and is more suited to the race track than the road. The bottom line is a weight saving of 85kg and a price saving of £4,797.' The author remembers that car with special affection: it was the last road test he helped prepare for the magazine.

It was still not enough. Plans were laid for a new 3-

CHAPTER 8

1977: 928, the big Porsche

Auto des Jahrzehnts.

PORSCHE

Dr. Ing. h. c. F. Porsche AG Stuttgart-Zuffenhausen · Printed in Germany August 1979 · Entwurf Werbeagentur Strenger · Foto: Strenger

There is a temptation to see the 928 as a kind of scaled-up 924 because it emerged a year after the 924, in 1977, with volume sales beginning in 1978. There is, after all, a similarity both of shape – a kind of smoothed-off rejection of the sharp-edged Italian mode of the time, as favoured by Italdesign and Bertone – and of mechanical layout, with a front engine and rear-mounted transmission.

To take this view, however, is to ignore the evidence of the Porsche archive. In fact, the 928 was conceived first, and the 924 followed it along the same pathway of design logic. But while the 924 (originally intended, it should be remembered, to emerge as the EA 425 VW sports coupé) made extensive use of VW group mechanical components, the 928 was all Porsche, and when work began on its design, it was seen as the key to the company's future.

Product planning in Porsche around the year 1970 was all about life after the 911. It was assumed that the rear-engined car had no long-term future and that the company had to establish a new direction for itself. One obvious move was to create a car which was bigger, more practical, more expensive – not so expensive as to shrink its potential market too far, but rather pitched at a level where the demand would be reasonable (and within Zuffenhausen's ability to manufacture), but the profit margin would be sufficient to ensure a healthy future. As always, this gave rise in some minds to the idea of a four-door car. In the end, however, the 928 took shape as a two-door sports coupé, big enough to provide four proper adult-sized seats.

The prime mover behind the 928 concept was Dr Ernst Fuhrmann, the designer of the high-performance 4-cam Carrera engine for the 356. He left Porsche during the 1950s but returned in 1971, after the company had been restructured and ceased to be an entirely family business. He became managing director in 1972 and saw the future as non-911, moving to modern front-engined cars. Fuhrmann eventually left in 1981, replaced by Peter Schutz, after losing his personal battle (with Ferry Porsche and Ferdinand Piëch), to kill off the 911.

Because it was to be a big and powerful car, the 928 was going to need a larger engine than the flat-6. In fact the power requirement more or less forced the adoption of a V8 configuration. To achieve something in excess of 175kW in a naturally aspirated engine, with the kind of relaxed delivery and mid-range punch that Porsche had in mind, would require a capacity in excess of four litres, and this would have resulted in

six uncomfortably large cylinders. The logical choice was eight cylinders, and while a flat-8 might have been possible, in effect a flat-6 with two extra cylinders, the vee configuration made far more sense. It was well-tried and resulted in a far more compact unit. Again, it might just possibly still have been air-cooled and even rear-mounted, following the example of a whole series of Tatra models from the T77 to the late post-war T700.

However, the appeal of liquid cooling was overwhelming. Porsche engineers were well aware that the 911 flat-6 was not really an air-cooled engine anyway, but rather an air-plus-oil-cooled engine, witness the steady growth of 911 oil coolers over the years. Liquid cooling meant fewer problems with internal airflow, no huge cooling fan to absorb power and create noise problems, and the chance to equip the new car with a high-capacity heating and air conditioning system without risking any of the criticisms which blighted the early (and indeed later) 911s in that department.

The 928's V8 engine was conventional in some respects but ground-breaking in others. It was a 90-degree unit with single-toothed belt-driven overhead camshafts, directly operating in-line valves via bucket tappets. Nothing strange there, then. It was a substantially over-square engine, with 95mm bore (as in the 3-litre flat-6 911 engines)

Following its introduction, the 928 was elected "Car of the Year" by a European jury, clearly swayed by its futuristic appearance, its performance, and the fact that it seemed to point a new way ahead for Porsche. The company certainly made the most of its accolade, witness this poster design.

and a stroke of 78.9mm for a swept volume of 4,474cc. Thus even as a V8 its individual cylinder capacity was 559cc; it is easy to appreciate why, eventually, a 6-cylinder engine was seen as out of the question. It is even easier when one realises that the original plan was to launch the 928 with a full 5-litre engine, something which in the event didn't happen until 1986. The back-tracking to 4.5-litre was a gesture towards the politics and economics of the 1970s, which saw the two great energy crises of 1973 and 1978/79, with fuel prices rising to what then seemed stratospheric levels.

As it was, the over-square dimensions meant the engine was relatively long, which didn't matter, but low enough to allow a swooping bonnet line, which did – although some commentators felt the designers failed to take sufficient advantage of this. However, the biggest talking-point was that this was an all-aluminium engine, without benefit of iron or steel cylinder liners. It needed the capacity but it could not be heavy, and risk spoiling the overall balance of the car. By the time 928 development was underway, Porsche had mastered the Alusil process and applied it to the individual cylinders of the 3-litre 911s. They saw no reason why it should not be adapted to a complete V8 cylinder block, and so it was done.

In order that the pistons should not wear themselves out against the etched-silicon cylinder walls, they were coated either with iron or with chrome. The block was low-pressure cast (by the piston specialists Mahle) and the casting was open-deck, each cylinder standing isolated within the surrounding casing. The cylinder centres were 122mm apart, allowing plenty of 'stretch' and betraying the fact that the engine had been developed as a 5-litre and then shrunk in the most convenient way, by reducing the bore; the left and right-hand banks were staggered by

The 928 needed an 8-cylinder engine to provide the target performance in a car of its size and weight. Porsche designed this unit, a conventional V8 in many respects although with single overhead camshaft per cylinder bank, and of all-alloy construction. Originally developed as a full 5-litre unit, it was launched as a narrower-bore 4.4-litre, only to "grow back" again later.

27mm. In the final analysis the complete engine, fully 'dressed' but dry, weighed 246kg (of which the steel crankshaft accounted for 25kg), so the all-alloy approach had certainly worked.

The engine introduced several other features which have become more familiar over the years. Principal among these was a substantial cast-alloy ladder-frame which bolted into place beneath the block (which extended only down to the crankshaft centre-line) and not only stiffened the whole assembly, but also carried the main bearing caps, and the lower oil galleries, cast in place and closed by special sealant. The lower void could then be closed by a cast alloy sump. The two-plane steel crankshaft itself ran in five main bearings, each crankshaft throw carrying the big-ends of opposite cylinders side-by-side (hence 27mm was the width of each connecting-rod big-end).

By the standard of the day, the cylinder heads were simple and straightforward. The valves were in-line, canted outwards by 20 degrees from the cylinder centres to create a classic wedge-shaped combustion chamber shape. The cylinder head section was trapezoidal, the top surface horizontal, and housing both the spark plugs and the inlet ports. Then the surface turned 65 degrees, so to speak, to form the base for the valve gear and the camshaft carriers. A further turn through 65 degrees created a face, parallel to the cylinder centre-line, at which the exhaust ports met the inlet manifolds. It was an arrangement which left plenty of space for coolant on the exhaust side, and the engine's over-square dimensions meant the in-line valves could be made big enough to allow the engine to develop the relatively modest required power. At 54bhp/litre, the 928's specific power output was nothing exceptional, but this was to be a much 'lazier' engine than any 911, with a fat torque curve. This was further emphasised by the conservative valve timing, 8-55-38-2 degrees.

Both camshafts were driven, along with the vital accessories of water and oil pumps, by a single, extremely long (all but 7ft long, in fact) toothed-belt. Considering this was still quite early in toothed-belt history this was a bold step, but one typical of Porsche's two-sided approach to innovation: not to adopt it without being sure it works, but not to be afraid of it either, if it does. At launch, the company called for cam belt changes every 60,000 miles (100,000km) or five years, and it does seem that adherence to this schedule avoids trouble. Apparently the valve timing and lift in the earliest 4.5-litre V8s meant that a cam belt failure would not result in

This cutaway drawing of an early 928 shows the V8 engine installation, the 4-seat cabin, still rather cramped in the back, the rear transaxle with gearbox located forward of the final drive, and the characteristic rear "buttresses" and triangular rear quarter windows aft of the substantial B-pillars.

valve-to-piston contact, but this benign feature vanished as soon as the timing was altered to extract more power.

The first 928s used Bosch K-Jetronic fuel injection, a neat mechanical-balance system which gave good results by the standards of its day, at moderate cost. It soon succumbed to increasingly severe emission regulations and the superiority of electronics, however. The V8 also used Bosch solid-state ignition, with a distributor driven from the end of one camshaft. As for that strange feature, the water cooling system, careful design seems to have ensured that it worked well and reliably.

As to where the engine should be installed, rear-mounting was out of the question. Quite apart from the stability and handling problems which would inevitably ensue, this was to be a luxury-class car in which owners would expect to open the back end and find generous luggage space. Mid-mounting was equally out of the question, given the requirement for two proper back seats. Thus the engine would have to

go in the front. That did not mean the transmission would have to live there as well. With a stroke of imagination which preceded the adoption of the same configuration for the smaller 924, the design of which (as explained in Chapter 7) began after that of the 928, it was decided that the gearbox should be installed in unit with the final drive.

The rear-mounted transaxle was by no means a new idea in itself. Vittorio Jano had adopted it for the Lancia Aurelia in 1950, Ferrari had used it in the 275 and the formidable Daytona. Alfa Romeo had also chosen it for the 116-series cars – the Alfetta and its successors – which replaced the 1750/2000 from 1972 onwards. Its great appeal was that it made for a more even static weight distribution. It also avoided having a big transmission cover between the front footwells, making more space and allowing a better pedal layout. The design of the manual gearshift was a little more problematic, but only a little; a slightly bigger problem was containing a propeller shaft which would always run at engine speed, but again, satisfactory solutions already existed.

In many ways the 928 layout resembled that drawn for the 924, with a rigid tube joining the rear of the engine to the front of the final drive. In the 928, however, the gearbox was installed forward of the final drive. The chosen 2,500mm (98.4in) wheelbase, a full 10cm longer than that of the 924, allowed this without the gearbox intruding into the back seat space, while the central chassis tube – 100mm in outer diameter, with 3mm thick walls – and the 25mm diameter propeller shaft could be made usefully shorter. As in the 924, the clutch was installed at the engine rather than the gearbox end of the propeller shaft, although in view of the much higher engine torque output, the clutch was a specially engineered twin-disc unit.

The standard gearbox was 5-speed manual, specially engineered to minimise noise levels which might be fed through the rear seat pan. Instead of having five all-indirect speeds as in a conventional transaxle, it exploited its position forward of the final drive to provide a direct-drive fifth gear. While the manual clutch was at the engine end of the propeller shaft, the torque converter for the optional 3-speed automatic – sourced directly from Mercedes-Benz – was at the rear. Consequently, a large cut-out had to be provided in the rear seat pan, to be closed by a shallow pressing in the case of the manual gearbox, or a much deeper one when the automatic was fitted. Creating the automatic transmission option was deemed essential, however much of an engineering nuisance it might be, because it was appreciated that a car like the 928 would be very difficult to sell in the USA in manual-only form; and sure enough, the majority of 928 sales in the USA were of automatics.

One odd feature of the 928 arose because of the desire to mount the complete drivetrain – engine, transmission and intermediate tube – to the body at just four points, two at each end. In order for these points to coincide with vibration 'nodes' of the assembly, a lot more weight was needed at the back end than the transmission itself provided. For this reason, a tray was added aft of the final drive, and in this was placed, lengthwise, the battery, all 35kg of it. It was a technically satisfactory solution, but the battery position was poor from the maintenance point of view and after the first year's production it was moved further aft to sit under the space-saver spare wheel. The drivetrain mounts were recalibrated and nobody complained.

For the 928 chassis, Porsche engineers exploited the space on either side of the V8 engine to do something for which they had never had the room in the 911: create a proper double-wishbone front suspension with parallel arms. The dampers, concentric with their coil springs, picked up on the big lower wishbones. Space was found for negative-offset 'auto-stabilising' steering geometry, and the wishbones were angled to provide anti-dive. An anti-roll bar was standard, and so was ZF power-assisted steering. Without it, the 928 would have needed perhaps five turns of the wheel between locks to keep the steering loads tolerable. The brake discs were ventilated front and rear, the rears carrying small auxiliary drums for the benefit of the parking brake.

At the rear, after some head-scratching and a period of careful development, the 928 introduced what Porsche called the 'Weissach axle'. This was a considerable elaboration of the semi-trailing arm principle, and replaced the double-wishbone layout first proposed, in which the upper 'wishbone' would have been a single transverse link. When it was found that, with suspension bushes soft enough to achieve low noise levels and tolerable high-frequency response, this layout produced unwanted rear-steering effects due to bush deformation, the 928 team sought a way of turning these deflections to advantage, and the Weissach axle was the result. The extended wheel hub was located by two independent links, one semi-trailing, one transverse, with bushes deliberately arranged so that when the wheel was subjected to braking or sideways cornering forces, its alignment would change in a way that compensated for the effect of the original force on the handling. Under braking, for example, the rear wheels would toe-in slightly for improved stability. The angles involved were very small, but all good chassis men (and Porsche has some of the best) know that even small changes of rear wheel alignment can exert a significant effect on the handling. The Weissach axle was one of the first systematic approaches to the idea of making sure that any change of geometry was beneficial to handling and stability; and it worked.

The 928 body looked much odder in 1977 than it does today. It was one of the first cars, at least in Europe, to have flexible, moulded plastic front and rear ends forming a completely styled shape and covering the mechanisms which would absorb impact energy and so provide the necessary safety. The main cross-beam at each end was mounted on collapsible struts for Europe, but self-restoring damper struts for the US market, which at that time demanded zero visible damage following a 5mph impact. In other respects the 928, styled by a team led by Anatole 'Tony' Lapine, fulfilled its specification in a package which provoked a few negative comments. It was a big beast, only 6 inches longer than a contemporary 911S but an important 9 inches wider. Nobody could ever have called its pillars, especially the rear 'buttresses', slender, and the rounded wings made it difficult to position the car precisely, or to judge the width in tight situations. As for the cabin, the requirement for four proper adult seats had clearly not included easy entry to and exit from the back seats, or the headroom when sitting there. Compared with the 911's rear perches, however, the 928 back seats were in a different league.

The 928 was ecstatically received by the motoring press, the author included. I find it worth quoting myself from *Autocar* of 9 April 1977: 'The handling, no less than the sheer grip, is astonishing. Faster round each succeeding corner, surely with a sideways force approaching 1g. Even a mid-corner bump seems not to worry this astonishing car. The 911 would flick out its

tail and call for instant correction, but not the 928: if it goes at all, it skitters sideways with all four wheels, a few inches of give to regain its composure.' Along with near-perfect brakes and beautiful steering, it seemed the 928 could do little wrong where dynamics were concerned. Yet this was, perhaps, also its Achilles' heel. It was just too good, therefore not 'involving' in the 911 sense.

Be that as it may, and despite the fears over the future of big, thirsty cars in an era of what seemed to be expensive fuel, and with the second great energy crisis just around the corner, the 928 was voted Car of the Year 1978. Since the rules of this election required the jury to take account of value for money, this was a surprising result, good though the 928 was in other respects. The author, a CotY judge at the time, can now confess he gave his maximum 10 points to the original Honda Accord, which was far better aligned with what seemed likely to be the spirit of the 1980s. But the 928 garnered 261 points ahead of 231 for the equally new BMW 7-series (and 139 for the Honda; a European jury was not yet ready for the idea

From the outside, this early 928 looks much more at home in the world of 2007 than it did in 1977. At that time, the lack of a visible front bumper was distinctly unusual, *especially in Europe. The big polyurethane moulding was collapsible, and concealed the energy-absorbing mechanism required by American regulations.*

of a Japanese Car of the Year), and it was, in some senses, the car's finest hour. Although eventually production of the 928 series ran to over 61,000 units, it was never a favourite among Porsche customers, most of whom remained stubbornly loyal to the 911 series, and thus proved Ferry Porsche and Ferdinand Piëch right and Ernst Fuhrmann wrong.

Even so, the 928 was developed beneath its skin, although it never changed its shape except in detail. Production began slowly, Porsche records showing a modest 1,290 cars built in calendar year 1977, including the pilot-production examples used for the press launch. In 1978, the figure rose to over 4,900 cars and the production rate to around 20 a day. By 1979, a second production line had been installed in Zuffenhausen to handle 928 manufacture. It was the first time Porsche had used a hanger system to enable the running gear to be offered upwards into the body and was sufficiently successful to result in a change being made to the 911 line shortly afterwards. Even then, however, these were not conventional, continuous-movement production lines. The cars remained stationary at each workstation, and were automatically moved forward to the next station at regular intervals. It was only much later that Porsche accepted the continuous-flow principle.

Because the 928 had in effect been launched into the teeth of a major energy crisis (sparked by the departure of the Shah from Iran, the US Embassy siege crisis in Tehran and for the second time in a decade, the use of throttled oil supplies as a political weapon), some effort was devoted to making the car more economical. After all, *Autocar* had measured its overall test fuel consumption at 14mpg (imperial) for the manual car and an appalling 12.1mpg for the automatic, and these figures were not untypical. For several years the Porsche engineers worked on the idea of cylinder-switching, deactivating four of the cylinders in order to turn the V8 into a V4 when cruising at modest speeds, thanks to reduced pumping losses and higher thermal efficiency in the four cylinders that remained operational. A journalists' technical seminar in Weissach in 1979 included a paper which suggested fuel savings of around 20 per cent could be expected, depending on driving conditions. A radically downsized, turbocharged engine was also considered. In the end, however, none of these solutions could be made to work seamlessly, and gradually the panic of the energy crisis was left behind.

Instead, if anything, work continued in the opposite direction. By the early 1980s the most influential magazines in Germany, the USA and the UK were all implying, in their tests, that the 928's performance if anything fell short of its aspirations and its positioning in the market. New benchmarks such as the Jaguar XJ-S had shifted the perspective of the opinion-formers. There was a ready answer to this, since the 928 engine had originally been sized as a 5-litre before being 'shrunk' prior to launch. It was the easiest thing in the world to restore that capacity, although in practice it was done in two stages, first boring-out by 2mm (to 97mm) for a swept volume of 4,664cc, and then proceeding to the full 100mm bore and the originally planned capacity of 4,957cc.

The first stretch, to a nominal 4.7-litres, came in 1980 with the creation of the 928S. Changes were also made to the 4.5-litre engine, with a raising of compression ratio both for the USA and Europe. Tuned for more torque rather than more power, the engines became notably more economical; in fact for the European version, an improvement of no less than 18 per cent was claimed (on the other hand, the new compression ratio of 10:1 called for the use of super-premium fuel). For the US market engines, three-way catalytic converters were now needed to meet emission regulations, and the Bosch K-Jetronic fuel injection gave way to the electronically controlled L-Jetronic which was compatible with lambda sensors and closed-loop control.

The real interest however was the 4.7-litre, which was deliberately tuned for higher power rather than extra torque. Thus it was a higher-revving engine, with its whole induction system resized to handle higher airflow – the throttle in the K-Jetronic system was enlarged from 66mm diameter to a massive 84.5mm. In this way the power was increased from the 240bhp of the original engine to 300bhp (221kW) at 5,900rpm in European form. The increase in torque was modest – the new output was 385Nm – but the transmission was uprated to match, and the chassis also received attention, with stiffer (now tubular) anti-roll bars and thicker, better ventilated brake discs. An extended chin spoiler, and a wrap-around rear spoiler, improved the aerodynamics. The enthusiast magazines generally approved, although *Autocar* mentioned hesitant low-speed response and high road noise. However, its 928S reached 60mph from rest in 6.2sec, and that was the real point of the exercise, along with a maximum speed comfortably over 150mph. Eventually the 928S became the standard model, the original, standard version being phased-out during 1982.

The worrying thing was that the 928's sales resolutely refused to grow – and before long, they began to shrink. In calendar year 1979, production (standard plus S) was 4,706 units. For the following years 1980, 1981, 1982, 1983 the figures were 4,195, 4,087, 4,510 and 4,200 respectively. It was all rather disappointing for a car for which so many hopes had been entertained, and which it had been planned to produce at a rate of 5,000 units per year. This did not prevent the engineering effort from continuing. In 1983 the output of the European 928S rose modestly to 310bhp (228kW) and 400Nm of torque, courtesy of a higher (10.4:1) compression ratio, new Bosch LH-Jetronic fuel system, a new ignition system and revised valve timing. For automatic transmission buyers, a new 4-speed unit replaced the original 3-speed, to the benefit of both performance and economy. In addition, ABS was offered (and was standard in the UK). The whole package was marketed as the 928S Series 2, and represented a serious attempt to kick-start a second phase in the 928's career. Sure

enough, in calendar years 1984 and 1985 output rose slightly, first to 4,601 units and then to no fewer than 5,356. Even so, it had become monumentally evident that 928 buyers and 911 buyers were completely different kinds of people, and that the only hope for the 928 was to soldier on as a flagship with almost nothing in common with the company's best-seller.

It was not, in practice, something which could be achieved, but Porsche gave it their best. After all, the alternative was to write off all that investment dating back to 1971. The way forward was moderately obvious. Up-gunning the original 928 from 4.5-litres and 240bhp to 4.7-litre and 300bhp had been a mild success. More of the same was indicated, but this time the process would be taken further. It had always been an option to bore-out the V8 to 100mm and 5-litre capacity, but now it was proposed also to adopt the growing trend towards 4 valves per cylinder. Rather than design a completely new cylinder head and valvetrain, the Porsche engineers retained the original outboard camshaft, but now to operate only the eight exhaust valves per bank, and added a second inboard camshaft driven by a short chain from the first, to operate the inlet valves. The included angle between inlet and exhaust valves was 28 degrees, indicative of a desire for economy rather than maximum output (for which an angle of 40 degrees or more would be preferable).

Little appears to have changed in the 10 years between the previous picture and this shot of a 1987 model year 928S4, other than the addition of the rear aerofoil spoiler. Under the bonnet, however, the engine had grown to full 5-litre capacity and had 32 valves instead of 16, and power output was now 320PS.

Despite the apparent economy in creating the valvetrain, the cylinder head itself had naturally to be all-new, incorporating twice as many ports and a completely different cross-section to provide a footing for the second camshaft. The combustion chambers became near-symmetrical wedges, with (naturally) the spark plug upright in the centre of the crown.

The main purpose of these major changes was not – as it might have been – to create a super-engine with an output of 400bhp, but rather to make it much more efficient and therefore economical. This was because the USA had introduced its CAFE (corporate average fuel economy) regulations and the 928 S2 had been branded as a 'gas guzzler'. So, despite the increase in capacity and the move to 32 valves, the engine in US-market form with a compression ratio of 10:1, valve timing of 11-50-30-5 degrees and a fully 'emissionised' exhaust system with larger catalytic converters, delivered just 292bhp at 5,750rpm – but 410Nm of torque, allowing the final drive ratio to be raised. There was no point in offering such an engine in Europe where 310bhp was the 928 norm, and it was only in 1986, for the 1987 model year, that Europeans were offered a 5-litre, 32-valve V8, in the 928 S4.

The Porsche GB press release of the time heralded it as 'the greatest ever changes to the 928 series embodied in the new Porsche 928 Series 4', although it went on to explain that 'the original USA-specification 292bhp 32-valve engine was the third major development but was not available for UK specification.' Even as released for Europe, the 5-litre's output was modest, especially for a 32-valve unit, but it had to produce more power than the preceding Series 2, so it did: 320bhp (DIN) at 6,000rpm and 430Nm of torque at 3,000rpm. Although the compression ratio remained at 10:1, the engine now incorporated knock sensors so that 95RON petrol could be used, the control system retarding the ignition (and reducing output) if knock was detected. Along with this higher power, the 928's aerodynamics had been substantially

Below: A cutaway view to compare with the original, this being a late-series 928GTS. Now beneath the bonnet, a 5.4-litre 32-valve engine delivering 350PS, still in relaxed style. The nose shape has substantially changed and the rear spoiler is evident, but as with the 924, the basic shape and especially the distinctive "glasshouse" remains unaltered.

Right: Parting shot: a 1995 model year 928GTS, therefore one of the final 300-odd examples to come off the Zuffenhausen line. Comparison with the similar-angle picture of the very early car shows how little the basic shape and the styling features had changed, even down to the 5-spoke alloy wheels, though they had become much wider. Only the nose shape is substantially different.

improved, with new, smoother nose and tail sections and new spoilers, so that its drag coefficient was reduced from the original, rather shocking 0.39 to a far more acceptable 0.34, to the benefit of economy, but also of maximum speed, which was now claimed as in excess of 270km/h (167mph).

In March 1988, a stripped-out, nominally higher-performance version of the 928 was announced, designated Club Sport for most markets although the UK insisted on a higher equipment level and called it the Sport Equipment version. The reaction proved that this was not the right way to go. In particular, the stiffened suspension raised the road noise to intolerable levels. Thus less than a year later, the far superior 928 GT was announced, according to the UK distributors 'as a direct result of the success of the Porsche 928 Series 4 with Sports Equipment, which was introduced in limited numbers on 1988 …' The GT was a more carefully considered package, with the most powerful V8 engine yet (330bhp at 6,200rpm, thanks to improved breathing and recalibrated engine management), but torque output unchanged. A limited-slip differential was standard, and acceleration was improved with a shorter final drive ratio; 0–60mph was now claimed in 5.8sec, and maximum speed had risen to 275km/h, near enough 170mph. In the UK, for the 1989 model year, the 928 GT became the standard manual-transmission version.

The final engineering flourish came in 1991, when the engine grew to 5.4-litre capacity. This time the change was more radical. Further boring-out could not be safely achieved, so a new crankshaft was designed with its stroke increased by 7mm to 85.9mm, yielding a swept volume of 5,397cc. Output, in European tune (and now, of necessity, with catalytic converters) rose to 350bhp at 5,700rpm, and torque to an impressive 500Nm at 4,250rpm. Improved though these figures were, the 5.4-litre had originally been planned as a stepping-stone to a full 6-litre. This programme, however, had been discontinued when it became clear that the 928's career was in terminal decline. The introduction of the 32-valve engine in the USA had won it a temporary reprieve, production reaching 4,617 units in calendar year 1986 and 5,407 units (the all-time record) in 1987. Thereafter, the decline was steep. From 1988 to 1995, the final year of production, the annual output figures ran: 3,663, 2,919, 3,088 (1990) and then 768, 1404, 721, 384 and 382. Beautifully engineered and capable though it had become, the 928 had been seen off by some highly capable – and generally cheaper – rivals. This could not happen to the 911, of course, because in a very real sense it had no rivals. That was the difference, and that was why the 911 survived while the 928, once seen as its successor, eventually fell by the wayside despite all the engineering effort thrown at it.

CHAPTER 9

1978: 911 reaches three litres

In the autumn of 1977 the Porsche 911 reached a watershed. The standard engine was enlarged to full 3-litre capacity, with the same dimensions (95 x 70.4mm for a capacity of 2,994cc) as the Turbo of 1974. In practice, this meant the 2.7-litre engine had been bored-out by a further 5mm. This really was the final evolution of the original 2-litre flat-6, the last engine which could properly trace a stage-by-stage derivation from the 1967 power unit. By this time, however, there had been so many stages that the 3-litre engine resembled its ancestor very much in the manner of George Washington's axe: the two had no components in common other than the odd nut and bolt, and probably not even that.

The first version to have a 3-litre naturally aspirated engine was, as pointed out in Chapter 4, the 911 Carrera 3 which was announced in 1975 for the 1976 model year. This Carrera proved to be short-lived, since the standardisation of the 3-litre engine for the 1978 model year meant the 911 was reduced to a single version, the 911SC. For this application the output of the 3-litre engine was 180bhp at 5,500rpm, compared with 200bhp at 6,000rpm in the Carrera 3, and 165bhp at 5,800rpm for the final-series 2.7-litre. This was not simply a detuned version of the Carrera 3 engine, though, any more than the Carrera 3 had been a naturally aspirated version of the 3-litre Turbo engine. In each case development had been specific to the perceived needs of the market. The new 911SC engine incorporated a new crankshaft with larger main and big-end bearings, and thus with greater overlap for more strength and stiffness. Meanwhile the revised valve timing meant that although peak power was down on the Carrera, torque was actually increased over most of the rev range. To some extent, in any case, the loss of power was due to the standard installation of an air pump in response to increasingly severe exhaust emission regulations, mainly in the USA but also elsewhere.

At last, with the 911SC, a 5-speed gearbox became standard equipment rather than notionally optional; in practice, it had for some time been difficult to lay hands on a 4-speed 911 even if you wanted one. In theory, especially given the fatter torque curve, the car would have been eminently driveable with just four well-chosen ratios, but at the end of the 1970s we had reached an era in which the market expected any high-performance sporting car to have five speeds, whether it needed them or not – it was simply part of the territory. Shortly afterwards, at the end of the 1980 model year, and apparently without any official

announcement, the Sportomatic clutchless transmission was abandoned. It had been a bulky and performance-sapping system, and while some drivers enthused over the ability to shift gears without heaving a clutch pedal, the wider opinion was that if you had an automatic, it should be a proper automatic that took care of everything. The 928 had one, of course, but its Mercedes-derived unit was far too big to fit into the constricted space of the 911, at least without turning it into an even more tail-heavy two-seater.

In any event, through most of the 1980s, if you bought a new 911, you accepted 'stick-shift' – something which was indeed of most consequence in the US market. For much of the decade Porsche mulled over its automatic options, even including a 'new and improved' 5-speed Sportomatic, but in the end it opted for a 'proper' automatic with positive driver override, in the form of Tiptronic. That, however, was for the beginning of the 1990s, for a new car (the Type 964) and a new chapter. On the chassis side, the 911SC also bowed to the inevitable in fitting a standard brake servo.

As though to maintain the differential between models not merely in performance but also in engine size, as the 3-litre became the standard 911, so the Turbo was opened out to 3.3-litres, as described in Chapter 6. This really was in effect a new engine, and in many ways it set the scene for what was to come. For the 911SC, however, the existing 3-litre engine continued with further improvements. The whole pace of 911 development at this stage definitely slowed, since the 1970s Porsche management under the direction of Ernst Fuhrmann had more or less decided on dropping the 'old soldier' 911 and evolving a new front-engined, water-cooled range built around the 924, 944 and 928. It was only with the retirement of Fuhrmann at the end of 1980, and his replacement by the German-American Peter Schutz, that the cloud was lifted from the 911's long-term future (and transferred, to a significant extent, to that of the 928).

The direction in which the 3-litre naturally aspirated engine evolved was not altogether expected,

The tough, high performance sports car image of the 911 was boosted through further development and entry in carefully chosen events. This is one of the three-car team which claimed success in the 1984 Paris–Dakar event. No ordinary 911, though: a 3.2-litre engine, 4WD and radically increased ground clearance were among the changes which made the win possible.

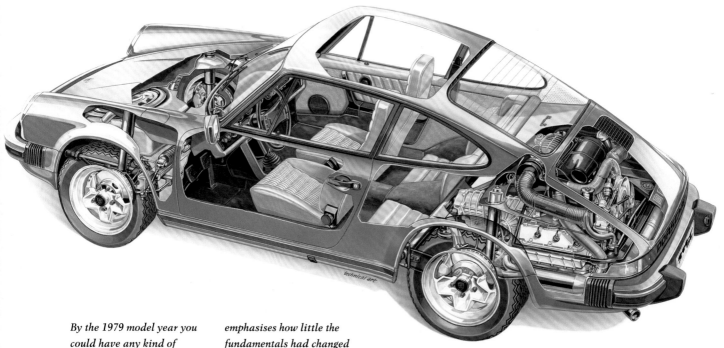

technical art

By the 1979 model year you could have any kind of naturally aspirated 911 you wanted, so long as it was a 3-litre 911SC with 5-speed gearbox and 180bhp. This cutaway of such a car emphasises how little the fundamentals had changed over the years, although it is worth searching for the host of detail changes. More refinements were to come in the future.

though it was entirely logical. Having shocked enthusiasts a decade before by adopting low compression ratios and the ability to run on regular-grade fuel, for the 1981 model year Porsche raised the European compression ratio back to 9.8:1, by fitting new pistons with higher crowns. The power output rose sharply from 180bhp to 204bhp (150kW), still at 5,900rpm, the torque output remaining – rather surprisingly – unaffected. Regular grade fuel was no longer available but this was more than compensated for by the reduced thirst for 98RON, the consumption being down by a claimed average of 21 per cent.

Meanwhile, urgent moves were in hand to broaden the appeal of the 911 and to take it into market areas with higher margins. The first sign that this would be so came at the 1981 Frankfurt Show, where Porsche displayed a highly 'political', yet technically significant concept car. This was a full soft-topped Cabriolet (as distinct from the Targa), equipped with four-wheel-drive transmission. The political angle was that here was proof that 911 development was back on the burner. The technical angle was that here were two avenues that would be explored all the way to full

production. The detailing of the Cabriolet was interesting, showing that a proper soft-top could be engineered in accordance with US safety regulations. The 4WD transmission was crude, without any centre differential, and implied (correctly) something much further down the line.

Sure enough, only six months later, in March 1982, the definitive 911 Cabriolet was shown at the Geneva Salon, and it entered series production shortly afterwards. The Cabriolet body was in no sense a revolution, since it was based on the Targa but with the hoop removed, and some extra strengthening built into the lower body to compensate for the modest degree of

Above right: At long last, in 1982 the definitive 911 Cabriolet became available, in effect a 911 Targa minus the famous hoop. Both Targa and Cabriolet versions were built in parallel. The Cabriolet was fitted with a manually-operated hood for the first four years of production, power operation finally becoming available for the 1987 model-year.

Right: The 911 had pioneered the Targa open-top treatment and claimed the name as its own. This 1984 car is a late-series example of the original 911 Targa, with the B-pillar hoop and the fill-in roof panel between that and the windscreen arch. By the mid-1980s, this body style was coming close to the end of its run, and its successor would adopt a radically different approach.

stiffness which had been lost in the process. The result was satisfactory, but it was certainly not the stiffest body in the business, and Porsche at that time, and with that body structure, resolutely refused to countenance the idea of a Turbo Cabriolet – the far higher torque would have been too much for long-term structural integrity. The actual soft-top was manually operated – unthinkable in this power-operated day and age – although it was cunningly designed for ease of operation, and it was decently weather-proof and quiet when raised. A crude feature was the zip-out plastic rear window, which would otherwise have folded, and perhaps cracked, during fold-down. There was some debate about whether the Cabriolet would effectively replace the Targa, but in the event demand for both versions continued strong, with annual production of each well into four figures. A power-operated hood for the Cabriolet arrived in 1986, for the 1987 model year.

Naturally aspirated, 3.2-litres

Meanwhile, further work had been conducted in the engine department. A new engine capacity of 3,164cc was created by combining the standard 95mm bore with the Turbo's longer 74.4mm stroke, and was introduced for the 1984 model year. Other major changes included a further increase in compression ratio, to 10.3:1 for European cars and 9.5:1 for the USA and Japan with their tighter emission requirements, and the adoption of fully integrated engine management for the first time, fuel injection and ignition timing being controlled from a single 'black box'. Conventional cylinder head gaskets were dispensed with, the sealing between head and cylinder now entirely (and dependably) reliant on metal-to-metal contact. The timing chain tensioner – long a pain for 911 owners, possibly the least reliable component on the car – was redesigned, with special attention paid to its lubrication. For the first time, oil pressure in the tensioner cylinder was maintained constant via a bleed from the main oil circuit. The upshot of all these changes was an increase in European power output to 172kW (231bhp), still at 5,900rpm, and a useful lift in torque from the previous 264Nm (195lb ft) at 4,300rpm, to 283Nm (209lb ft) at 4,800rpm. For the USA and Japan, the corresponding figures were a much less impressive 202bhp and 185lb ft of torque.

The gearbox was new, with higher fourth and fifth gears to the benefit of fuel economy and cruising noise levels, and was provided with an integral oil cooler.

Such was the improvement in performance which came with this larger engine, with European-specification cars running to a maximum of over 150mph and comfortably under 6sec to 60mph (or indeed to 100km/h), that a change of designation was thought to be called for. The clear favourite was to resurrect the Carrera name, and consequently the 3.2-litre 911 became the 911 Carrera, replacing the 911SC. The engine was not the only change, naturally. There were thicker brake discs and a larger-diameter servo, plus a pressure limiter in the front brake line to prevent, or at least discourage, premature locking of the front wheels during panic braking. Although there was a clear distinction between the Carrera and the Turbo,

By 1985 the 3-litre 911SC had evolved into the 3.2-litre 911 Carrera. In most markets it was possible to order the Carrera with what amounted to a Turbo body, creating a naturally aspirated "Turbo Look" car. This could be done with any of the variants in the range, such as the Turbo Look 911 Carrera Cabriolet seen here.

it was possible in most markets (other than the UK, for some reason) to order the Carrera with a body and equipment package that made it look virtually the same as a Turbo – but it could be ordered for the Targa and Cabriolet as well as the basic Coupé (the apparent anomaly was rectified in 1986 when Targa and Cabriolet versions of the 3.3 Turbo were finally offered).

Through the mid-1980s, 911 development once again appeared to stagnate. Changes were of detail, not fundamental. The oil cooler was redesigned, complemented by a new air intake in the front bumper moulding. The Cabriolet was given a power-operated hood, following many complaints about the original manual operation. The chassis was fine-tuned with new Boge twin-tube dampers, stiffer anti-roll bars and uprated rear torsion bars. For the 1987 model year, US and Japanese market engines were revised to run on 95RON unleaded 'premium' petrol, resulting in an increase in output to 217bhp (162kW) and 264Nm (195lb ft). The European specification was unaffected, although customers were now being offered the option of a catalytic converter – at that time still a European novelty for the environmentally conscious – with output reduced to US levels.

More significant than this fiddling with engines was the introduction, again for 1987, of a completely new transaxle, the Type 950. This had its primary and secondary shafts wider apart, 85mm instead of 75mm, allowing the gears to be made larger and stronger. It also provided the space for six forward gears, if required (which it soon was). As a result, the 950 was rated at 550Nm and so could cope with any Porsche torque output, including that of the Turbo which was thus for the first time provided with five forward speeds. Its larger size was complemented by a larger 240mm diameter clutch, with hydraulic rather than cable operation. Another change which came in with the Type 950 transmission was a revised shift pattern. For a long time, Porsche had laid out its gearchange gate in three planes, with first opposite reverse, and second through fifth in an H-pattern. Most other five-speed gearboxes kept the lower four gears in an H and offset the (usually overdrive) fifth gear to the right. Journalists of the time, including the author, often referred to a 'Porsche-pattern' gate to distinguish it from the others. Opinions differed as to whether it was a good thing, but it came to an end with the Type 950 which had a shift moving in four planes, the forward gears conventionally arranged and, opposite the overhung fifth, a slot where a sixth gear would soon be introduced for some purposes.

No doubt some American dealers were by now reminding Porsche that it had been a long time since they had been able to offer automatic transmission, but they didn't have much longer to wait. Since 1984, American customers had been offered a very small consolation in the form of a dashboard-mounted upshift warning light to indicate when the engine would pull just as well, and more economically, in the next gear up, but it was not a popular feature and was soon dropped. In later years, no doubt, it would have been dubbed a 'Formula 1-type upshift indicator', but as things were, it was an idea before its time.

Club Sport

Some measure of excitement was provided, during 1987, with the introduction of the 911 Carrera CS (Club Sport). The rationale for this version was that the inexorable uprating of equipment, such as electric windows as standard, had made the production car heavier and blunted the edge of its performance. Accordingly, the Porsche development team went over the Carrera and deleted any item which was not considered essential to the normal day-to-day operation of the car – starting with the electric windows and moving on to the back seat, and much of the sound-deadening material. The list of deleted items extended, with Teutonic thoroughness, even to the coat hooks and the PVC underbody treatment (as a result of which, Porsche's celebrated ten-year warranty against body rot was reduced to three years). Various other items, including the spare wheel and some electrical components, were lightened where the opportunity arose.

To go with this simplification and lightness, the engine was mildly breathed upon, with the valvetrain inertia reduced by the fitting of hollow inlet valves, and the red line raised from 6,200 to 6,600rpm. The actual rev limit set within the engine management unit went up from 6,600 to 6,850rpm. The damper setting were stiffened, as indeed were the engine mounts, and the wheels were wider, with 7-inch rims at the front, and 8-inch at the back. Reaction to the Carrera CS was mixed. The British, to judge by contemporary published road tests, quite liked it, especially the improved acceleration which resulted from the weight saving. The Americans hated it, although this may have been as much to do with the price as the car; the British importer charging around 8 per cent less for the CS (a saving of some £3,000) in acknowledgement of its lower standard of comfort and equipment, while the US importer retained the standard Carrera price. All sides agreed, however, that driving the CS was a noisy experience, and one best left to the dyed-in-the-wool enthusiast.

In retrospect, the 911 was lucky to survive the 1980s. It had entered the decade under the shadow of 'the plan' which foresaw a switch to front-engined cars, and it had received only a small share of the engineering development capacity available in Weissach and Zuffenhausen. Yet it did survive, mainly because the market refused to let it go. By the end of the decade the 911 had become almost the only car with an overhung, rear-mounted engine: the VW Beetle had become a Mexican-assembled oddity, Skoda's rear-engined range was history. The only rear-engined production cars in Europe were the under-rated Renault Alpine V6, and the Polish-built Fiat 126bis, whose engine was so light it scarcely mattered where it was.

Somehow, the 911's near uniqueness, and the ultimate threat to stability and handling which came with the configuration, simply added to its appeal. The engineers had done most of what they could,

One last pre-964 addition to the range, in 1987, was the 911 Carrera CS (Club Sport), aimed at enthusiasts, with weight saved through the stripping out of all non- *essential items, even to the underbody PVC protective treatment. From the outside, you would be hard put to see the difference without being close enough to see the badge.*

given the technology of the period, to tame the handling although there was less they could do about the stability, especially in gusting sidewinds. Driving a 911 at very high speed somewhere like the Millbrook Proving Ground 'bowl' with a wind blowing could still be a hair-greying experience. By the end of the 1980s it was clear that the experience would continue to be offered.

Something, however, was about to change. In all the quarter-century-plus since its introduction, the 911 had been just that – the Porsche Type 911. But with the approach of the 1990s, things would become more complicated. A new car, a 911 replacement, had been designated Type 964, although it would still, for

obvious reasons, be marketed as a 911. There followed a whole series of new Porsche type numbers, each of which represented a further major iteration of the 911 theme, all with rear-mounted flat-6 engines but otherwise with less and less in common, unless one counted the 'family likeness' of body shape. For the sake of easy reference, although the cars themselves are covered in later chapters, it may be worth noting here that the later Type Numbers run as follows, with their dates of introduction and discontinuation:

Type 964 1989 to 1993
Type 993 1993 to 1998
Type 996 1998 to 2004
Type 997 2004 to date

Within these changes of series would come completely new engines, further evolutions of transmission, all-new body structures and major revisions to the suspension, especially at the back. The essence would remain: the 911 would always be a 911.

CHAPTER 10

1984: 959, a technical pinnacle

One might well ask whether the Porsche 959 has a place in a book which specifically devotes itself to production cars rather than the company's many competition cars. After all, the 959 was developed to comply with the FIA regulations for Group B cars, and it made its first real impact by winning that toughest of all motor sport events, the Paris–Dakar Rally. On the other hand, in order to comply with the Group B regulations, a minimum of 200 production cars had to be made and sold, and in the later 1980s these cars formed part of the wave of 'supercars' which washed through the upper strata of the motoring world and whose merits were endlessly debated by dedicated motoring enthusiasts. It was also a fierce expression of just how much technology Porsche could deploy, and how advanced its engineering could be, when most of the normal constraints were removed.

Looked at in retrospect, the late 1980s were a very silly period in which a significant number of companies, some of them specially formed for the purpose (and some of which, in the end, failed to produce even a single prototype), set out to make money by designing and building cars which were road-legal yet capable of exceeding 200mph (322km/h), and selling them in deliberately small numbers to rich enthusiasts for extremely high prices. Part of the advertised appeal was that such 'limited edition' cars would surely increase in value (they didn't). Porsche, of course, was nothing like so cynical, yet by virtue of its performance and its road-going abilities the 959 fell naturally into this group of models and was arguably superior to any of them.

Was it the fastest road-legal car of its time? Possibly not quite. Did it provide the strongest combination of performance, handling and roadholding, achieved through the ruthless deployment of the most advanced technology? Yes, almost beyond serious dispute, except on the race track where a couple of back-to-back tests suggested Ferrari might have the slightest of edges. Such was the mystique which grew up around the 959 that for a while, it became an object of almost ridiculous adulation in the pages of the 'enthusiast' press. The author took serious issue with *Autocar*, to which he then contributed, when for a time, the magazine seemed to publish a Porsche 959 story almost every week, sometimes on flimsy pretexts, but it was certainly not alone in this. In almost all such stories the emphasis was on driving the 959 on the road, exploiting its capabilities so far as the writers were able. As a competition car, the 959 had already long since had its day by 1990.

Beginnings

The genesis of the 959 lay in the emphasis placed on FIA Group B competition during the early 1980s. Group B, as the designation implied, lay between Group A, covering competition between true production cars of which at least 5,000 examples had been made and for which the regulations were written deliberately to exclude two-seat sports cars, and Group C, for what amounted to purpose-designed competition two-seaters. Porsche had been outstandingly, almost crushingly successful in Group C, but it had no product which would ever allow it to compete in Group A events and series. Enter Group B, for which the technical regulations were far more liberal (no vehicle weight regulations, no power output limit, free use of special materials) and which required the series production of only 200 nominally identical, road-going examples. One of the unspoken objectives of Group B was to enable other manufacturers quickly to build 4WD rally cars with which to challenge the Audi Quattro, which otherwise threatened to carry all before it. It was generally (although not universally) accepted that any serious Group B car would have four-wheel drive.

After a period of consultation, Group B was introduced by the FIA in 1982 to replace the existing regulations covering Group 4 (modified grand touring) and Group 5 (prototype) cars. It was anticipated that Group B events would be run both as circuit races and rallies. Porsche was mainly interested in the first rather than the second. The company had achieved success with the 911 in the Monte Carlo Rally and the East African Safari Rally, but it had long regarded full-season rallying as extremely expensive even compared with GT racing, and also took the view that technically speaking, where lessons which could be applied to its road cars were concerned, it had (paradoxically) learned less from its rallying programmes than from its racing experience.

The 959 won the 1986 Paris–Dakar event. This was a very different car from the relatively crude 1984 winner – and also significantly different from the road-going cars which would eventually find their way to rich enthusiasts. For one thing, to cope with the running conditions seen here, the ground clearance must be substantially increased.

Sadly from Porsche's point of view, Group B quickly established itself as a rallying rather than a racing formula, and in so doing sowed the seeds of its own destruction. Very soon, the cars proved to be so fast and to impose such high loads on their occupants that even the fittest and most professional drivers could not drive them consistently to the limit for the distances and surfaces over which international rallies tended then to be run. It became a case of pacing oneself or of risking the potentially catastrophic consequences of misjudgement brought about through sheer fatigue. A string of serious accidents, culminating in the death of Lancia works driver Henri Toivonen and his co-driver Sergio Cresto in Corsica, resulted in the termination of international Group B events after 1986. Many of the surviving Group B cars ended up taking part in top-level rallycross, where speeds tended to be lower and events much, much shorter.

The problem for Porsche was that by the time the 959 had been fully developed to a satisfactory standard, the 1986 season-end axe had fallen and the car was left without any real purpose, other than to serve as a technology demonstrator promoting the image of the company via the 'halo effect'. In this, for a time, it was outstandingly successful. Unlike some of the 'supercar' manufacturers, Porsche had no trouble selling its production run of 329 959s at a standard price of DM 420,000 ($225,000 at the then-current rate of exchange). This was about the going rate for a

A precursor of the 959, and indeed of much subsequent Porsche technology, was this 4WD Cabriolet exhibited at the Frankfurt Motor Show of 1981. Not only was it the first 911 Cabriolet to break cover, but under its skin was the germ of the transmission which would help to make the 959 such a formidable proposition.

'supercar', but it has been estimated that the cost of building a 'production' 959 was well over 1 million DM. This implies that Porsche lost nearly DM 300 million on the 959s it sold. That was the difference between the 959 and some of its rivals which achieved their performance through sheer power and with relatively little regard to the quality of chassis engineering or aerodynamics. That was why the 959 was so demonstrably superior. Porsche could probably have sold 500 examples or even more, but the programme's losses would have been commensurately greater. Enough was enough – and it must be admitted that once the fevered interest in 'supercars' died away in the early 1990s, the 959 became part of motoring history remarkably quickly, and the focus of Porsche enthusiast interest returned yet again to the 911 in its later series.

Shaping the 959

Although the 959 project was officially launched in January 1983, under the direction of Professor Helmuth Bott with Manfred Bantle as engineering project leader, most of the major decisions concerning its specification had already been determined. The extent to which this was so is evident from the fact that it took Bantle only a week to produce a target engineering specification. It had been accepted from the outset that a Group B car would need 4WD, and that eliminated the 924 and 928 as any kind of basis for development. Given their front engine, rear transmission layout, there was simply no tidy way to split the drive and take a proportion of it forward to the front wheels. That did not stop a number of manufacturers (BMW, Ford, Mercedes) doing that with originally front-engined, rear-driven models. Audi of course had simply taken a front-driven car and added to the existing final drive a differential and an output to the rear wheels.

Porsche's distaste for running a front propeller shaft alongside a front engine and finding room for the accompanying final drive left two alternatives: to base the Group B project on the 911, or to start from scratch. Helmuth Bott had considerable enthusiasm for an all-new mid-engined design which would undoubtedly have been the optimum so far as competition was concerned. One only has to look at the most successful Group B rally cars, during the formula's brief currency, to see that. It might have been rather less satisfactory, however, for those 200 very special

customers who would have to buy the 'production' cars. Given the necessary power output and the size of the engine bay, a road-going version would have been cramped and noisy at best. Also, bearing in mind the lessons learned even with the modestly powered 914, it seemed likely that from the handling point of view, a mid-engined car might prove a real handful for some of these customers.

The clinching argument, however, was that the 959 could serve not merely as a Group B competition car, but more importantly as a test-bed for technologies and concepts applicable to future generations of the 911. It was already clear that that the 911 would continue in some form more or less for as long as Porsche made cars. It had survived the arrival of the 914, 924 and 928, all in their different ways intended to supplant it. And the thing that made the 911 different was its flat-6 engine installed aft of the transaxle. Thus whatever else, the 959 was going to have its engine in the same place, though it would be equipped with 4WD. In fact, its mechanical layout, if one forgets the actual engine configuration, would be that of the Audi Quattro in reverse.

The standard front-drive Audis mounted their engine ahead of the transaxle (making them inherently nose-heavy) and the Quattro added a centre differential to the transaxle, and an output to a rear final drive. The 959 would take the standard 911 layout, with engine aft of the transaxle (making it inherently tail-heavy) and would add a centre differential and an output to a front final drive. Unlike the Audi, which used a conventional centre propeller shaft and a rear final drive located within a rear sub-frame, the 959 would adopt the 924/928 arrangement of a stiff central tube which would tie together the front and rear final drives.

The 959 was shaped to resemble a 'high-tech' 911, with the same general outline but with features which would substantially reduce its aerodynamic drag coefficient. This was, of course, with generous use of advanced composite materials, although only for the cladding, rather than the main structure which took the 911 steel frame plus the central transmission tube and strengthened sill sections, to which was added the obligatory Group B roll cage. The result was an immensely strong and stiff safety cage. The cladding was made in a variety of materials, according to purpose, but always with the aim of saving weight. Thus the doors and 'bonnet' were of a carefully chosen aluminium alloy, containing magnesium and silicon, which enabled the weight to be reduced by

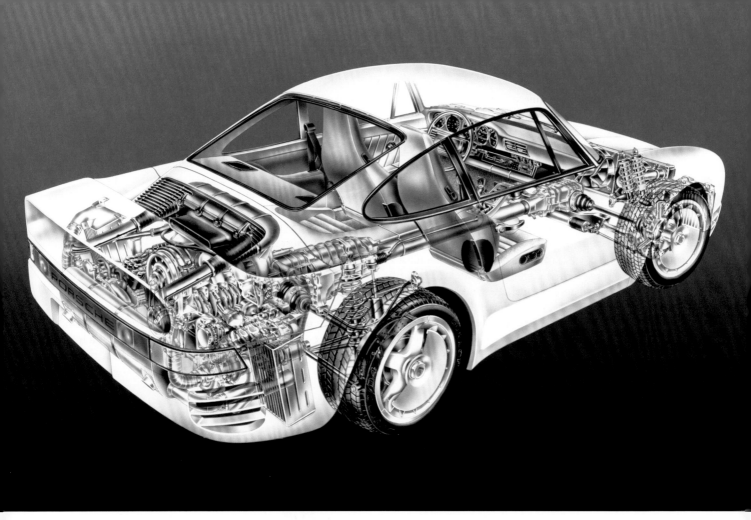

nearly 60 per cent when compared with standard 911 steel components.

The nose cladding (other than the bonnet) was moulded in glass-reinforced RIM (reaction injection moulded) polyurethane, a material which the motor industry was closely studying at that time. In RIM, the two chemicals which react to form the polyurethane are injected together into the mould, where the reaction takes place and the component emerges as a 'clean' part with excellent surface finish. Extra stiffness can be added by also injecting a proportion of chopped or hammered glass fibre; Porsche, which had already employed RRIM for some parts of the 924 and 928, used 15 per cent glass filling for the 959. The remaining panels, some of them complex in shape and incorporating air intakes, were made out of layered glass fibre and Kevlar aramid fibre in an epoxy matrix, with additional stiffening for the roof and floor.

If nothing else, producing the 959 body in modest quantity must have convinced Porsche that advanced composites were still years away so far as a proper production car was concerned. The constraints involved were considerable. At that time, Kevlar was far less well known and extremely expensive, but it

Above: There was seemingly no limit to the technology thrown into the 959 mix, some of it visible in this cutaway. The high-output engine (of only 2.85-litre capacity), the complex and sophisticated transmission and suspension, the composite outer panels grafted onto the strong steel core, all contributed to making the car the most dynamically competent model of its time.

Right: Although it was a flat-6 like any 911 engine, the 959 power unit broke new ground in many respects, not least its use of 4 valves per cylinder which in turn forced the adoption of water-cooled cylinder heads – in addition to the substantial oil-cooling which was a familiar if under-appreciated 911 feature. Twin KKK turbochargers worked in series rather than in parallel.

was preferred to carbon fibre for its mechanical characteristics. Carbon fibre is extremely strong but rather brittle, while Kevlar is very tough, in other words it resists high shear loads (which is why it has become an essential component of vehicle and body armour). The moulding and curing of each composite panel took three hours in a pressurised autoclave; subsequent trimming was by water-jet rather than mechanical. The panels were then mounted to the steel frame with adhesives, the remaining panels added, the paint finish applied, and the whole cured in a low-bake (80°C) stoving unit.

The 959 body proved aesthetically and aerodynamically effective. One could not look at the 959 without 'seeing' the 911, but in a smoothed-over kind of way. Because this was to be an ultimate-performance car, every detail was studied in the wind tunnel to reduce both the drag coefficient (C_d), for the sake of maximum speed, and the lift coefficient (C_l) for the sake of stability and roadholding. Pure aesthetics mattered less. The wheels and wheel arches, the air intakes and internal aerodynamics, even the shape and the manner of fitting of the windows were subjected to this treatment, along with the basic body shape, and especially the underside and back end. It was perhaps remarkable in the circumstances that so many

echoes of the 911 remained, but the work was highly effective. The drag coefficient was reduced to 0.31, no mean achievement considering the amount of air which had to be passed through as well as around the car, and that a proper, inverse-camber rear wing was integrated into the rear deck to kill any rear lift. The wing did its job, because the net (front plus rear) lift coefficient was zero – no lift at any speed, a major contributor to the impression of almost stubborn stability and absolute control which the 959 provided.

Ultimate engine?

Given the power output that would be required of it, and its secondary role as a technical pinnacle which would enhance Porsche's engineering reputation, the

959 engine needed every worthwhile feature then available. Most specifically, it needed a sophisticated turbocharging system for ultimate output, and four valves per cylinder if it was to provide the permeability (the gas flow rate capacity) to allow the target power to be achieved in an engine of modest size. Here was a classic illustration of the engine's purpose and the engine designer's challenge: power depends on the rate of burning fuel, and the rate of burning fuel depends on how much air can be delivered to oxidise it all. Turbocharging, up to whatever boost pressure will not destroy the engine, is one huge step, but the air still needs to be able to flow. The biggest valve ports, and the biggest valve area that can be fitted within the engine's dimensions, are vital when seeking ultimate power. Thus, four valves per cylinder it had to be.

This led to an immediate problem, one which would be reflected in much later decisions concerning the production 911. The 959 engineers wanted to base their new power unit on the 911 flat-6, but it was clear that by the time the 12 valves and ports had been fitted into each cylinder head, there was absolutely no way enough heat could be removed from the critical areas around the valve seats – especially the exhaust valves – with air-cooling. The cylinder heads would have to be water-cooled. Did that mean the whole engine might as well be water-cooled? In fact, this was not an option, in terms either of engineering capacity or politically. In the end, the 959 engine consisted of an adaptation of the existing vertically-split crankcase with modified bearing dimensions, a familiar-looking seven-bearing steel crankshaft, individual Nikasil-surfaced air-cooled cylinders (as in the 911), and brand-new 12-valve cylinder heads each incorporating a water cooling system. The chosen dimensions were 95mm bore by 67mm stroke, for a swept volume of 2,849cc.

The technical awkwardness of the layout was that the 959 needed both air cooling, with a fan-and-ducting system much like any 911, and also a water cooling system, with a nose-mounted radiator and twin electric fans. Water circulation was ensured by a pump for each cylinder bank, driven off the inlet camshaft. Further positive cooling of the engine was achieved by spraying the undersides of the pistons with jets of oil, keeping their crown temperatures within bounds. Twin oil coolers flanked the water radiator at the front of the car. The pistons were indeed heavily loaded: given the maximum permitted boost pressure of 14psi, the geometric compression

ratio of 8.3:1 was actually equivalent to 13.5:1 at times. Consequently, titanium was chosen to make the connecting rods. The boost pressure was delivered by twin water-cooled KKK K26 turbochargers working in series – one turbo only at lower speeds, both together at high speeds – and complex measures were undertaken to avoid the problem, of which everyone was very conscious in the 1980s, of turbo lag, but also of perceptible 'steps' in the system's operation. An intercooler was used, naturally.

The cylinder heads with their four valves per cylinder carried twin overhead camshafts, operating the valves directly via inverted bucket tappets. The included angle between the inlet and exhaust valves was only 28 degrees, and slim 12mm sparking plugs were needed to reach the centre of the combustion chamber crown. Because the engine was turbocharged, the valve timing did not require excessive overlap, and was set at 1-40-37-2 degrees. Double-row chains drove the camshafts, after it was discovered early in development that the single chains originally proposed were simply not up to the task. Despite the use of hydraulic automatic lash adjustment, the engine would run happily beyond the 8,000rpm to which it was normally limited.

The result of all this work was – officially – a power output of 450PS at 6,500rpm, and peak torque of 500Nm at 5,500rpm. The drive was taken through a 6-speed derivative of the then-standard 5-speed gearbox, with fifth and sixth gears, plus reverse, in a bolted-on nose extension to the main casing. The gearbox included an output taken via a thin propeller shaft, 924-fashion, but from rear to front rather than vice versa. At the front was a differential to which the torque was fed via a multi-plate wet clutch device, the PSK (the 'Porsche controllable clutch'). Varying the pressure on the clutch plates controlled the torque split – the amount of torque being fed to the front. Control was exercised by a computer taking instructions from a number of sensors. Its basic task was to decide, from moment to moment, how much torque could beneficially be fed to the front. The system also governed operation of the limited-slip rear differential.

The design of the PSK limited its torque capacity to 250Nm. Things were arranged so that at steady speed, the torque split matched the car's weight distribution, 40:60. During hard acceleration, resulting in an effective rearward weight shift, the front wheels' torque share might drop to 20 per cent. Should the rear wheels hit a patch of ice and spin helplessly, 100 per cent of the drive might reach the

The more one looks, the less like a Porsche 911 it becomes. If anything, the 959 resembles a 911 hidden inside a slightly larger, smoother body, even though so many of the styling cues were carefully retained. In practice, the 959 body had a far lower drag coefficient than the contemporary 911, thanks to the huge attention paid to every detail.

front – but subject to that 250Nm limit. Anything in between was possible, and although in 2006 one might quarrel with the system's basic parameters and the way it was programmed, in its time it was a sensation: simply the most ingenious transmission around, leading to impeccable road manners in the most difficult conditions.

Competition chassis

For the 959, there was no compromise in the design of the suspension, no consideration of cost or of leaving space for luggage, as there had to be in the 911. It was a simple choice: double unequal-length wishbones all round and twin dampers per wheel. At the front, each damper was concentric with a coil spring and picked up on the upper wishbone. At the rear, a single, large coil spring wrapped around the rearmost damper on each side, which picked up on the lower wishbone. Beyond the scope of normal competition suspension were two additional features, variable ride height and variable damper rate. The driver-selected ride height adjustment was hydropneumatic, and could increase ground clearance from its nominal 120mm by an additional 30mm or 60mm, although the latter would be overridden at speeds of more than 80km/h, and the 150mm selection at over 160km/h. The choice of damper setting, soft, medium or hard, was also left to the driver, although again, selections were overridden above 160km/h and the hard setting automatically reselected. Apart from spreading the damper loads equally on either side of the hub, the use of twin dampers per wheel meant that one could be used as the ride-height actuator while the other provided the variable damping, simplifying the design and development of both.

Care was taken to provide the 959 with brakes equal to its potential performance, and the ventilated discs were 12.7in in diameter at the front and 12in at the rear, all with four-pot calipers, providing stopping power on a par with that of the monstrous racing 917. ABS was standard. The original specification also called for the 17-inch wheels (with 8-inch rims at the

front and 9-inch at the back) to be equipped with safety rims compatible with Dunlop Denloc tyres, and also with a low-pressure sensor and warning. The production cars, however, were fitted with Bridgestone tyres, the standard size 235/45-17 front and 255/45-17 rear, the latter on 10-inch rims which would also accept 275-section tyres.

Below: Seen from the rear quarter, the shape of the "glasshouse" makes the 959 resemble a 911 even more closely, even though the subtly reshaped external panels are made from advanced composites which are then applied to the steel core structure. Even the shapes of the wheel arches were carefully studied, and that rear spoiler worked!

Right: For the doubters who saw pictures only of white or silver 959s, the car did exist in other shades. Bear in mind this is one of only 329 produced. From this angle the 911 resemblance is far less obvious, and the car is very plainly sitting at the lowest setting of its height-adjustable suspension, one of its many advanced features.

And in the end …

The road-going 'supercar' 959 was officially announced at the Frankfurt Motor Show in September 1985. Its stated price of DM 420,000, around £100,000 at the time, did nothing to discourage a queue of rich enthusiasts to form, a queue far longer than the stated production batch size of 200, needed for Group B homologation. As it was, Group B had already more or less ceased to exist, and the 959's only competition triumphs were in the Paris–Dakar Rally, a type of event completely divorced from the arena in which the Group B cars were supposed to have competed. That failed to prevent ecstatic road tests and allied features in the most respected motoring magazines, and the 959 built its alternative reputation as the ultimate road-going car.

Sadly, the first customers did not receive their cars until 1987, when the enthusiasm was already beginning to slip, ever so slightly. It was further doused when it emerged that instead of sticking strictly to the production target of 200, Porsche eventually built 329

– enough to reduce the financial expectations of those who had bought the 959 purely as an investment. Another severe blow came when the American authorities resolutely refused to allow any 959s into the USA, where it lacked road-car homologation (and this despite emerging from its crash-tests with the best safety rating achieved up to that time).

The curtain fell on the 959 as the last car left the Zuffenhausen works late in 1988. Ferdinand Piëch is on record as stating that each production example sold for nearly DM 900,000 less than it had cost to make. That made the 959 a very expensive programme, the more so because there was nothing gained from it, once the show was over. Even now, it seems surprising how quickly the disinterest set in – not only in the 959, but in the supercar concept generally. The best one can say is that well within two decades, Porsche was building new-generation 911s with almost the same performance and road manners, but in full production, for (in real terms) much less money. Some of the young engineers who had worked on the 959 were the senior engineers who brought cars like the 997 Turbo to fruition.

CHAPTER 11

1986: Porsche the engineering consultants
– and a sortie into aero engines

It should never be forgotten that Professor Porsche created his company in the first instance as an engineering design consultancy, or that his interest extended to almost anything mechanical. Although almost by default, Porsche became one of the most celebrated manufacturers of high-performance sports cars, its immediate post-war survival being largely ensured (as explained in Chapter 2) by the securing of a contract with Cisitalia. Throughout its existence the company has always been willing, where contractual obligations permit, to undertake studies for other manufacturers.

The main constraint on Porsche was that from 1949 to 1974, the company had an agreement with VW which stipulated that in return for a lump sum and a royalty on each Beetle built, to say nothing of a steady flow of work from Wolfsburg, Porsche was forbidden to design a car for any other company with an engine of between 1.0 and 1.3 litres displacement. In theory, the proscription only applied to complete cars, but in fact Porsche undertook no identifiable engine work for anyone but VW prior to 1973. It did carry out a great deal of transmission work, as might be expected, being commissioned through the 1950s to develop gearboxes for Bugatti, Ferrari and Vanwall Formula 1 cars.

The bulk of the company's work in this period, much of it destined never to see the light of day, was concerned with the eventual, inevitable, need to replace the Beetle. Many of the earliest suggestions fell at the same hurdle: how does one replace a car which is selling outstandingly well and has no serious rival in its class? This state of affairs persisted until the early 1960s when two things happened. First, BMC developed its transverse front-engined, front-driven cars under the design leadership of Alec Issigonis, and the Austin/Morris 1100/1300 clearly had the potential to give the Beetle a run for its money, so long as it was produced with sufficient quality to please customers and keep down warranty costs which, as we all know, it failed to do. Second, Opel introduced a new Kadett in 1962. The Kadett was stunningly ordinary in many respects, front-engined, rear-driven and with a live rear axle, but it was pretty, cheap, well put together and easy to drive, with none of the Beetle's waywardness in a sidewind or if the accelerator was released in the middle of a sharp corner. It was also, of course, a challenge to the Beetle on its German home ground, where its success was most evident and most damaging to VW.

Heinz Nordhoff, still firmly in charge at VW, apparently hoped the Beetle would see off the challenge and made no positive move until 1966, when he acknowledged that a new car would need to be developed. Porsche, naturally, would do the developing. The trouble was that despite, or perhaps because of, the BMC 1100/1300 it was decreed that front-wheel drive was out of the question. To adopt a front engine and rear drive would have been to concede that Opel had been right (and besides, the car's conventional mechanical layout meant the Kadett interior was distinctly cramped in relation to its package size). Thus there was only one way forward – another car with the engine mounted somewhere at the back, driving the back wheels. At the same time there could be no question of repeating the Beetle layout with an engine cantilevered behind the rear axle line. Something even more drastic and imaginative was called for.

Porsche came up with a whole series of layouts, in essence all carefully integrated powertrain studies for installation at the rear of a compact saloon car. Type 1834 embraced a series of possibilities, mostly with transversely mounted in-line engines but also including one in which the engine was installed longitudinally, laid on its side directly above the final drive. Types 1866 and 1872 continued the transverse-engined theme, with powertrain packages in some cases looking remarkably like those later adopted by other manufacturers for front-driven cars (such as the Peugeot 104 of 1972 with its transverse, 4-cylinder engine laid back at an acute angle above the final drive). With the benefit of hindsight, some of the Porsche packages look practical as well as interesting, the drawback in most cases being that their rear-axle installation meant a high deck above the engine bay, placing constraints on the cabin interior layout at a time when the hatchback configuration, in the fashion of the Renault 16, was quickly becoming popular.

The layout actually chosen by VW was perhaps the least practical, since it not only laid the 4-cylinder engine on its side, on a level with and ahead of the final drive, but sufficiently far forward that a 4-speed gearbox could be installed between the two. This had the advantage that, in the same way as a conventional front-engine, rear-drive layout, the gearbox design

In 1979, Porsche prepared this full-size engineering mock-up of the Type 955, a projected new sports model which would have been extremely eco-friendly by the standards of its day, and was therefore arguably 25 years ahead of its time. Despite its appealing features, it did not proceed beyond prototype stage.

could be simplified by using a direct-drive (therefore quiet and efficient) top gear. From Volkswagen's point of view it seems the attraction was that the layout would allow a near-flat rear load platform within a hatchback body, while avoiding the perceived drawbacks of front-wheel drive. The strong traction of a rear-driven car with a rearward weight bias would be maintained, but without the extreme rear-heaviness which compromised the Beetle's stability and handling. The drivetrain layout was also compatible with other body configurations, from sports car to Microbus.

It is a tribute to Porsche's development skill that it made everything work. Designing an in-line engine to operate while lying on its side is not fundamentally difficult but it has rarely been adopted in light-duty passenger vehicles; the most recent instance seems to have been in the first-generation Toyota Previa MPV of 1990. The Porsche-designed engine was well oversquare to minimise its installed width; two versions were built, both with a bore dimension of 87mm, one with a 57.6mm stroke (1,289cc) and the other with 66.8mm stroke (1,588cc). There was a single toothed-belt driven overhead camshaft driving the in-line valves directly via bucket tappets. These incorporated hydraulic lash adjusters, since with the engine where it was, adjusting valve clearances manually promised to be a nightmare. So far as access for routine maintenance was concerned, Porsche did its best, designing access panels into the rear load plat-

form and beneath the back seat (the VW Transporter/Microbus had broadly similar arrangements although in this case the engine was much easier to access, while the transmission was more difficult). The engine was water-cooled, with a wide, low radiator and forced-induction cooling fan installed where (so to speak) the 'other half' of the engine would have been if it had been a flat-8.

Perhaps the most astonishing thing about this study, which crystallised into the car referred to by Porsche as the Type 1966 and by VW as the EA 266, was how far it managed to progress. Of the original Type 1866, it appears that eight complete examples were built, plus another 15 powertrains which were mostly installed in outwardly unremarkable Opel Kadett body shells. For the definitive Type 1966,

Below: Porsche's studies for a VW Beetle replacement homed in on a mid-engined layout in which the in-line 4-cylinder engine was installed on its side beneath the rear floor, as seen in this drawing showing the main technical features. The project began as the Type 1866 and evolved into the Type 1966, otherwise the Volkswagen Type 191 (Project EA 266).

Right: Porsche undertook external design work as well as engineering studies for the EA 266. Here, stylists work on a definitive clay model in the design studio in Weissach. At this point it appears possible that the design might have extended to a 4-door version, but all the manufactured prototypes featured 2-door bodies.

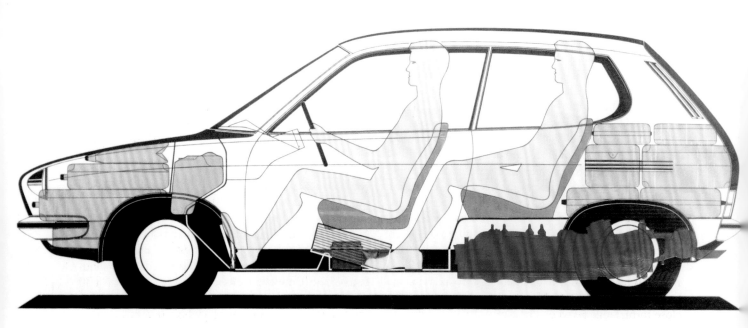

Porsche made 100 engines and 50 transmissions, and a prototype fleet of some 50 vehicles was built, 35 by Porsche and the final 15 by VW itself. No figures have ever emerged or are ever likely to, but the expenditure to reach this stage must have been considerable, even if nothing was ever spent on production tooling.

Certainly, nothing of significance was ever spent on production tooling, since in 1971 the entire Type 1966/EA 266 programme was brought to an abrupt halt. It had been born during the reign of Professor Nordhoff, and after his death its gestation had proceeded with the approval of Nordhoff's successor Kurt Lotz. But Lotz departed late in 1971, to be replaced by Rudolf Leiding, a tough, technocratic pragmatist who had been running Audi. It remains a matter of some dispute whether Lotz, prior to his departure, instigated a serious parallel programme which led to the original Golf, but it is beyond doubt that Leiding dismissed the EA 266 almost out of hand as complex, expensive and impractical, and overturned all previously expressed Wolfsburg objections to front-wheel drive. VW retained one prototype for its own museum, but Porsche scrapped every material vestige of the EA 266 that remained in its possession.

The end of the EA 266 was almost the end of the close formal link between Porsche and VW. As already pointed out, the contract of 1949 with its exclusive small-car development clause was due to expire in 1974, leaving Porsche's engineering consultancy arm free to pursue other projects with other eager customers. To this end, and to serve its own internal needs, ever since 1961 the company had been steadily investing in a whole series of facilities at Weissach, about 20km west of Stuttgart and thus within easy reach of Zuffenhausen. The original layout with a test track and test car workshops was expanded by stages to include laboratories, engine and transmission test cells, rolling roads and offices, enabling the bulk of Porsche's development work – including almost all the consultancy work undertaken for customers – to be conducted remote from the factory where Porsche's cars were built. By the early 1980s, the Weissach staff numbered over 1,000, a large proportion of them highly qualified engineers.

Karl Ludvigsen in his scholarly work on Porsche suggests that the EA 266 cancellation was a major blow for Porsche. He takes the view that the Porsche team 'had been well on its way to the creation of a modern classic small car that would have been as innovative in its time as the Beetle had been more than 30 years earlier'. There is evidence that the company was studying the development of a whole series of engines

Above: Type 1966 prototype complete, seen at Weissach in 1970. The neat but simple design probably falls more easily on modern eyes than it did then, with cars like the Golf several years in the future. The only external clue to the unusual mechanical layout is the clean, "closed" nose and the air intakes in the rear flanks.

Left: Interior shot of the Type 1966, with front seats and engine bay covers removed, seems to suggest the spare wheel and battery have been moved to clear the view. Reference to the engineering

drawing on page 130 shows that in fact, they are in their correct positions, to the detriment of back seat passenger foot room!

Right: An aerial view of the Weissach technical site and proving ground, very much the focus of Porsche engineering activity since it was established. While the shape of the test track, and especially the celebrated high speed handling circuit, has changed little over the years, the number and size of buildings located on the technical site has steadily increased.

based on the EA 266 power unit, including one with a DOHC cylinder head, and a flat-8 comprising two cylinder blocks on a common crankshaft. These might indeed have provided Porsche with a different way forward – and it would have been a water-cooled way.

The author feels more sympathy with the Leiding point of view, which was that the EA 266 would have remained unique not least because everyone else would have been offering front-driven cars that were cheaper to build, roomier in relation to their package size, lighter and much easier to maintain. The possibility has to be admitted that if Lotz had remained in charge and the EA 266 had been committed to production, VW would have ended in such trouble that the German government would have been forced into an expensive support operation – which, according to some writers, is why Lotz was persuaded to resign under pressure from the government's existing interests within the company.

One should not ignore the fact that the times were, in a proverbial Chinese sense, 'interesting'. Leiding took over in October 1971 and instituted the crash programme that remarkably quickly gave birth to the Passat, Scirocco, Golf and Polo – all of which were based largely on Audi front-drive technology, VW/Audi in-house engineering and the design skills of Giugiaro at Italdesign. Over this remarkable achievement hung the shadow in the first great energy crisis – the steep increase in crude oil prices that accompanied the 1973 war in the Middle East. That move led all car manufacturers, including VW, to draw up plans for ultra-economy cars. Porsche weighed in, at the very end of its exclusive contract, with detailed studies for what seems to have been almost an updated version of the two-seat, rear-engined 'bubble car' concept so beloved of the Germans in the 1950s (and so comprehensively upstaged by the BMC Mini). This car, the Type 1997, would have had an air-cooled in-line 2-cylinder engine – not unlike that of Fiat's Nuova 500 – providing up to 18bhp, for excellent economy but barely acceptable performance. It remained a paper project. VW adopted the much more practical step of developing a diesel version of the Golf engine, a much more practical way of evolving a highly economical compact car.

Independent consultancy

Through the latter half of the 1970s, the results of Porsche's new freedom to work with any customer it chose, on any car it liked, began quickly to emerge. Because Porsche is a significant car manufacturer in its own right, with substantial design and development needs, strains could arise when the balance between in-house and external consultancy work had to be decided. Karl Ludvigsen points particularly to the period around 1990 when much of the total capacity was taken up with work on the four-door Type 989 (described later in this chapter), which eventually came to naught but which swallowed effort which might have been more profitably expended elsewhere. Porsche has never been short of potential customers and has said that up to 150 projects may be in progress at any one time, ranging from limited problem-solving exercises to the development of complete vehicles including their powertrains.

As is usually the case when a consultant is involved, it is up to the customer to decide whether he wants to claim the project as his own, or to admit to some degree of assistance. In common with other design and engineering consultancies, Porsche discovered that its contributions would never be publicly acknowledged. The reward came strictly in the form of payment on completion of contract. Such was Porsche's reputation, however, that a handful of customers decided to exploit its association in product promotion. This was never more so than in the case of SEAT, which at that time had progressed from being a Spanish subsidiary of Fiat, to a nationalised company. Fiat had rarely allowed its more advanced car or engine designs to be built in Spain, and consequently during the 1970s, with emissions regulations beginning to loom, it had need of an all-new engine range suitable for transverse installation in front-driven cars, beginning with the original Ibiza and Malaga.

In many ways this was hardly a challenge for Porsche's engineers, other than in terms of keeping things simple for the sake of low unit cost. A team headed by Herbert Ampferer came up with an elegantly simple design, a compact 4-cylinder, five-bearing unit with a 67.5mm stroke and a choice of either 75mm bore (1,193cc) or 83mm bore (1,461cc, with 'siamesed' cylinders). One of the most notable features of the engine was the extension of the cylin-

der block skirt well below the crankshaft centre-line, making the engine notably stiff and its operation more refined. The cross-flow alloy head used the flat-faced Heron principle, the combustion chambers being formed in the piston crowns. A single toothed-belt driven camshaft operated the in-line valves via bucket tappets with hydraulic lash adjusters (an echo of the Type 1966?). The design of the inlet ports, imparting substantial swirl, allowed the use of higher than normal compression ratios without danger of misfiring or detonation. Economy was good, the exhaust emissions targets easily achieved, and power output was adequate at 63bhp for the smaller engine and 86bhp for the larger one.

The SEAT engine was a good, solid, workmanlike, state-of-the-art engine but hardly a major breakthrough or a notable step forward – except in the eyes of the Spanish company, which proudly cast the words 'System Porsche' on each cam cover, and made extensive use of the Porsche name in its European advertising. SEAT was, after all, then seeking to establish itself as an independent manufacturer, and few would have predicted that a quarter-century later it would have become a member of the VW Group! Porsche, however, was not amused at what it perceived to be the profligate use of its name, and future contracts apparently included clauses to the effect that the use of names in promotion by either side would require the agreement of both parties. A lesson, although not in engineering, had been learned.

Thereafter, development relationships proceeded along more normal lines, to the extent that very few of them have been revealed to public view. Among those that have are the extensive programme which led to the development of the Lada Samara as a front-driven replacement for the Fiat 124 derivative, which was the original product of the Togliattigrad factory in Russia, and at almost the opposite extreme, the development of a whole range of air-cooled motorcycle engines for Harley-Davidson in the USA. Porsche also worked with Volvo to conceive and develop its modular range of 4-valve engines, with four, five or six cylinders in-line, for a new range of cars. These engines proved highly successful and remain in production at the time of writing. They have proved amenable to turbocharging for spectacular performance. By contrast, a project to develop an OHC conversion of the old Rolls-Royce V8, dragging it into the last quarter of the 20th century, was stillborn.

Another success with which Porsche is known to have been associated is the Opel/Vauxhall Meriva midi-MPV, which was developed extremely quickly as a riposte to the Renault Scenic and whose versatile and adaptable interior notably caused the planned MPV derivative of the Ford Focus to be 'pulled' at a late stage, a move which Ford executives admit cost them sales and market share. Such can be the advantages of calling in a capable and imaginative consultancy.

Whatever its activities in Europe – and these extended to the development of military vehicles, some of which went into production (although not at Porsche) for the German army, the *Bundeswehr* – a great deal of Weissach effort went into seeking out customers in the Far East. One notable project was the C88 'basic car' developed under a contract with the Chinese government. The C88 emerged in 1994 as a pleasant looking four-seater saloon with a nicely rounded shape and some clever detailing, but its basic

engineering was perfectly straightforward. In the end it came to nothing (except that as part of the programme, Porsche oversaw the training of a cadre of Chinese engineers). China did not really want a basic car; its emerging middle class was looking for something better, and it appears likely that the Chinese were looking to evolve an industry in which its, domestic manufacturers would evolve their own designs to serve the lower end of the market – eventually. There is equally no doubt that Porsche has been consulted, over the years, by a number of Japanese manufacturers but the details of these associations have always been closely guarded.

From basic research to four doors

Over the years, Weissach has performed a great deal of research, not only into engines and transmissions but complete vehicle concepts. Porsche thought these well worth pursuing at the time but from which it took only parts – if anything – to apply to its future production cars. To take one obvious example, there has never

Engineering section drawing of the Type 995 shows it projected as a generous 2+2 but probably not a full 4-seater, with front-mounted engine and rear drive.

Particular attention was paid to the aerodynamics, and the engine was encapsulated to reduce external (and indeed internal) noise levels. Tyre noise remained a challenge.

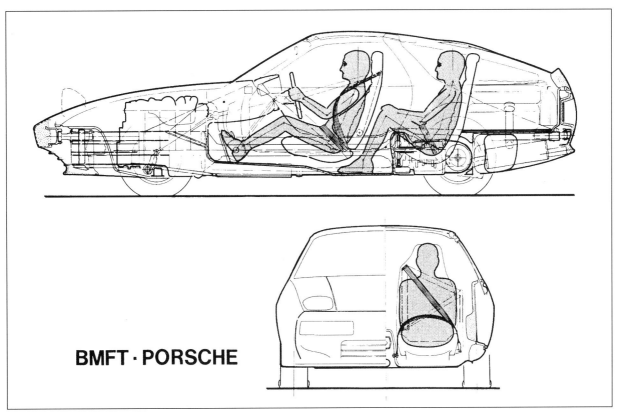

BMFT · PORSCHE

been a diesel-engined Porsche – yet during one press facility visit to Weissach in 1979 (at the height of the second great energy crisis) very obviously diesel-engined 924s were being driven around the site.

By this time, Weissach had already undertaken a series of specialised studies to demonstrate its abilities. Unlike some of its fellow-manufacturers, Porsche never produced a dedicated 'safety car concept' although it was quick to investigate both passive and active safety, using specially installed equipment. But the company was ahead of the game in seeing the need for cars to become more environmentally friendly, and one avenue of research led to the 'long-life car' concept, first shown at Frankfurt in 1973. Although it bore a passing resemblance (as it turned out) to the imminent VW Golf, it was 'not a production proto-type but rather a pathfinder for new development trends; leave the 'throwaway car' and move towards longer life span, rust-protected bodywork, lightweight construction and simple exchange of body parts or components.' Loyal to its principles, and leading the way for the industry is some respects, Porsche soon pioneered the use of zinc-coated steels and the offering of multi-year warranties against body corrosion.

In 1979, Porsche announced its Type 995 'Research Passenger Car' which it described as a sports car concept for the future. In this study the Weissach team did its best to combine economy with performance, plus 'new standards of safety and quietness'. External noise levels were at this time something of a worry for Porsche, since quantitative legal standards were being laid down for the first time and in some cases special measures had to be taken to allow the 911 to comply. The Swiss standards were (and to this day remain) especially severe. To achieve economy with performance, the Type 995 was conceived with an aluminium body and the low drag coefficient, by the standards of the day, of 0.3. A 4-cylinder, 16-valve 2.2-litre engine was envisaged, with the alternative of a 3-litre V8. Porsche said it had ruled out diesel and turbodiesel engines on the grounds of weight and noise. An electronically controlled 5-speed automatic transmission would have been used. To reduce noise, it was proposed that the engine would be encapsulated, but 'tyre noise is an unavoidable complication'. It was reckoned that this lightweight car, running on suitably narrow tyres, would achieve an external noise level of 72dB. The current European standard (at the time of writing) is 74dB.

Also in 1979, Porsche hosted a major technical seminar, the Porsche Consumption Symposium, at

Weissach to discuss technologies for improving fuel economy without hurting performance. One paper discussed the Thermodynamically Optimised Porsche (TOP) engine in which compression ratio was increased to around 12.5:1, with high squish to ensure strong fuel/air mixing and the consequent ability to run lean mixtures when on part-load. Porsche suggested that varying the mixture strength from rich (lambda 0.85) to lean (up to lambda 1.2) according to operating condition, would result in up to 25% better fuel economy. Sadly, of course, all this work proved to be for nothing as soon as exhaust emission regulations became tight enough to call for catalytic converters, and the holding of mixture strength at lambda = 1 in almost all circumstances.

Other engineering approaches favoured by Porsche in the 1979 symposium included lower and much better regulated idling speeds, a technique now taken for granted. Other measures discussed included automatic stop-start, always a good idea in principle, but doomed to suffer problems until the arrival of hybrids twenty years later, and partial cylinder cut-out, running a V8 on four cylinders when on part-load. Porsche never took this technology anywhere near production, however, and in view of the adverse experiences of some other manufacturers in the early 1980s, probably just as well.

Another idea which occupied the Weissach engineers was the PDK twin-clutch transmission, in which gearshifting was accomplished by the near-simultaneous engagement of one clutch and the disengagement of another. Today we are fairly familiar with the concept, which is offered in Audi and VW models and under development by most of the major transmission specialists. However, Porsche's in-house development began in 1982 and ran through many iterations in racing applications, suffering a host of problems. When it was judged to be production-ready by 1988, it was then dropped because it would have been uneconomic to produce unless Porsche's own volume was supplemented by that of another customer. To be viable, the PDK would have needed a production rate of at least 40,000/year, far more than was required for the 944, which would have been its only Porsche application.

For a while, around 1990, Weissach also found itself deeply concerned with the project to develop a four-door Porsche, the Type 989. There had of course been previous Porsche projects for full four-seaters, culminating in the 928, but as already pointed out, when that model was launched a deliberate decision

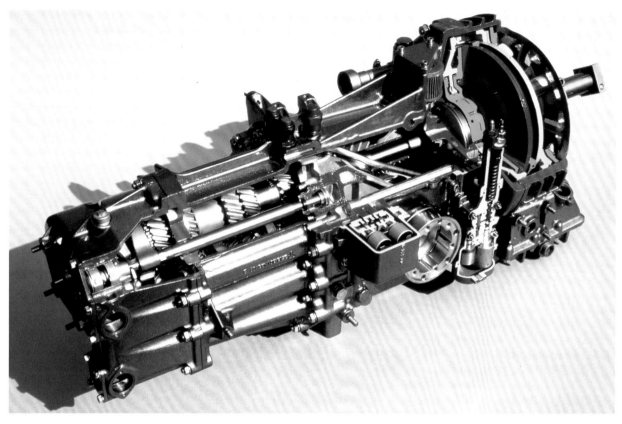

Long before the idea gained its current popularity, Porsche studied the concept of the twin-clutch layshaft transmission, using pre-selection and shifting by simultaneously releasing one *clutch and engaging the other. Although the PDK transmission was made to work very effectively, Porsche used it only in its racing cars, this unit being fitted to the Type 962.*

was taken not to make it a four-door, because that would have brought it into direct competition with Mercedes. But when it came to the 989, developed under the energetic leadership of Ulrich Bez, all such reservations were forgotten and Porsche set out to develop what Bez called 'a Lear jet for the road'. It would move the company even further up-market and make use of all the technology which could be thrown at it.

It was an era in which some of Porsche's contemporaries also flirted with four-door models to broaden their ranges. As ever, Ferrari resisted the temptation of extra doors but there was the Maserati Quattroporte/Royale, the Aston Martin Lagonda, and even the de Tomaso Deauville, for example. Those who wanted to develop the 989 had plenty of evidence to support their ambitions. The basic plat-

form was defined on a wheelbase of 2,826mm (111.3in), making it a big car but still more compact than the Aston Martin Lagonda (wheelbase 2,915mm/114.8in) to take an existing benchmark.

On this platform, two teams developed competing external designs. One came from Giugiaro at Italdesign, while the winner was the in-house study by Harm Lagaay. Despite the fact that this was a big, front-engined car, his design created a strong family resemblance to the 911. This, in fact, was the era in which the 911 had become recognised as a more or less permanent part of the Porsche range, and the tendency was to make its sister models look more, rather than less like it – witness the design evolution which turned the 944 into the 968.

One arguably strange decision was to create an all-new engine for the 989. It seems that the existing all-alloy V8 from the 928 would not fit without compromising the bonnet line. Thus the engine design team under Herbert Ampferer worked hard to design an all-alloy 32-valve V8 with chain-driven DOHCs per bank, with well over-square dimensions of 92mm bore by 68mm stroke (for a capacity of 3,616cc), helping to keep down the engine's overall height, but ensuring that it would need to run at high speed to develop significant power. The design target was 300bhp, which was achieved at 7,000rpm. Outline plans existed both for a smaller (3.3-litre) and a longer-stroke (76mm, yielding 4,219cc) version. An odd feature of the engine was that the angle between its cylinder banks was 80 degrees rather than the conventional 90 degrees, to make sure the unit was narrow enough to sit between the double-wishbone front suspension and big wheel arches. A V6 derivative, shorn of two cylinders, was also sketched (with balancer shaft), but apparently never built.

Unlike the 928, the 989 kept the gearbox in unit with the engine, helping to save weight at the expense of static balance and traction. Ambitiously (remembering that this was around 1990) the transmission was intended to be a 6-speed Tiptronic. The idea of four-wheel drive was flirted with. Double wishbone suspension all round promised excellent and predictable handling, and the 989 would have been a first application for the system Porsche was developing (as part of the pan-European EUREKA research programme) to enable road surface coefficient of friction to be continuously monitored. Complementary rear-wheel steering – at that time, recently introduced by Honda in the Prelude and Mazda in the 626 – was also seriously considered, as a further aid to both stability and manoeuvrability, but rejected.

At least eight Type 989 'mules' were built and tested, with all the running gear installed in Mercedes 300CE bodies. Production of the new model was scheduled for the 1995 model year, with a press and public launch in the autumn of 1994. Sadly, it never happened. The whole development process began to get out of hand. The target ready-to-run weight, which had originally been set at 1,400kg with the extensive use of aluminium (although the basic structure was steel), escalated to 1,742kg, a 24 per cent increase which did nothing to help acceleration or economy. Even more alarmingly, the calculated cost of production had risen even more, while the target market appeared to be shrinking. Sales of the 928 at least, were shrinking (to well under a thousand in 1991) and likely 989 sales were reckoned to be a percentage of these. The logic was inescapable and early in 1992 the decision was taken to kill off the 989 project, after something approaching £100 million had been spent on the programme. It was money which Porsche could ill afford at the time, but even more damaging was the waste of time and effort at Weissach, which – with the benefit of hindsight – could valuably have been spent on other tasks. Some

attempts were made to sell the V8 engine to customers for Porsche's consultancy business, but nothing came of them, and the idea of a four-door Porsche had to wait until the appearance, a decade later, of the Cayenne, a very different beast.

Excursions into aviation

For the past half-century the classic purpose-built light aircraft engines, from Continental and Lycoming, have been air-cooled flat-4s and flat-6s. That made it inevitable that aviators, especially in Europe, looking for cheaper and more readily available alternatives would consider converting the flat-4 Beetle or flat-6 Porsche 911 power units for light aircraft. A light single or two-seat aeroplane can have a surprisingly low power requirement by car standards, and many designs fly quite happily on less than 100bhp, so the idea of adapting car engines for aircraft use is by no means far-fetched.

However, such conversions are not straightforward. With some (although not entire) justification, airworthiness authorities take a highly conservative view of some features which car manufacturers happily accept. The problem with aircraft is that if the engine stops when it is not supposed to, the pilot cannot simply pull over and park in the emergency lane. Thus for example, aircraft engines are required to have fully duplicated ignition systems, generally fired by magneto as protection against failure caused by complete loss of electrical power. Similarly, anything but a geared drive to the camshaft is usually frowned upon (which explains why the purpose-built light aero engines still use overhead valves with pushrods and rockers).

There is also the contrast between a conventional car engine, which has a flywheel at the rear of the crankshaft, and an aero engine which drives a relatively massive propeller at the front. Crankshaft stressing and precautions against torsional vibration have therefore to be carefully studied. Lubrication issues also arise, because unlike a car engine in which oil levels are affected only by gradient, acceleration, braking and cornering, an aero engine may be rolled through 360 degrees and subjected to sustained positive and negative g. Finally, there is the question of optimum engine speed. Aircraft propellers rarely exceed 3,000rpm, for efficiency and quietness, while modern car engines generally develop their peak power at much higher speeds, typically 6,000rpm.

Some kind of gearing is therefore needed between the engine and propeller if both are to operate efficiently.

Acknowledging all these potential problems, Porsche began to develop an aero version of its 1.6-litre Type 356 flat-4 in 1955, under the designation Type 678. To some extent this was an acknowledgement that 'unofficial' adaptations, some even of the original 1.1-litre Type 369 power unit, had existed for some time. The Type 678 had revised cylinder heads to incorporate the obligatory second spark plug per cylinder, and dry-sump lubrication to avoid oil-surge problems. It eventually existed in a whole range of versions, the most basic of which was the 678/3 which delivered 52bhp at just 3,200rpm for take-off, and was therefore compatible with direct drive to a sufficiently small propeller. It was started by hand-swinging the propeller, but the later 678/3a had an electric starter added. Later versions, developing more power at higher speeds, needed reduction gearing. The Types 678/0 and 678/1, differing in their reduction gear ratio, offered 65bhp at 4,500rpm, while the Type 678/4 produced 75bhp at 4,600rpm. This engine was also fitted with a radial-flow fan to assist cooling (the others all depending on 'natural' cooling which meant temperatures had to be watched when taxying or holding prior to take-off) and was offered with a choice of propeller-drive reduction gear ratios from 0.472 to 0.685. The German airworthiness authorities certified all these engines for use on light aircraft and motor-gliders, allowing 600 hours of operation between overhauls.

Interest in the Type 678/4 by the US military, for possible use in helicopters, led to the allocation of an official designation (YO-95, the Y indicating trials status, the O for a horizontally-opposed engine, the 95

Above: Through the 1960s, Porsche developed versions of the 1.6-litre "boxer" engine as a power unit for very light aircraft, with the designation Type 678. One of the first definitive units in the series was the Type 678/3, which produced 52bhp at 3,200rpm, well down on the output of similar units for road-going cars, mainly because the speed had to be limited to the needs of direct drive to the propeller.

Right: A later aero engine in the 4-cylinder series was the Type 678/4, fitted (like the cars) with its own integral cooling fan rather than relying on "natural" cooling provided by propeller slipstream and forward motion. It also featured a reduction gear, allowing the peak power speed to be raised, and hence delivered a rather healthier 75bhp at 4,500rpm.

for the swept volume in cubic inches) and the development by Porsche of a revised engine, the Type 702, which was designed to spend its life on end, so to speak, being vertically installed to drive the rotor of a light helicopter. This engine delivered 72bhp at 4,500rpm but seems, rather sadly, to have signalled the end of Porsche's efforts in this field for a couple of decades.

The 911 engine takes to the air

Interest was renewed under the chairmanship of Peter Schutz, who arrived in Stuttgart in 1981. Schutz, among other things a keen light-aircraft pilot, decided the time was ripe for the 6-cylinder 911 engine to be adapted for installation in a more serious kind of aeroplane, the four-seat 'business express' capable of cruising close to 200mph with an engine delivering over 200bhp for take-off. Schultz argued that many Porsche 911 owners in the USA also owned light and business aircraft: what could be nicer than providing them with motive power in both environments?

The 911 engine seemed a good basis for such an exercise, and by 1983 the 3.2-litre (95 x 74.4mm, 3,164cc) engine from the then-current 911 Carrera

had been adapted, and redesignated PFM 3200, with twin-plug heads, racing-style gear drive to the camshafts replacing chains, and accessory drives rearranged at the rear of the engine, and including twin alternators (avoiding the need for magneto ignition) and twin vacuum pumps. The fuel system was a specially adapted version of the standard Bosch K-Jetronic. A ducted fan ensured adequate cooling during ground handling and at low speeds. The compression ratio was 9.2:1 (compared with 9.5:1 in the US-market car version of the engine). Take-off power in this naturally aspirated form was 217bhp at 5,300rpm at sea level.

Porsche made considerable play of the fact that the PFM 3200 was environmentally sound. With its standard reduction gearing of 0.442, giving a propeller speed of 2,350rpm for take-off, and an exhaust engineered to car standards, it was extremely quiet by light aero-engine standards, its emissions were low and it was notably economical. From the flying point of view, it was also simple to operate, with 'one-lever control' replacing the more conventional trio (in the average business aircraft) of throttle, mixture control and propeller pitch. In the PFM 3200 the Bosch fuel injection took care of mixture control in all circumstances, while a single management computer ensured that the throttle and propeller pitch always combined to provide the best power, for take-off and climb, or the best economy, when cruising.

The future seemed set fair for the PFM 3200 in 1983 when it began flight trials in a Cessna 182, with notable success so far as the engineering targets were concerned. A search began for a higher-performance aeroplane which would serve as a more convincing performance demonstrator, and the choice fell on the

Left: A return to the aero engine scene during the 1980s, when Porsche's chairman was the aviation-minded Peter Schutz, saw the 911's flat-6 engine undergo development into an extremely well-packaged light aircraft power unit with several advanced features including electronically controlled fuel injection. The 3.2-litre PFM3200 produced a healthy 217bhp at 5,300rpm.

Right: During the late 1980s, the American general aviation manufacturer Mooney produced a series of 40 of its high-performance M20 4-seaters powered by the PFM3200. The aircraft was extremely well received by the specialist press which praised the refinement and ease of operation of the engine, but the project sadly failed to break into a market dominated by Continental and Lycoming.

Mooney M20K, a sleek four-seater which was arguably the fastest aircraft in its class. During 1986, with the Porsche engine installed, the Mooney completed a 100,000km round-the-world demonstration flight. With the naturally aspirated engine, the Mooney proved capable of cruising at 300km/h (186mph). It had a fuel consumption of 13 litres/100km (21.7mpg) with the engine at the economy setting, delivering 176bhp. In any single-engined aircraft, reliability is at a premium when flying over water, and the Mooney's longest flight time (with extra tanks) was 17 hours non-stop.

Encouraged by the good results achieved with the PFM 3200, Porsche began work on a logical further development stage, with the addition of a Garrett turbocharger. This would have increased the take-off power to 241bhp, and maintained it all the way up to 18,000 feet. The turbocharger itself was installed underneath the engine, and a big intercooler on the engine's left. Sadly, it was in the end a wasted exercise, even though it had resulted in an excellent engine which made existing products look distinctly old-fashioned. A Porsche press release of 1986 says that 'the market potential for the PFM 3200 engine is considerable. It is estimated that there are more than 200,000 light aircraft in the 180–230hp class worldwide which could utilise the engine, some 160,000 of which are in the USA.'

Despite these hopeful words, the market did not materialise. Hard times were coming, the general aviation market began to shrink, and the owners of existing aircraft were happy to soldier on with the engines they already had. Mooney built a series of 40 M20s with the Porsche engine, but that marked the end of the project. Peter Schutz departed from Porsche at the end of 1987, and he had been very much the prime mover for the venture into aviation. Apart from the PFM 3200 for fixed-wing aircraft, during this period the company had also developed, or adapted, both the 3-litre and 3.3-litre 911 engines to power the Airship Industries Skyship 500 and 600 respectively. In these non-rigid airships the engines were housed in fireproof containers within the control gondola, and drove external ducted fans which could be tilted to provide vertical control as well as forward propulsion.

Although the PFM 3200 programme lingered until 1991, honouring existing commitments, Porsche management post Peter Schutz examined the figures (including the reported $75 million cost of the project) and decided there was no prospect of being able to produce its aero engine at a price which would both be profitable and command a market. To the continuing regret of some, who were justly proud of what had been achieved in engineering terms, the concept was quietly shelved in the early 1990s.

CHAPTER 12

1988: Carrera 4 – 4WD in production – and a new 911

The 959 might never have been more than a technology demonstrator, but Porsche still felt the need to offer its top-end customers the superior traction and more secure handling of four-wheel drive. Technically, however, any such car would need to be much less ambitious than the 959, to bring its price within the reach of a few thousand, rather than a few hundred buyers, and the system would have to be built into the 911, to exploit that model's impregnable owner loyalty.

To the interested onlooker, the first hard evidence that something was afoot came in the form of some 'preview' photographs of a new model which, as stated in the deliberately terse accompanying press release of May 1988, would be launched during the course of the 1989 model year. The purpose of the pre-release, it said, was to 'dispel conjecture surrounding its future 911 model line-up'. 'The car pictured,' added the release, 'is code-named 964 and is in fact a 4WD 911. It will be called the 911 Carrera 4 and will be an <u>additional</u> [Porsche's underlining] model to the existing 911 range, i.e. the existing 911 Carrera in all its forms will be continued.'

In fact, that press release was disingenuous. There was a great deal more to it than the addition of a 4WD version to the existing 911 range. The 911 had by now weathered the storms of the late 1970s and early 1980s, and seen off managements that planned a Porsche future heading off in the entirely logical direction of a front-engined range, which would grow out of the 924/944 and 928. It had simply become too much of a classic ever to kill off, yet there was no denying that it could by now be improved in so many respects as to make it a new model. Thus a classic compromise was struck within the walls of management at Zuffenhausen. There would indeed be a new model, carrying the internal Type Number 964. It would, however, still look remarkably like a 911 and in the marketplace it would be called a 911, no matter how different it was under the skin.

The design brief for the 964 was that it should retain the external appearance of the existing car above the 'lower belt line'. In other words, the only visible panels which could be significantly changed were the lower sections of the front and rear bumpers, and the sill panels. Beneath the skin, out of sight, it was a case of anything goes. Most notably, the rear suspension was to be completely new, which involved doing away with the cross-tube, containing the transverse torsion bar springs, which had been a feature of the 911 ever since its inception. This was one reason why it was necessary to allow those lower side panels to be reshaped.

The engine would not be new, but it would be heavily revised. It would still be an air-cooled flat-6 and it would still be rear-mounted, but to keep up with the competition (which in the USA, was now recognised as coming increasingly from Japan) it would have to deliver 240PS even when tuned to meet the ever more severe Californian exhaust emission regulations. In fact, the decision was taken in principle that the 964/911 would provide 240PS wherever it was sold: universal homologation was the goal. Areas with less demanding regulations would benefit from better fuel economy and driveability, but there would be no more American customers complaining that their cars were 'gutless' when compared with their European counterparts.

From these starting points, the 964 evolved and, naturally, not simply as a 4WD but as a replacement for the whole existing 911 Carrera series. The official beginning of the programme came with management board approval in April 1984, clearing the way for development of the Type 964 (naturally aspirated) and the Type 965 (the equivalent Turbo). Both would be developed as 4WD models, although using a transmission simpler than that of the 959, and as rear-drive ones. It would have been possible to retain the existing 911 body for the rear-drive cars and have a new shell only for the 4WDs, but in the end it was decided that it would be technically better (and in the long term, perhaps also cheaper) to develop a brand-new body shell which would serve both purposes.

Making a fitting header for this chapter, the 964 Targa was the last of the "original" Targa-body versions. Although the Cabriolet had been expected to supplant the Targa, demand for the latter was still strong and the two variants were built and sold in parallel for some time, until eventually the Targa concept was rethought when the body was reworked for the 993.

A potential drawback was that because the shell would need to incorporate provision for the drive to the front wheels even when it was not fitted, the luggage space of the rear-drive versions would be reduced. In the end it was so, although the adoption of a more compact, accurately moulded (and slightly smaller) plastic fuel tank took away some of the sting. On the credit side, the all-new body would allow provision to be made for power-assisted steering. This would be essential for the 4WD but also highly desirable for the rear-drive models, given the way wheel and tyre sizes (and especially widths) were evolving.

Above: Externally, the 964 was hard to distinguish from previous generations, unless you were a dedicated Porsche enthusiast. The effect is a tribute to the way successive Porsche design chiefs managed to house wholesale product improvements within a skin whose lines were only subtly altered over the years, helping to strengthen the whole mystique of the 911.

Left: The back seat of the 964 was, like its predecessors, nicely finished but strictly nominal in size, suitable only for young children. Legroom was limited by basic packaging requirements, and the cushion width not least by the massive central tunnel whose origin was the need to house the drive to the front wheels in Carrera 4 versions.

The redesign of the body – visibly 911, yet structurally completely new under the skin, with extensive aerodynamic revisions – was carried out under the direction of Anatole 'Tony' Lapine, who had also overseen the design of the 928. Some of the technology evolved for the 'soft' 928 front and rear ends found its way into the lower bumper areas of the 964. The main aerodynamic features were a carefully shaped and faired nose, a smooth undertray beneath the nose and some way aft, and a retractable spoiler which looked

Below: Cutaway of the Carrera 4, the first version of the Type 964 to be announced, shows the familiar-looking but actually much changed 3.6-litre engine, the drive to the front wheels, and the completely new suspension design, with torsion bar springs nowhere to be seen – and all packaged into a body which remained recognisably 911, though the sills and undertray were redesigned.

Bottom: Spot the difference: to achieve a common body across the range, the rear-driven 964 Carrera 2 retained the transmission tunnel and front final drive housing used on the Carrera 4, though in this case empty. As a result, there was a slight reduction in front compartment luggage capacity, despite a reshaped and smaller fuel tank.

for all the world like an air intake trim until it moved aft and upwards at 80km/h. The spoiler made no difference to the drag coefficient, which was 0.32 as defined by the product definition paper, but it reduced rear lift to zero. Once deployed, it only retracted again at 15km/h. Close detail attention to things like the window trims and the guttering did the rest. The result

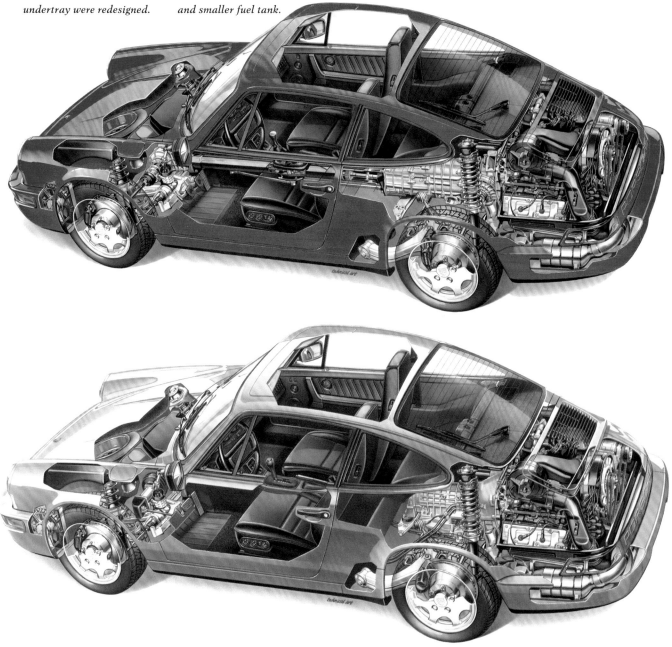

was a body which was quite visibly, to any but the most eagle-eyed of enthusiasts, simply another 911.

Under the skin, the structure had been shaped by a number of factors: by ever more severe crash-safety requirements, certainly, but also by the completely redesigned running gear. This was the area where the old 911 had been largely abandoned. The new chassis was destined to use concentric coil springs and dampers all round, although the original intention was far more radical, calling for the use of air springs. In the end, these could simply not be developed to the required standard by the launch date of 1988, but the decision did force the abandoning of the 911's beloved torsion bars.

The front suspension layout was still MacPherson strut, but with a completely new lower wishbone to which the inclined strut was located so that clearance existed for the front drive shaft (in the 4WD) to reach the wheel. The layout was such that the line of the steering axis continued downwards to meet the ground at the centre-point of the tyre contact patch, something which could only be contemplated with the adoption as standard of power-assisted rack-and-

The 3.6-litre capacity of the 964 engine was achieved by increasing the bore to 100mm, and the stroke to 76.4mm, calling for a new crankshaft as well as revised blocks and heads. This was the ultimate "stretch" of the air-cooled engine, with a limit imposed by exhaust valve heating, but it resulted in a reliable 250PS output for all markets.

pinion steering. At the rear, the former semi-trailing arm layout had been modified into something resembling, albeit with different detailing, the 928's Weissach axle, with similar results: a beneficial change to rear wheel alignment under cornering side-load. Anti-roll bars were fitted at both ends.

As for the all-important engine, one might as a starting point quote the text of the UK market press release issued in August 1988 for the 1989 model year: 'At the heart of the 911 Carrera 4 is the most powerful naturally aspirated flat 6-cylinder air-cooled production engine in 911 history: a twin-ignition 3.6-litre unit producing 250bhp … Indeed, in the 25-year history of the 911, the classic "boxer" engine has never undergone such a radical change and the 3.6-litre unit can be regarded as a new design.'

It could indeed, and its evolution had been painful. Starting from the existing 3.2-litre unit, delivering 207bhp in catalyst equipped US-market form, the most apparently obvious way to achieve 240bhp in a 'universal' engine, homologated for all markets, would have been to open it out to 3.6-litre capacity. Yet in practice, this seemed so difficult to do that other, very determined measures were taken to extract the required power from 3.2 litres. In the end they failed, and the stretch in capacity was achieved.

The decision to move to a twin-plug configuration, 'developed from Porsche PFM 3200 aero technology' was by no means perverse. Tests had shown that twin plugs, firing together, led to more even combustion cycle-to-cycle, more stable idling and improved tolerance of lean mixtures. The root of the problem lay elsewhere.

It would have been easier without the impact of the latest US emissions regulations, which, from 1985, imposed stricter limits on levels of NOx as well as CO and HC. Any air-cooled 3.2-litre engine – at least, any 2-valve engine, and it was much too early to think about four valves per cylinder – seemed destined to suffer excessive heating around the exhaust valve seat some time before 240bhp was available. Various measures were tried. The cooling fin area was increased, the air-cooling fan and ducting where made more efficient, and more heat was extracted from the engine by spraying oil on to the underside of the pistons, to keep them cooler. Even taken together, these measures were insufficient.

A small increase in capacity was contemplated, a boring-out to the Turbo's 97mm which would have resulted in a swept volume of 3,299cc. This promised 235bhp, was still not enough, and so, in the end, the team capitulated to the obvious. The bore was increased to a full 100mm, which required some redesign of both the crankcase halves and the cylinder heads, because the locating studs had to be moved outwards (by 2mm) to maintain sufficient clearance. Having done this, and apparently just to make sure, the stroke was increased by 2mm to 76.4mm; with all the other changes, why not a new crankshaft as well? As it turned out, this was a good move, because the new crankshaft, designed with the aid of the new-fangled CAD/CAE, was around 10 per cent lighter than the old one. The new capacity, 100mm bore by 76.4mm stroke, is always quoted as exactly 3,600cc; in fact, taking π as 3.1416, it works out at 3,600.27cc!

This opening-out enabled the 'universal' engine not only to achieve the specified 240bhp, but a more satis-

factory 250bhp, the quoted output when the Carrera 4 was launched. But it was certainly the ultimate sensible stretch of the air-cooled, naturally aspirated flat-6 which had clearly hit the buffers, at least without resort to a 4-valve head. Indeed, so long as the engine remained air-cooled, a 4-valve layout was more or less out of the question, because the additional valve stems, guides and seats would have 'stolen' too much of the cylinder head volume needed for air-cooling fins.

Naturally, the key interest in the 964 Carrera 4 when it emerged lay in its 4WD transmission, which had inevitably to be simpler than that of the no-cost-barred 959. In fact, as in the 959 (and in some degree reminiscent of the front-engine, rear-driven 924 and 928) the front and rear drivelines were tied together by a substantial tube enclosing the propeller shaft to the front differential. The necessary centre differential was in unit with the rear transaxle, and was a planetary arrangement in which outer ring-gear drove the back wheels, while the inner sun gear drove the front, the geometry of the unit providing a front-to-rear torque split of 31:69. Porsche certainly wanted no more on the front than this, since it was by then well appreciated that tail-heavy 4WD cars were only too ready to understeer to excess when power was applied to the front. In fact the static weight distribution of the Carrera 4 was 41:59, so there remained a considerable element of rear-bias. Porsche's stated intention was that the Carrera 4 should handle as much like the

Below left: The Carrera 4 driveline looks deceptively simple when laid out for photographic purposes. In fact, the gearbox and rear final drive assembly incorporated two electronically controlled multi-plate clutches, limiting slip in both the centre and rear differentials. A stiff torque tube joined the centre

and front differentials, housing the propeller shaft. Basic front:rear torque split was 31:69.

Below right: The Carrera 4 front differential was relatively simple, and had to be as compact as possible to avoid eating into the capacity of the front luggage compartment.

rear-drive car as possible. However, the differential was bridged by an electronically controlled multi-plate clutch, so that wheelspin at one end of the car would not bring it entirely to a halt. A further such unit bridged the rear differential. Control signals were generated by a microprocessor accepting signals from the ABS wheel-speed sensors and a lateral accelerometer. The system was christened the Porsche Dynamic All-wheel Drive System (PDAS) and all told, it added 100kg to the car's kerb weight, which partly explains the need for that reliable 240–250bhp.

Universal 964

The myth that the 964 Carrera 4 was, and would remain, a separate model took only a year to evaporate. In 1989, the year of Ferry Porsche's 80th birthday, it was made plain that from the 1990 model year, the old 911 was dead and the 964 had taken over. Not only had the front-drive components of the 4WD system been removed from the Carrera 4 to create the rear-driven Carrera 2, but the new internal structure had been made compatible with the Targa and Cabriolet body styles. There was no hint of regret at the previous model's passing. As the Porsche UK press release said: 'The introduction of the new Carrera 2 in Coupé, Targa and Cabriolet versions powered by a 3.6-litre, 250bhp flat-6 cylinder, air-cooled, naturally aspirated engine heralds in (sic) a new era in the 26-year-old history of the 911 as it succeeds the 3.2-litre model which has borne the Carrera name since 1983'.

Among other things, the 1990 model year was one for which all Porsche models were equipped with three-way catalytic converters as standard; Porsche UK observed that lead-free petrol could by then be bought in 50 per cent of UK filling stations. Within a couple of years, that rose to 100 per cent as new EC regulations made catalytic converters obligatory for all new European-market cars from 1992.

The removal of the front driveline made the Carrera 2 some 100kg lighter than the Carrera 4, with the promise of slightly better acceleration. It also shifted the static weight distribution perceptibly rearwards, which together with the absence of drive to the front wheels, meant that the Carrera 2 was much more of a 'traditional' 911 in its stability and handling. Little else was changed except that a twin-mass flywheel was fitted to damp otherwise excessive torsional vibration in the transmission. The excitement for this vibration came mainly from the wheel

end during acceleration. Even as it was, press testers found the Carrera 2 suffered from rear wheel hop during full-bore acceleration in search of the best 0–60mph time. Those testers also commented that the rear-drive version felt less naturally stable and more susceptible to gusting cross-winds. On the other hand, the car seemed also to have regained some of that character and controllability (for the skilled and quick-witted driver) which the Carrera 4 had to some extent lost. The 4WD version was easier and safer to drive quickly, but back-to-back tests appeared to prove that the Carrera 2 was the more agile in particular situations, whether in slalom tests or around the Nürburgring – in the hands of drivers who knew what they were doing.

Automatic

At this point the 964 also introduced a brand-new technical feature in the form of the first 4-speed Tiptronic automatic transmission. Since 1979/80 – depending on market – there had been no kind of automatic option for the 911, following the demise of the Sportomatic semi-automatic, beloved of some and cordially detested by others (including the author). But the lack of an automatic was bad news for the US market, and all through the 1980s Porsche had sought to remedy the deficiency. The problem was an indecisiveness of engineering management. The choice vacillated between Porsche's own twin-clutch (PDK) concept, proven in competition (in the 956 racing car), an updated 5-speed Sportomatic, and an adapted ZF automatic transmission. At first the Sportomatic was favoured, but the packaging turned out to be a nightmare requiring the use of angled drive shafts. After that the choice swung between the PDK and the ZF solutions, mainly it seems according to which one Audi would prefer to use in its upcoming A8. If Audi could be persuaded to take the PDK, production would be at economic levels and Porsche could use it too. If not, it would have to be the ZF transmission even though Porsche would have to pay for its adaptation to the needs of the 911.

In the end, but not until 1986, Audi chose the ZF solution and thus forced Porsche in the same direction. However, the end result of the programme, the transmission which Porsche christened the Type 943, differed significantly from the original ZF 4HP in the way it was controlled. To outward appearance (or rather, when viewed in section) the transmission was

The Carrera 2 was the first application of the highly satisfactory, indeed groundbreaking Tiptronic automatic transmission with its manual "flick-shift" mode, now almost *universally copied. For the 911, a short shaft transferred drive aft from the gearbox output to the rear final drive. A Tiptronic Carrera 4 was not contemplated.*

a conventional 4-speed epicyclic automatic with a compact lock-up torque converter, adapted to the 911 configuration with a transfer gearset and a short propeller shaft which took the drive output back aft to the final drive. Its installation involved a fairly modest weight penalty of 34kg (75lb). None of this was strange to ZF, which had made a name for itself as the bespoke supplier of automatics for a range of driveline configurations, including front-wheel drive. The important thing was that the unit was far more compact than the huge, though effective, Mercedes-Benz automatic which Porsche had adapted for the 928, but which would never have fitted the 911. The real innovation however was not mechanical, but electronic. Working with ZF and Bosch, Porsche had evolved an electronic logic for the transmission which enabled it to work either as a conventional

automatic, or holding whichever gear the driver chose.

There had previously been transmissions which worked on similar principles, not least the first version of the clever little unit which AP had engineered for the BMC Mini and 1100/1300, which began life with a PRND4321 selector in which each of the 4321 positions held that particular gear, regardless. The '4' position was eventually deleted when it was found some users selected it more or less permanently, instead of D, and then complained about sluggish performance! Porsche however had something else in mind, a feature which is today offered on most automatics and taken more or less for granted: the ability for the driver to 'flick-shift' up or down a gear at a time as an alternative to normal automatic self-selection. This entailed the provision of a selector with two parallel gates, one with the usual PRND positions and the other alongside with three positions, spring-loaded to the centre from the forward (upshift demand) and rearward (downshift demand).

It was felt, in developing the logic which Porsche and ZF jointly christened Tiptronic, that the transmission had to be protected from the awful things the

driver might do while the selector was in the flick-shift gate. Thus it retained automatic upshifting in the event of engine overspeeding, and would not downshift if the driver tried to select a lower gear at too high a speed. Equally, it would automatically select second gear if the car stopped with third or top still selected, and if the novel and complex electronics (as they were seen at the time) failed, the transmission would simply drop into third gear, enabling the driver to 'limp home'. Also significant, although more subtle and probably not even appreciated by all Carrera Tiptronic owners, the system's memory stored five different sets of shift timing parameters, and in D mode would switch between them according to the driver's behaviour – how often he (or she) used full throttle, for example. A further input from a lateral accelerometer ensured that no balance-disturbing gearshift would occur if the Carrera was cornering at more than 0.4g. For smooth progress, the computer also eased back the engine's torque output whenever a shift was taking place.

All this seems very straightforward now, but it was a revelation in 1989 when the Carrera 2 was presented to the motoring press. Some of the possibilities were not really to be recommended: the author,

Above: The 964-series 911 Carrera RS was billed as the high-performance version, but its additional 10bhp (to give 260bhp) was achieved mainly through reprogramming of its engine management system. Like the previous-generation RS it was stripped-out to save weight, with the result that acceleration benefited while interior noise and comfort levels suffered.

Right: With an eye as always to the US market, Porsche created a Speedster cabriolet derivative of the 964, following a long-established formula. Early Speedsters had been distinguished by their faired-in cockpits and aero windscreens, but by this stage the most prominent feature was the double-bulged "streamline" fairing over the retracted hood. Other colours, fortunately, were available.

starting that day in the passenger seat, realised he could drastically slow his over-enthusiastic driver with three unobserved forward flicks of the Tiptronic selector! More seriously, the debate began (and continues) about the relative merits of driving with flick-shift all the time, or selecting D to take advantage of the transmission's own smooth shifting and auto-adaptive capability. In most respects, however, the Tiptronic was a technical success. A number of tests, both of straight acceleration and around circuits,

proved that there was very little to choose between a Tiptronic 964 and a 5-speed manual car. Nor was there any great fuel consumption penalty if the automatic was chosen.

A step, or a stop-gap?

Thus the 964 brought both 4WD and a novel automatic transmission (although not both together) to the 911, along with other improvements. Yet it was not altogether a happy car. Both its air-cooled engine and its rear suspension were operating close to their limits, and in the event the 964 proved to be something of an interim design, with a 5-year life counting from the launch of the Carrera 4 to the announcement of its replacement series, the 993. Porsche went through the motions of developing the model in line with tradition, launching both a Carrera RS and a Speedster cabriolet version. But the RS offered only 260bhp compared with the standard 250bhp, and this through careful selection and matching of pistons and cylinders, plus recalibration of the engine management to assume the use of 98RON petrol instead of 95RON as standard. Otherwise, weight was saved in

time-honoured fashion by stripping out trim, most notably the noise damping. The suspension was lowered and stiffened, the wheels and tyres were larger and wider, and the internal gearbox ratios closed up (by raising first, second and third). The result, even more than in previous RS derivatives, was a car which was very much for the enthusiast, and preferably one wearing earplugs.

These, and other more specialised derivatives aimed more or less directly at club racing, could not disguise the fact that the 964, although still unique in character, now also had competition, especially in the US market. Opening up a sufficient margin over newcomers like the Honda NS-X would require some fundamental changes of approach, and it is clear that Porsche's engineers were working on this assumption even before the 964 range had been announced. As it turned out, the 964 enjoyed only three years of full production: in 1989 it was ramping-up and by 1993 it was already overlapping with its successor, the 993. For the three complete years 1990, 1991 and 1992, 964-series production was 20,666, 13,816 and 9,747 units respectively. The 993 could not come soon enough, and beyond that, the end of the air-cooled era would be at hand.

CHAPTER 13

1993: 993/996, the 911 goes water-cooled at last

As the Porsche sales figures quoted in Chapter 12 show, the 964/911 was in effect an interim model, an improvement on what went before but with enough deficiencies – in relation to a rising tide of competition – in the chassis and engine departments to be found wanting. Nobody was more aware of this than Porsche's engineers in Weissach, and they set about remedying the problems in a programme carrying a new Type number, 993, which began even before the 964 was properly off the drawing board. And even beyond the 993, plans were already afoot to take the boldest engineering change it was possible to apply to the 911, short of moving its engine to another position: the air cooling of the engine would be done away with, as a major part of the Type 996 programme.

It might have been preferable, in an ideal world, to wait for the 996, but that would have taken too long. Porsche's planners knew, although the world did not, that both front-engined models, the big 928 and its smaller sibling the 968, were scheduled for an imminent departure from production. An end was being called to the front-engined strategy. For one crucial model year (1996) the Porsche range would be reduced to the 911 alone. The 964 simply would not do, and the 996 with its inevitably massive engine development programme could not be made ready in time. So the 993 was slotted into the schedule, to incorporate some of the chassis elements which would be continued into the forthcoming 996 while making do with a final-generation air-cooled engine, essentially a reworked 3.6-litre 964 unit with its shortcomings engineered-out.

Thus in many respects, the most important change in the 993 was the abandoning of the semi-trailing rear suspension and its replacement with a double parallel wishbone arrangement. This ensured for the first time that there could be no significant rear wheel camber change to affect the stability or handling. The new layout allowed several features to be incorporated, notably (through the subtle angling of the wishbone mounts) powerful anti-dive and anti-squat forces to keep the body more nearly level during heavy braking and hard acceleration. The stabilising passive rear-steer effect of the old Weissach axle was very simply reproduced by making the rear attachment bush of the lower wishbone sufficiently soft to allow some wheel toe-in when drive torque was reduced, to counteract the basic lift-off oversteer tendency.

The rear hubs were given additional stabilizing links which – as Ludvigsen points out – could equally well

have provided the self-steering effect, but at this point Porsche chose not to do so. The new rear suspension could not be fitted around the engine package without making the rear track substantially wider. This was no bad thing, and accordingly the track was widened by a total of 70mm; the front track was wider too, and so were the wheels themselves. The concomitantly increased width of the 993 body gave it a 'broad-hipped' look with swelling rear wheel arches which most onlookers found attractive.

One of the main complaints about the 964 had concerned the amount of noise being fed into the cabin from the directly-mounted rear suspension. The new 993 overcame this problem by mounting the wishbones to a fabricated, and very light rear sub-frame which could in turn be mounted to the body via four well isolated bushes. The only part of the rear suspension that still fed loads directly into the body were the concentric coil spring and damper units which ran between the two arms of the upper wishbone, to pick up on the lower wishbone behind the drive shaft.

Spot-the-difference becomes easier when examples of the five generations of the 911 up to and including the 964 series are paraded as a group. In this way the changes to the front end become more evident, especially in the 996 (middle front), as does the progressive widening of the body to accommodate wider and wider wheels and tyres, especially at the rear.

Although the rear suspension change was wholesale, the MacPherson struts were retained at the front, partly at least because they were easy to fit around the front luggage space, leaving as much free volume as possible. Changes were indeed made, but they were more subtle, altering the suspension and steering geometry. A small amount of negative offset was introduced, while the castor angle was substantially increased – something which could be lived with only thanks to the standard power-assisted steering. Unsprung weight was saved through the extensive use of aluminium components and the steering ratio was increased (that is, reduced numerically) to quicken its reaction, while the turning circle was reduced.

The front brakes were larger in diameter, and thicker, there being the necessary space within the wider front wheels, now with 7in rims (9in at the rear). Standard tyres size were 205/55-16 at the front, 245/45-16 at the rear. A space-saver spare wheel was retained and ABS was standard.

The 993 body, as already implied, was new in many respects, although not all-new. The constraint on the

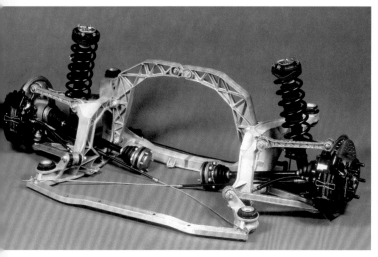

design of the 964 body – 'change nothing above the lower belt line' – was removed. Now the headlamps leaned backwards and the rear haunches hunched upwards as well as outwards. The only requirement was that the spirit of the 911 should be retained. The 'greenhouse' grew subtly but effectively, to the benefit both of interior space and of aerodynamics. The 964-type automatically extending rear spoiler was retained.

As for the engine, it was of course a case of taking the 3.6-litre 964 unit and methodically taking out its weaker points. The crankcase was only slightly changed but inside it, the crankshaft was very different in detail, even though it retained Porsche's classic seven-main-bearing configuration. The aim was to stiffen the crankshaft, in bending but especially in torsion, with the object of discarding the heavy torsional vibration damper fitted to the 964 crank. The new crank had thicker webs but narrower big-end bearings. The narrower bearings matched slimmer and therefore lighter forged-steel connecting rods. The narrower rods meant in turn that the pistons could be modified to reduce their weight. All in all, the reduction in reciprocating mass improved the engine's balance and made it feel smoother at high operating speeds, the engine's electronic speed limiter being set at 6,700rpm.

The cylinder heads were also reworked, but retained the basic 964 layout with two valves and two sparking plugs per cylinder. The valve train inertia was reduced through the use of slimmer valve stems and optimised rocker arm design. The valves themselves were slightly larger, but the most important change here was the adoption, for the first time, of hydraulic lash adjustment. Helped by improved inlet and

Above left: One of the most significant new features of the 993 was the completely redesigned multi-link rear suspension, mounted (except for the dampers) to a carefully optimised light alloy sub-frame. It was a radical attempt to rectify the handling problems which had always dogged the tail-heavy 911. The need to fit round the engine forced a 70mm wider track, resulting in the "swell-hipped" body shape

Above: For the 993, MacPherson struts were retained at the front, but the adoption of power steering as standard meant that castor angle could be increased and the steering ratio reduced. Weight was saved with a switch to cast light alloy for many components.

Above right: From the rear three-quarter angle, the gracefully swelling "hips" of the 993 (this one a Carrera 4) are not as evident as in other views. This was really the last extension of anything resembling the original 911 body to accommodate a wider and bigger-wheeled chassis, before the overall shape was (again) subtly but comprehensively reworked into the Type 996.

Right: From the high-view front three-quarter, "hips" are far more evident, giving the 911 a slim-waisted and rather purposeful look. The leaning-back headlamps represented a first stage towards the evolution of the far more complex optics of the 996.

exhaust porting and manifolds as well as the larger valves, the official power output increased to a nice round 200kW (272bhp) at 6,100rpm, and torque output to 330Nm at 5,000rpm. As in the 964, these were 'universal' figures, applicable in all Porsche's world markets.

Two remaining factors were the engine cooling and the catalytic converter-equipped exhaust system. The

increased power meant that even more heat had to be extracted from the engine by the oil, especially the supply generously sprayed into the piston undersides. Now the oil system was thermostatically controlled, first opening the passage to the cooler at the front of the car (at 87°C) and then switching on an electric fan to provide positive oil cooling if the oil temperature exceeded 110°C. Never was it clearer that the flat-6 was an air-and-oil cooled engine, and that it was in any case reaching the limits of what air cooling could do.

As for the exhaust system, its design was driven not by exhaust emission regulations but by those governing external noise levels, which were becoming ever more severe, especially in some important Porsche markets, notably Switzerland. The requirements were met with the adoption of a new layout in which all the exhaust pipes fed into the centre of a rear-mounted mixing chamber with a catalytic converter at each end. From these emerged the twin exhaust pipes. The layout worked, its only problem being potentially slow catalytic converter warm-up to 'light-off', calling for the use of ceramic exhaust port liners to reduce heat rejection in the upstream part of the system. It was clear, none the less, that noise level was another respect in which the air-cooled engine, with its generous noise-radiating area, was beginning to find life in the 1990s very difficult indeed.

To match the output of this last incarnation of the air-cooled, 12-valve flat-6, the Type 950 manual transmission was evolved into a 6-speed unit. The extended nose of the two-shaft gearbox now housed fifth and sixth gears plus reverse, with the remaining four forward gears in the main casing. The opportunity was naturally taken to re-space the gear ratios to provide an even spread. The 4-speed Tiptronic transmission introduced with the 964, which had been well

received in Europe as well as in the USA and Japan, was carried-over.

Especially in view of the fact that for a short while, the 993/911 Carrera would be the sole Porsche production model, it was essential that the Cabriolet and Carrera 4 versions (but no Targa, that configuration having run its course) should be developed in parallel with the rear-driven coupé and that they should arrive in the market place if not quite at the same time, then very soon afterwards. In fact, the Cabriolet was a fairly simple adaptation, with

Below: The naturally aspirated engine of the 993 series – the last in the long series of air-cooled flat-6 power units, and a last view of the prominent cooling fan. By this time, the problem of removing heat from some crucial areas, especially around the exhaust valves, had become so severe as to impose a limit on the further development of the engine for greater power output.

Right: The Targa variant of the 996, showing the new concept with sweeping pillar-arch. Changes included sharp-cornered rather than rounded rear windows, big rear window (with wiper) and panoramic sliding glass roof; an altogether tidier look, while still providing a kind of open-air motoring. For customers who wanted more, there was the Cabriolet.

1993: 993/996, THE 911 GOES WATER-COOLED AT LAST

strengthened sill sections to compensate as far as possible for the loss of the roof's contribution to torsional stiffness, while the windscreen pillars were strengthened for better roll-over protection.

The new Carrera 4 was another matter. Having tried a centre differential and a 31:69 torque split in the 4WD 964 and discovered the result was an extremely safe and stable car, but one which often understeered more than enthusiast drivers would have wished, Porsche decided to adopt an 'on demand' 4WD system. This replaced the centre differential with a viscous coupling of the type originally developed in the UK by Harry Ferguson, and now made by GKN. With the coupling installed as a 'bridge' between the main rear-wheel drive and the front wheels, all the drive would go to the back unless a rear wheel began spinning, in which case a speed difference would arise between the front and rear wheels and the drive would transfer torque forward until the difference had been reduced to zero. However the coupling was designed to transfer no more than 40 per cent of the torque at most. To make sure the message got through from a single spinning rear wheel, a lightly (25 per cent) limited-slip rear differential was made standard. Also standard was Porsche's own extension of the ABS principle into ABD (active brake distribu-tion) which was in effect a brake-operated traction control system for the rear wheels.

All told, the new 4WD system was simpler and lighter than its predecessor, adding only 50kg to the weight of the car; it was cheaper, and it reduced losses in the transmission as a whole, to the benefit of performance and economy. Better yet, press testers and enthusiast customers confirmed what the Porsche test engineers already believed, namely that the car had shed its former unwillingness and now combined extreme grip in demanding circumstances with a nimbleness much more appropriate to the 911. Eventually, the 993 Carrera 4 was launched a year later than the rear-drive coupé, for the 1995 model year.

The 993 was good, and almost ecstatically received, but it could not have done the job of turning around Porsche on its own. Its launch came at a time when Wendelin Wiedeking had arrived (he had only been away three years) first to become Director of Production, and two years later, in 1993, to head the company. Wiedeking swept through the old-fashioned, ultra-conservative company which Porsche had become like a new broom, introducing Japanese production and management concepts, reducing the headcount and the number of suppliers, and consequently slashing costs. That, plus the quality of the 993, set the company back

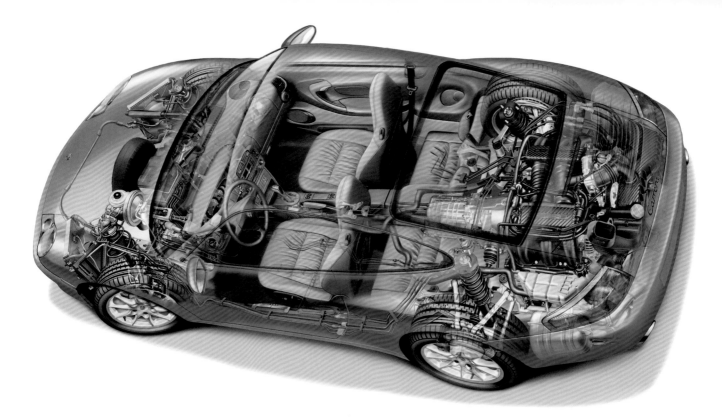

on the road to sustainable profitability. The way was open for the much larger development spend which would be needed for the Type 996.

Before the 996 could emerge, however, the air-cooled engine suffered one final capacity stretch. It was found possible – just – to open out the cylinder bores to 102mm diameter, which with the existing stroke yielded a capacity of 3,746cc. This final series of engines was built for a Carrera RS derivative, which was road-legal but really intended for competition. With larger valves and higher lift, plus a complex three-stage variable-length inlet manifold, the 'Varioram' which optimised intake duct length at three different points on the torque curve, the RS delivered 221kW (300bhp) at 6,500rpm, and 355Nm of torque at 5,400rpm. With lowered ride height and even wider tyres on 18in rims (8in wide at the front, 10in at the back) the RS was not an easy or comfortable drive, but it attracted over 1,000 customers and thus qualified for the necessary motorsport homologation. Several of the RS features, including Varioram, although not the increased capacity, were carried over to the standard 993 in the latter part of its production run, raising the power output to 210kW (286bhp) at 6,100rpm and 340Nm of torque at 5,250rpm.

The final twist in the 993 tale came with a new body style, launched for 1996. This took the Targa name although not the original Targa hoop. Instead, the name was applied to a version with a 'panoramic' two-piece roof, the aft section bonded into place, the

"Ghosted" overhead view of the 996 shows traditional-looking engine installation, even if the cooling medium has changed, plus the even further revised suspension, beneath an all-new body sitting on a wheelbase 8cm longer than before, with wider front and rear track. The characteristic "hips" of the 993 have vanished, and the new "greenhouse" is longer and smoother.

forward section sliding beneath it when opened. The whole package was engineered and supplied as a module by sunroof specialist Webasto, and the Targa was in fact assembled on a Cabriolet base. This interpretation of the Targa sold well into four figures.

The 993, and the company changes wrought by Wendelin Wiedeking, did their job. The production figures for calendar years 1994, '95 and '96 were 15,947, 16,041 and 18,391 respectively. Those figures deserve comparison with the three full production years of the 964 (and take no account of an additional 2,400-odd units of the re-introduced Turbo in 1996). Yet, good though it was, the 993 had to give way to the real 'new generation', the Type 996 with its all-new water-cooled engine, and its smaller cousin the Boxster.

Type 996

As described in a later chapter, the idea of the 'new generation' sprang from the notion that two different cars could share the same, or closely similar structure back to the B-pillar and mid-floorpan. After of that, everything could be different: a new 911, retaining the classic rear-engine installation, and a smaller, lighter, cheaper car, the Boxster, with the engine mid-mounted, and a shorter tail. As explained in more detail in the following chapter, development of both cars proceeded more or less in parallel and they were launched close together. The 996 – the new 911 – was the lead vehicle in the process, because it was the heavier and more powerful; anything developed for the 996 would do for the Boxster. But they could hardly be launched simultaneously, because it would not only stretch available resources beyond capacity, but also dilute the degree of interest in each.

The question of which to launch first was answered when it became clear that the 993 was doing well. It could be left to run for another year, and the Boxster would run through the launch process rather ahead of the 996. It was not, in fact, too far ahead: the definitive Boxster was exhibited at the September 1996 Paris Salon, and went on sale early in 1997. The 996 was first officially exhibited at the September 1997 Frankfurt Motor Show (the biennial Paris and Frankfurt Shows effectively alternate), and was available on the market very soon afterwards.

When it came to shaping the 996, there were no constraints at all on the body designers, other than the familiar requirement to come up with a shape that instantly said '911'. The result was a very smooth body with a drag coefficient of only 0.30. It was all-new: as the table (which for completeness also includes the Type 964) shows, its dimensions alone made that clear.

Most obvious feature of the new water-cooled engine is the one that isn't there – the cooling fan and its associated ducting has vanished. Moving to water-cooling allowed the adoption of 4-valve cylinders, a primary factor in pushing the output of the naturally aspirated engine to 280kW (375PS), previously unthinkable.

Dimensions: Type 996 vs Types 993/964

(units: centimetres)	*996*	*993*	*964*
Length overall	443	424.5	425
Width overall	176.5	173.5	165
Height overall	130	130	131
Wheelbase	235	227	227
Front track	145.5	140.5	138
Rear track	150	144.5	137.5
Kerb weight (kg)	1320	1370	1350

Thus, the 996 body was altogether bigger, as well as cleaner-looking than its predecessor. The additional width of the 993, which had been created by its bulging rear wheel arches, was absorbed into the overall shape. The longer wheelbase and further enlarged 'glasshouse'

made the cabin usefully roomier – partly in acknowledgement that the average Porsche customer, significantly larger than his father, needed the extra space. The smoother shape, and especially the more steeply raked windscreen, was responsible not only for the low drag coefficient but also for the low front and rear lift coefficients which made the car more stable. Extending the new rear spoiler (automatic extension now at 140km/h, retraction at 70km/h) further reduced both the drag and rear lift coefficients.

That the 996, although bigger, was marginally lighter than the 993 was due to Porsche being able at last to afford the latest computer-based design and engineering techniques – including 'virtual' crash-testing of highly detailed finite-element models – and the most advanced steel technologies, both high-strength alloys and tailored blanks, with steel thickness varied according to need. In the final analysis, the 996 body was stiffer and more crashworthy as well as roomier and lighter.

The new body served as the foundation on which an all-new engine, and a substantially revised suspension, were mounted. The engine, naturally, was the focus of attention at launch. It was all-new because to keep ahead of the pack, the 996 needed substantially more power than the 993. The stage had been reached where the only practical way to access more power in a naturally aspirated engine, without making it huge and heavy, was to use four valves per cylinder. The 4-valve layout was, by the mid-1990s, more or less *de rigueur* for European and Japanese sporting cars, so in a sense Porsche would merely be catching up with fashion. The crunch was that four valves, two inlet and two exhaust ports simply couldn't be accommodated in an air-cooled cylinder head without local overheating. So the heads at least would have to be water-cooled, and while there was some discussion about retaining air cooling for the cylinder barrels, for the sake of tradition, the result would have been a foul compromise, an engineering mess, and the notion was discarded. Apart from all else, a water-cooled engine would be much easier to make

externally quiet, something which had become a real concern for Porsche engineers as regulations became more demanding.

What was not discarded was the flat-6 layout. Yes, it was expensive to make, it posed some problems for routine maintenance, and the danger of oil surge during hard cornering had to be carefully guarded against, if not by dry-sumping then at least by 'remote sumping'. In the interests of simplicity and lower cost, the new engine would use an ingenious layout which provided good protection against oil surge without the need either for a scavenge pump or for a remotely

Moving coolant between the rear-mounted engine and the front-mounted radiators, one in each "corner", called for a long and complex plumbing system, taking advantage of the central tunnel to pass through the enlarged cabin. Previously, the oil had been required to run a similar distance to the front wing-mounted cooler.

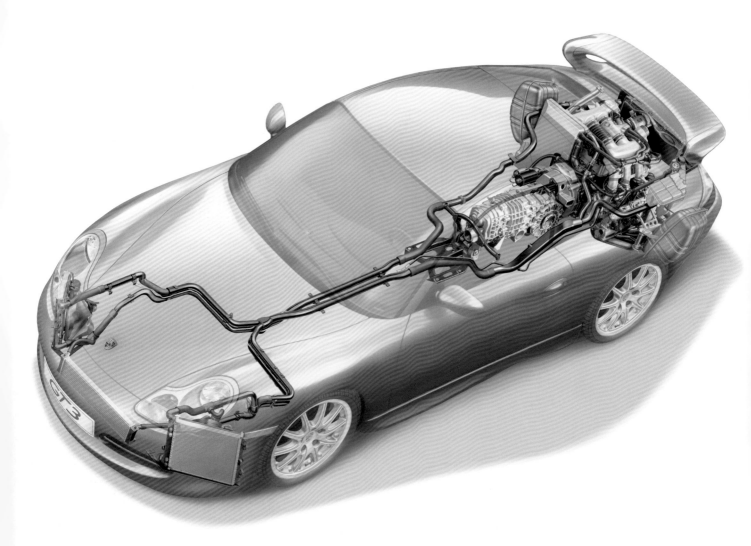

mounted oil tank. There had been plans, during the 1980s and 1990s, to create a range of V6 and V8 engines, which in many ways, would have been more practical from an engineering point of view. But by now, well over 30 years after the model's launch, the very essence of the 911 was its rear-mounted flat-6 engine, and there were things in favour of the configuration too, not least its low centre of gravity and its compatibility with good aerodynamics.

A flat-6 it was, therefore, and in a show of keeping faith with tradition, it was laid out with two characteristics carried over from the air-cooled engine. Its cylinder bore spacing was 118mm, as before, and there was a main bearing between every crankshaft throw, so that the crank ran in seven main bearings. The chosen engine dimensions were 96mm bore and 78mm stroke, for a capacity of 3,387cc – significantly less than the 993, but with the benefit of the 4-valve layout promising higher power, and leaving room within the blocks for some stretch. The twin plugs of the 993 engine, naturally enough, would give way to a single centrally mounted plug per cylinder. The same basic engine would be used in the smaller, lighter Boxster, the 'new generation' companion model, but it would be substantially smaller and less powerful.

In its actual construction the new engine was very different from its predecessor, adopting a form of sandwich construction. At its heart was a sturdy aluminium alloy 'box' formed in two halves, housing the main bearing shells and bolted together around the crankshaft. To this box in turn were mounted the two cylinder blocks, sandwiched between the box and their cylinder heads, with long bolts passing clear through the blocks to locate in the box at the centre. Additional 'skirts' forming part of the cylinder block castings surrounded the box so that externally, the engine appeared to resemble the old air-cooled engine, split and bolted together down its vertical centre-line. The difference was that the new engine was much easier to put together, so long as care was taken in aligning its main components.

The cylinder blocks, as well as the heads, were all pressure-cast aluminium alloy. The linerless blocks used Kolbenschmidt's Lokasil process, in which the silicon needed to resist bore wear was inserted as a pre-formed cylinder within the mould prior to casting. This meant the rest of the block was pure alloy and much easier to machine. The block castings were open-decked, the water passages closed-off by the cylinder heads once everything had been bolted together. The

With four direct-acting camshafts to drive, Porsche elected to drive the exhaust cams directly, and the inlet cams from the exhausts via a further short chain. The drive to the opposite cylinder bank is at the other end of the block, an arrangement which saved space and allowed some commonality of parts.

new construction bore evidence to the way in which the engine's design had been carried through with a determination (which might have seemed downright odd to the designers of its predecessor) to pay close attention to ease of manufacture and assembly. The 996 engine's parts count was well down, despite its having twice as many valves and camshafts, and the time needed to assemble it was but a fraction of that needed for the air-cooled 993 power unit.

Those extra camshafts were in part the result of a calculated decision on Porsche's part. The team's chosen combustion chamber layout was symmetrical, with the pairs of valves inclined 15 degrees on either side of the centre line. The included angle of 30 degrees is relatively narrow by comparison with many high-performance engines, but also allows a flatter-headed piston which weighs less. This narrow angle makes it entirely feasible to use a single overhead camshaft driving the valves via fingers or rockers. This would have made the engine more compact and further reduced its parts count, but Porsche felt four camshafts were necessary not only for 'image', but also to provide the maximum development potential – because if its predecessor was any guide, this was an

An engineering view of the new lubrication system used in the water-cooled 996 engine. As always, one of the key challenges was to prevent oil surge into the horizontal cylinders when cornering hard, while still ensuring adequate oil supply to all components, and the removal of heat from some crucial areas.

engine which would see a lot of development throughout a long life. The valves could thus be operated directly, via inverted bucket tappets.

One might not, at first, have thought the chain drive to the camshafts contributed anything to simplicity and the low parts count. Essentially, the drive to the exhaust camshafts was in two stages: from the camshaft to a jackshaft running beneath it, at two-thirds crank speed, and then from the jackshaft to the camshaft. The inlet camshafts were then driven, by single rather than double chain, from the exhaust camshafts. To make things even more complicated, there was a camshaft drive at each end of the engine, one to the right-hand cylinder bank and the other to the left. There was a threefold rationale behind the apparently needless complexity of this arrangement. First, it meant the camshaft drives could be slotted into the offsets of the cylinder banks, reducing the overall length of the engine. Second, it meant the cylinder heads themselves could be identical instead of 'handed', the one on the left being installed the other way round from the one on the right. This led to useful production economies. Third, the short single-chain drives to the inlet camshafts could incorporate Porsche's Variocam device.

The Variocam variable valve timing system, originally developed for the 4-cylinder 944, was adopted for the 996 because it was clear that variable valve timing would be useful not only in improving drivability without affecting power output, but essential in meeting future exhaust emission regulations. Variocam, in which the length of chain on one side of the camshaft sprocket is increased while on the other side it is reduced, is significantly different in principle from the camshaft phase-shifting variators within the camshaft sprockets, which by the mid-1990s, were becoming almost commonplace.

The use of water-cooling, with its carefully distributed passages around the upper cylinders and throughout the cylinder heads, meant the 'hot spots', which had plagued development engineers during the evolution of the air-cooled engines, were done away with. Even then, the importance of oil cooling was not overlooked, and the undersides of the pistons continued to be cooled by a generous oil spray. It was decided not to attempt a rear-mounted cooling radiator. Instead, twin cooling radiators were installed at the front of the car, ahead of the front wheel arches, a layout preferred to a single radiator which would have been more difficult to accommodate within the car's styling. Another unarguable benefit of water-cooling was that a 'proper' heater system could be engineered at last, without resort to bulky gas-to-air heat exchangers around the exhaust system.

In its finally developed form, the 996 engine developed 221kW (300PS) at 6,800rpm, and 350Nm of torque at 4,600rpm. The interesting thing here was that despite the reduction in swept volume, the 996 developed more torque as well as more power than the 993, an indication of its overall higher efficiency. The Motronic-imposed absolute rev limit was 7,300rpm. To make sure the torque was well contained there was an all-new 6-speed manual gearbox, now 'all in one' with a single casing, unlike the 993 which contained its highest gears in a separate extension casing. Equally new was the 5-speed, rather than 4-speed, Tiptronic automatic.

Chassis refinement

The front suspension of the 996 – in effect, shared with the Boxster – continued the tradition of the MacPherson strut layout; not the chassis engineer's ideal, but when developed as Porsche had done, an excellent compromise between structural convenience, minimum space demand and well-controlled front-wheel behaviour. The main development for the 996 was the adoption of conical 'beehive' coil springs which allowed long wheel travel without the strut needing more space.

At the rear, the approach was more radical. The 993 had led the way with its adoption of a double wishbone layout with an additional 'guidance arm' and with the outer end of the upper wishbone split into two separate attachments. The 996 took this approach to its logical conclusion with a true multi-link suspension, five separate links each serving to provide a particular element of wheel movement guidance horizontally, in camber and in alignment. To outward appearance the layout was still that of parallel double wishbones plus an auxiliary alignment guidance link, but the overall effect was more subtle. Computer analysis had at last enabled the engineers to investigate the effect of modifying each link in isolation, and multi-link was becoming a more popular

The Tiptronic automatic transmission option in the 996 provided five forward speeds rather than four, to the benefit of performance and smooth shifting. In all respects the Tiptronic principle had proved sound, and appreciated by customers especially in the USA, after such a long period of "stick-shift only" 911s.

solution across the industry, especially for models positioned towards the top of the market.

The new and more efficient body design of the 996 meant that the rear subframe, while retained, could be made much simpler. At the sharp end, the all-disc brakes received their customary attention, those at the front increased in size to 12.5in diameter, a new servo and the latest ABS. Extra space for the brakes was made with the adoption of 17-inch wheels as standard, still with 7in rims at the front and 9in at the rear. Tyre sizes were 205/50-17 front and 255/40-17 rear.

On the whole, reaction to the 996 was exactly what might have been predicted. The Porsche traditionalists hated it, as they would hate any car with a water-cooled engine. Some cursed the new arrival as a maladroit halfway house between the old 911 and the defunct 928, partly on the grounds that it was bigger and heavier than the 993. But the motoring press, and seemingly the majority of customers, took a different view. The specialist press ran back-to-back comparisons with the 993 which showed that in demanding conditions – in timed lapping of race circuits for example – the 996 was superior. All that was left for

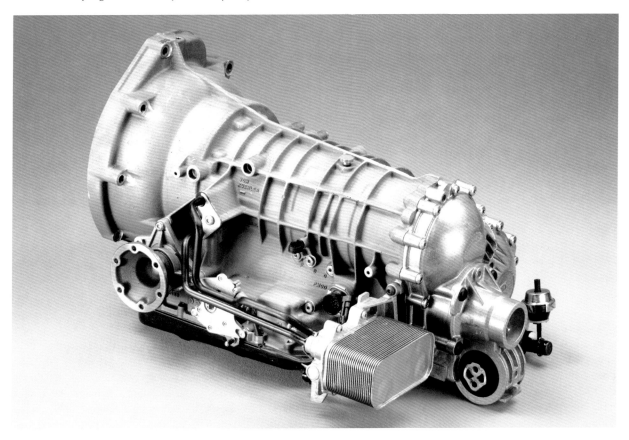

those who wouldn't believe was the claim that the 996 was somehow not as 'involving' for the driver as the 993, and those complaints slowly faded. The press even had the temerity to point out that anyone who wanted a lighter and more nimble Porsche could now opt for the Boxster; the increase in size from 993 to 996 had created a little more marketing space for the smaller model.

As with all previous iterations of the 911, the 996 soon evolved into a range of versions, some of them boasting new features. First on the scene was the Cabriolet, which appeared as early as March 1998, at the Geneva Salon. The Cabriolet had a suitably stiffened lower body, especially in its sill sections, and a Z-fold soft-top supplied and installed as a complete 'cassette' like the one in the Boxster. Roll protection was enhanced with spring-loaded 'pop-up' hoops behind the back seat headrests, their release triggered by a tip-angle sensor. The Cabriolet weighed 75kg more than the Coupé, a fairly hefty penalty which indicated, in effect, just how efficient its new basic body structure was.

Six months later, in October 1998, the new Carrera 4 emerged, with three innovations of its own. Tiptronic automatic transmission was offered for the first time, and with five speeds. The viscous coupling was moved from its original position on the nose of the transaxle, forward to be integrated with the front differential (thus allowing the Tiptronic to be installed). And the Carrera 4 was the first model to receive a new electronic system, Porsche Stability Management (PSM) developed with Bosch. PSM integrated the familiar functions of ABS and traction control with the new one of electronic stability enhancement, which was becoming more widely used under the acronym ESP. The system used data from various sensors to compare the car's path with the driver's input commands, and used momentary application of individual brakes to create yawing moments to reduce any difference that occurred. This was the ultimate guard against excessive understeer or over-steer – but, at the driver's discretion, it could be inhibited.

Once the basic range had been established, it was a while before the inevitable further developments appeared on the scene. In fact, work proceeded on two predictable fronts (or three, if one counts the discreet development of the next distinct model in the 911 line, the Type 997). The first move was an enlargement of the engine; the second was the revival of the Targa body style in its most recent glass-roofed incarnation, which had proved a popular version of the 993, but had 'died' with it.

The first official word of the bigger engine came in June 2001. Porsche UK issued a terse press release which stated that there would be 'A 3.6-litre engine and a new look for 911 Carrera models'. Apart from stating that power output would be 235kW (320PS), that the maximum speed would now be 285km/h (177mph) and that acceleration to 100km/h from rest would take exactly 5 seconds, it was also stated that the revised models, Coupé and Cabriolet, would also incorporate 'the headlight design of the 911 Turbo, a completely reshaped front, an extended rear end panel and two oval exhaust pipes'. It was also revealed that within the Cabriolet soft top, a heated rear window would replace the former plastic pane.

Another Porsche UK press release, in August 2001, heralded the return of the glass-roofed Targa version after a four-year absence, but with a new feature: for the first time, the Targa would have a folding rear window to ease the process of loading luggage into the load space behind the front seats. With the back seats folded, it claimed a luggage volume of 230 litres. Performance would be comparable to that of the Cabriolet, with marginally slower acceleration than the Coupé due to the extra weight of the conversion – the Targa weight was quoted at 1,415kg.

To complete the 2001 revelations, September saw the announcement: 'The new Porsche 911 Carrera 4S to be unveiled at the IAA Frankfurt'. The press release summed up the concept: 'As with the previous evolutions of the Carrera 4S concept it combines the wide-track body of the 911 Turbo with the new 3.6-litre flat-6 boxer engine ... the Carrera 4S will be the ultimate naturally aspirated 911 in current production.' More specifically, the body came with the 911 Turbo front splitter, 'to maximize straight-line stability and provide consistent mid-corner aerodynamic balance'. Apart from its 4WD, standard features included 10mm lower suspension and Porsche Stability Management. Unlike the previous Carrera 4S, the 996 version would also offer the Tiptronic S automatic option.

Back to 3.6 litres

The increase in engine size was achieved by lengthening the stroke to 82.8mm, an increase of just over 6 per cent. The new capacity was thus 3,596cc – but note, its dimensions differed both in bore and stroke from the 993's air-cooled 3.6-litre. The new dimensions, less under-square, probably helped emissions and meant the cylinder heads could be left alone, but at the expense of a new, longer-throw crankshaft which, since it was new, was also given 3mm larger main bearings to maintain its stiffness. The increased capacity would have been sufficient to increase the power output in any case, but Porsche decided this was the right moment to standardise on a system already introduced in the latest Turbo, VarioCam Plus.

While retaining the familiar alteration of inlet valve timing (by up to 40 degrees) provided by VarioCam, the new system added variable valve lift, using a new two-piece tappet design in which a slender centre tappet, operated directly by a single cam, delivered a valve lift of only 3.6mm, while the surrounding bucket-type tappet, driven by twin cam lobes on either side of the centre one, delivered the normal 11mm maximum lift. All that remained was to provide an electro-hydraulic pin-switching mechanism in each cam cluster so that either all three cams moved in unison, for high lift, or the centre cam alone rotated, for low lift.

This meant the new output of 235kW (325PS) at 6,800rpm, and the peak torque of 370Nm at 4,250rpm, could be combined with a much fatter torque curve especially at low speeds, with better engine behaviour at idle, when warming-up and at low loads (minimum valve overlap and minimum valve lift). The Motronic ME 7.8 engine management system was equipped with extra processing and signal outputs to switch to high valve overlap and high lift as appropriate, depending on the operating condition. Reduced friction and pumping losses throughout the engine speed range resulted in better economy, with a mixed-cycle EC figure of 25.4mpg.

Just as important, the new system helped excellent driveability to be achieved with low exhaust emissions. The 3.6-litre water-cooled engine was homologated in Porsche's usual 'world-wide' basis, and thus had to comply with the then-current Euro 3 regulations as well as meeting the US Federal LEV standard. To achieve this, the engineers fitted no fewer than four exhaust system lambda sensors (one for engine management, another for the new on-board diagnostic or OBD system) plus auxiliary air injection and the latest metal-substrate catalytic converters. The OBD system, taking its data from the Motronic control and monitoring unit, was able to store information resulting from a malfunction (such as a misfire) and relay it back to a workshop interrogation unit.

Signing-off

There was no great story to tell about the naturally aspirated 996 after the engine enlargement. It may have seemed as though the water-cooled 911 had only just arrived, but it ran an average seven-year career, introduced in 1997, withdrawn – as it turned out – in 2004, to be replaced by the Type 997. That, however, gave time for two more stages of evolution, one entirely predictable, the other less so.

The predictable one came in the late spring of 2003. We had been presented with the 996 Cabriolet; we had seen the Turbo-bodied Carrera 4S. Thus it had to be that there would also be a 911 Carrera 4S Cabriolet, and there was. As with the 4S Coupé, it was mechanically identical with the standard model. Adding the drop-top to the wide-haunched Turbo body added 70kg to the kerb weight, slowing the acceleration slightly down but still impressive: 5.3sec to 100km/h. In announcing the derivative, Porsche pointed out that the zig-zag folding hood could be deployed in 20 seconds, and that this could be done with the car travelling at up to 50km/h. No longer, then, the interlock with the handbrake which prevented earlier power-operated hoods from being operated with the car on the move.

The final 996 derivative was by way of a celebration. The 911 turned 40 in 2003, and an anniversary edition was created in honour of its long career. This was a strictly limited edition, running to 1,963 examples with allocations to all the major Porsche markets. If you made it on to the list, you could have your rear-driven 911 40th Anniversary Coupé in any colour you liked – so long as that was the GT metallic silver previously seen only on the new V10 Carrera GT. The list of standard equipment was long, but of more interest to some buyers might have been the extra power which had been persuaded out of the naturally aspirated engine – 254kW (345PS). This was enough to raise the maximum speed, if you needed it, to 290km/h (181mph). Acceleration was marginally improved also, as was road behaviour, ensured by a 10mm lowering of the suspension and a standard limited-slip differential. It was a fitting swansong for the variant which had weaned Porsche enthusiasts (most of them, at least) away from their love affair with the air-cooled engine. The stage was now set for yet another interpretation on the 911 theme, the Type 997 (Chapter 15).

CHAPTER 14

1996: Boxster

The Boxster grew out of the situation in which Porsche found itself at the end of the 1980s, making three disparate series of cars (911, 928, 944/968) which had nothing in common, and two of them being manufactured at over-high cost in penny-packet numbers. To make matters worse, the company had been contemplating a fourth product line, the four-door 989, which in all probability, would have added further weight to these woes. A dramatic rethink was needed, and it crystallised into a 'New Generation' which would embrace – to begin with – only two cars, yet another reincarnation of the 911 (the 996), and a new, lighter, more affordable companion model. One might choose to regard the smaller car as a replacement for the 944/968, but it wasn't essential; the Porsche planners would prefer it to be regarded as a new start, harking back only to the dear, but already distant memory

This, of course, was a route Porsche had travelled twice before, with the 914 and the 924, and the lessons of those two had been thoroughly learned. There would be no more watering-down of the image through the use of cheap but non-Porsche parts from volume manufacturers. The key decision was that cost would instead be saved by using what amounted to a common front end for both of the new models. That way, the majority of the platform and its front upper structure – with all its vital safety implications – plus the front suspension, the steering and any other nose-mounted systems, would need to be developed only once. The vital difference between the two models would be at the back, where it was intended that the smaller and lighter car would have a smaller engine within a more truncated tail. This meant that any front-engine options were ruled out.

This key decision came after some early work on a completely distinct smaller model, the Type 984, which included studies of both front and rear-engined layouts with 1.9 or 2.1-litre flat-4 engines. The costs remained obdurately high and the results were not overly inspiring, other than to convince the planners that the smaller car would have to be a proper, soft-topped sports car rather than a coupé which might be adapted (like the 911) into a Cabriolet. While the 984 studies were in progress, the appearance and instant success of the Mazda MX-5 meant that much of the lower ground, from the point of view of size and price, was effectively denied to Porsche. Also, the Mazda being front-engined, the alternative of mounting the engine behind the driver become even more attractive to Porsche, as a further differentiator.

Before long, the 984 programme was officially abandoned and replaced by the 986, which was eventually to grow into the Boxster. There was no doubt from the outset that the 986 would have its engine aft of the cabin, but should it be mid-engined or rear-engined? Either was possible, but the mid-engine was the clear favourite. The new 996/911 was rear-engined because 911s had always been rear-engined; it was an article of faith. But despite the apparently awful lesson of the 914, the mid-engine looked the better bet, for all kinds of reason. A mid-engined 986 could never be dismissed as a 'shrunken 911'. For years, all serious road-racers had been mid-engined; any other layout would be dismissed more or less out of hand by the enthusiast customer, aided and abetted by the writers of the specialist press. More to the point, it would be entirely feasible to take the larger front half of the 996 platform and install the right kind of engine the 'other way round', eating into cabin space (but the 986 was to be a strict two-seater, so that didn't matter) but creating the opportunity to pull the entire back end of the body aft of the rear axle line, shorter and tighter.

The 996, further along the engineering development line, would always be the lead chassis design but the 986 would benefit from its mid-engine configuration with better static balance and lower polar moment of inertia. It was widely appreciated that the low polar moment could also lead to over-abrupt turn-in and generally twitchy handling, as exhibited by the 914/6 and by a number of mid-engined road cars launched by various manufacturers during the 1980s, but the Porsche chassis experts reckoned they could tame this propensity through careful tuning, and in any case, the company's electronics partners, notably Bosch just up the road, were already promising a different kind of solution with the system that became known as ESP.

The Porsche stylists had already decided they wanted a short and tapering rear overhang, although a wedge-shape with a tall, flat rear panel – the classic Kamm tail – would have been better aerodynamically. The view was that it would also be ugly, unavoidably so, and the 986 would have to sell at least partly on

The original Boxster was quickly "up-gunned" to create the Boxster S, seen here in 2005 model-year form. Evident in this view is the way the nose structure, back to the A-pillars, is shared with the 911. Aft of this point the Boxster is unique, its mid-mounted engine allowing a shorter rear overhang to make the car significantly more compact – at the cost, naturally, of eliminating any back seat space.

visual attraction. In the end, a concession was made to aerodynamics with the fitting of a retractable 'pop-up' rear spoiler, aft of the folding hood well, which rose at 120km/h and then remained in position until the speed fell below 80km/h. With this one aid, the Boxster achieved satisfactory stability (it reduced the rear lift coefficient by 31 per cent) and allowed the car to achieve a drag coefficient of 0.31.

The best of the ideas in and around the Porsche studios were assembled into a concept car which was shown in Detroit at the beginning of 1993. This model, which was not a runner, was overseen by Grant Larson, an American designer who had come to Porsche via Audi. It was the first project to carry the name Boxster, a simple combination of 'Boxer' (for the engine) and 'roadster' (for the open two-seater concept) which the styling studios had begun to use as a shorthand name for the project. To say the Boxster concept was well received would be an understatement, especially since Porsche sources hinted that the US market price would be under $40,000. All that

Below: Seen from any front angle, the Boxster showed a clear family resemblance to the 996 – not surprising, since the engineering of both front ends was essentially the same, to save on development costs. Thus like the 996, the Boxster needed front air intakes to feed its front corner-mounted radiators while at the back, the induction needs of the mid-mounted engine had to be met.

Above right: In this packaging drawing, the relationship between 996 and Boxster becomes clearer. The structure and systems are 996 as far back as the B-pillar,

aft of which a completely different rear structure accommodates the mid-mounted engine and rear transaxle. Strict 2-seater nature of the car is evident.

Middle right: Vertical-view counterpart of the package drawing gives an even clearer indication of the radically different engine installation and the challenge of fitting a decent rear suspension round it – hence the move to MacPherson struts at the rear as well as in front. Smooth line of tail was thought essential, though a "chopped-off" Kamm tail might have been better aerodynamically.

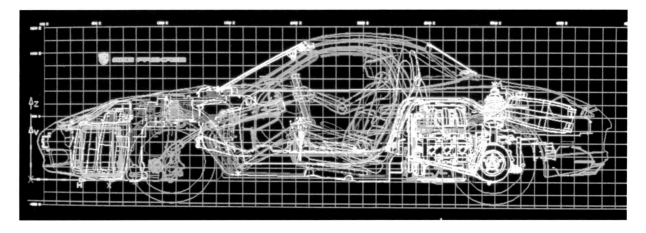

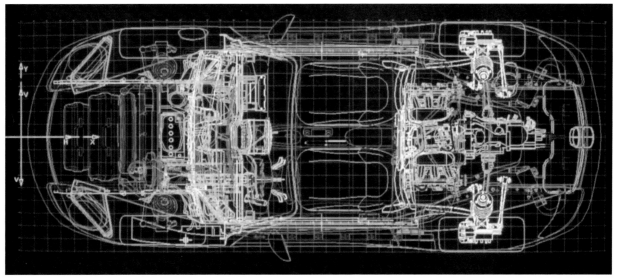

remained was actually to achieve this target. In the end, 'base version' Boxsters were indeed offered in the US market for $39,950 although the vast majority of cars were built to a higher specification, with 'options' that added both to the price and to the margin.

The Boxster team had more cost-saving tricks up their sleeve. Principal among these was what amounted to a common engine. This would be developed initially for the 996 but would be reduced in capacity and output for the 986. It would of course be a flat-6, a completely new one, with four valves and a single sparking plug per cylinder, developed from scratch to be water rather than air-cooled. That the Boxster-to-be should have a smaller-capacity version of this engine made perfect sense, so long as it fitted 'the other way round', which it did. There was then no point whatever in deriving a shorter, smaller, 4-cylinder version. That would have cost far more, and

risked depriving the 986 of its status as a 'real Porsche'. The fact that owners would know they had behind them a version – even a smaller one – of the 911/996 engine would be a distinct plus point. It also meant that within the constraints of the mid-engine installation, the Boxster unit could be 'stretched', if desired, all the way out to the 3.4-litre capacity of the 911 itself.

The question remained: how much smaller should the engine be made? Porsche insists that it decided upon the appropriate performance level first, and reduced the engine capacity to the minimum which would comfortably achieve it. As described in the previous chapter, the all-new 996 engine would emerge with a bore and stroke of 96 x 78mm, for a capacity of 3,387cc. The Porsche 986 team decided that reducing the bore and stroke to 85.5 x 72mm, for a capacity of 2,480cc, would produce the desired result. One benefit of downsizing a basically larger

Above: How it all came together, as seen in ghosted view. Restricted cabin space was accepted as inevitable, and problems of access to mid-engine for service were minimised with "remote" access for level-checking, and long service intervals. But rather like its mid-engined precursor the 914, the Boxster had to make do with two medium-sized luggage compartments rather than one big one.

Left: Satisfactory aerodynamic qualities were achieved through the fitting of a retractable rear spoiler, which emerged above 120

km/hour and then retracted below 80 km/hour. Final drag coefficient was 0.31, and the extended spoiler reduced rear lift by 31 per cent.

Right: In one respect at least the mid-mounted engine made life easier – there was more room for the exhaust system, without the engineering gymnastics needed to create a system for the 911 which was both legally quiet and provided space for catalytic converters. Even so, the short tail meant designers could not be spendthrift with space and still needed to use a large transverse box arrangement.

engine was improved refinement, mainly thanks to longer connecting rods (as a result of the shorter stroke) and lighter pistons – the full seven-bearing crankshaft configuration being retained. Power output was quoted at 150kW (201bhp) at 6,000rpm, with

245Nm of torque at a fairly high 4,500rpm. The 'red line' – actually the cut-off imposed by the Motronic engine management system – was set at a conservative 6,700rpm. A big advantage of front-end commonality with the 996 was that most of the cooling system could be carried over, with the slant-fitted radiators in the wings ahead of the front wheels. The lubrication system was likewise virtually identical.

There was a good deal more to the downsizing of the 3.4-litre engine than shrinking the bore and stroke, naturally. The cylinder heads needed redesigning, with port sizes matched to the lower gas flow rates which were the consequence of the smaller capacity – retaining the existing port sizes would have drastically slowed bottom-end gas speed and created a big hole in the low-end torque curve, Variocam timing and the dual-length manifold ducts (both recalibrated for the Boxster) notwithstanding. The inlet and exhaust systems were completely different because of the mid-engine installation. In particular, because the inlet manifold was so close behind the cabin, it needed careful design to achieve an induction sound which was both pleasant and not too loud. Meanwhile, the

exhaust system was engineered to provide a feature of which the stylists were especially enamoured, a single, large central exhaust pipe. This actually emerged from the centre of a large and complex stainless steel silencer box running across the car aft of the gearbox, with the twin exhaust manifolds running, via their catalytic converters, into each end.

The potential nightmare of all mid-mounted engines, that of reaching it to perform routine maintenance, was largely overcome to the point where an owner would rarely if ever need to perform the chore of lifting the first section of the soft-top before lifting the engine cover in turn. Porsche made provision for checking and replenishing both oil and coolant without having to lift the lid, and all engine components subject to wear in normal use, including the spark plugs and belts, were long-lifed.

If money was to be saved by using bought-in parts, it was in the transmission. Here, Porsche bought-in a complete 5-speed manual transmission from Audi, which was capable of accepting the 2.5-litre's reduced maximum torque. The Audi gearbox has the advantage of cable-operated shifting, which helped over-

come that familiar bugbear of extreme rear-mounted gearboxes, the problem of achieving a satisfactory linkage around the intervening mass of the engine. As an alternative to the manual gearbox, the Boxster was also offered with a 5-speed Tiptronic automatic supplied by ZF.

From the chassis point of view, the Boxster of course used the highly developed MacPherson strut front suspension of the 996, benefiting from the fact that a system developed for a considerably more powerful car would have a lot in hand in the lighter one. The rear suspension was another matter, but the final solution was both neat and economical. In effect, the front suspension was turned round so that the rear suspension was also MacPherson strut, by no means an original layout by that time (the original Datsun 240Z used rear struts), but was especially well suited to fitting around the 'box' formed by the engine – whose dimensions would have made the engineering of a double-wishbone layout difficult if not impossible. To create its MacPherson struts, Porsche used Bilstein twin-tube gas-filled dampers as the struts themselves, together with separate lateral links and trailing radius arms, all picking up of the cast aluminium hub carrier. The hub carriers and the lateral links were identical front and rear (the hub carriers in effect corner-to-corner, being 'handed'). The rear radius arms,

Above: The rear transaxle – 6-speed manual gearbox plus final drive – was sourced from Audi, who were able to provide a high-quality "off the shelf" unit at moderate cost. Engineering the shift linkage to pass around the engine and aft to the gearbox was something else, a challenge outside Audi's experience.

Above right: Boxster rear suspension used MacPherson struts with lower transverse arms and lengthwise radius arms to provide good

location. While theoretically inferior to a multi-link suspension, the geometry of the strut system meant it could be fitted easily around the engine, while still providing the necessary clearance for passage of the drive shafts.

Right: Seen "in the metal" (and the other way round) the sub-assembly of struts, lower and radius arms, wheel hubs and subframe clearly leave space for the flat-6 engine and the Audi transmission.

however, were much longer than those at the front, not least because there was the room to make them so, to the benefit of rear suspension geometry – the longer the arm, the less the unwanted fore-and-aft movement of the wheel during vertical movement. All that then remained was to lock the rear hubs at a suitable alignment, and make provision for the drive shafts to pass through the hubs to the wheels. Anti-

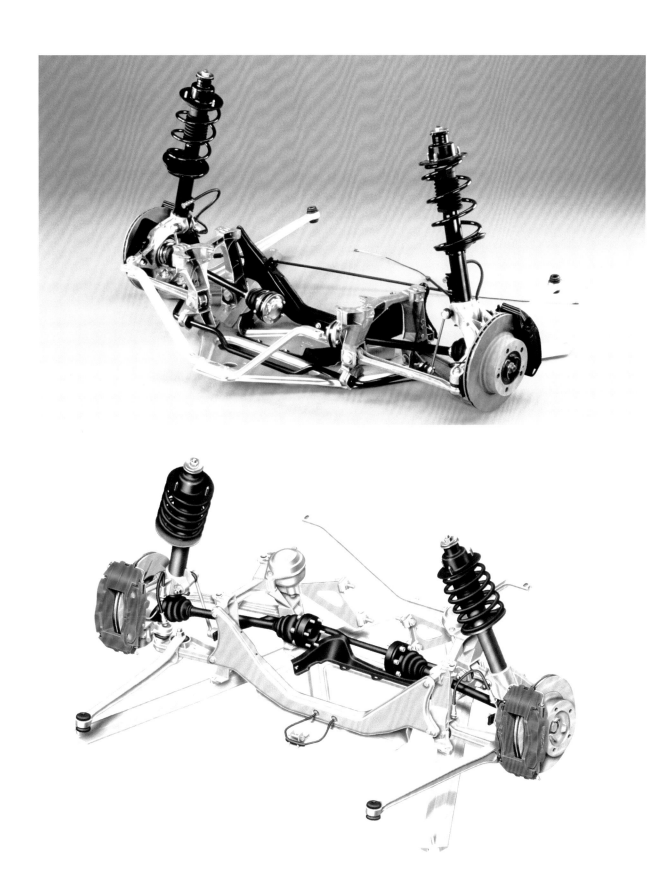

roll bars were provided at both ends, although with different forms of attachment.

The front coil springs provided a neat solution to the problem of allowing sufficient wheel travel without spoiling the swooping nose line. They were 'beehive' shaped, the coil diameter becoming smaller towards the top, so that when fully compressed the spring collapsed almost into a disc without suffering from coil binding. This space-saving solution, more often found in the rear suspensions of small, front-driven cars, proved an admirable solution and the MacPherson strut configuration left sufficient space (at both ends of the car) for a useful if not generous luggage compartment. Like any mid-engined car, the Boxster abhors big suitcases and forces you to split your stuff between two smaller ones. As for the remainder of the chassis, ventilated discs were fitted both front and rear, an easy decision in a high-performance car with near-even weight distribution, while the standard tyres, on 16in rims, were 205/55 front and 225/50 at the back – an indication that there was still an oversteering tendency to be overcome. With the optional 17-inch wheels, the tyre sections went to 205/50 at the front and 255/40 at the back. A space-saver spare was installed in the front luggage compartment.

There were two imperatives for the Boxster body design: stiffness, and (since it was going to be launched purely as a roadster) a decent soft-top and excellent weatherproofing with the hood up. Stiffness, especially torsional stiffness, is never easy to achieve in a soft-top design. Through the vital centre-section, the loads can only be carried via the central tunnel, the floor and the sill sections, with the latter the most vital of all when it comes to torsional stiffness. There was a centre tunnel of sorts although it was, so to speak, non-functional. The hollow sill sections were made as generous as possible without compromising cabin space or ease of entry and exit (these considerations applied equally to the 996 and the Boxster, remember). It would have been difficult to achieve satisfactory results without the help of the higher-strength steels which were by then available. It allowed the stiff, energy-absorbing 996 nose section to be tied to the equally stiff Boxster rear section – its strength derived in part from a substantial steel-tube assembly which also provided integral roll-over protection – by a short but adequately stiff centre section.

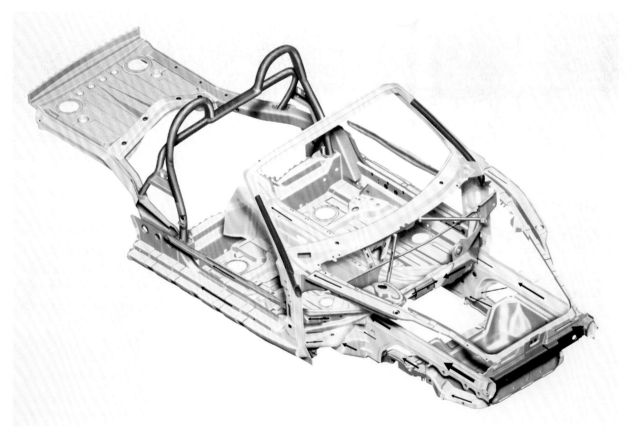

The hood was a challenge, since the engine (or rather the induction system above the engine) left little depth for neat stowage out of sight. Also, the hood had to be power-operated: the days had gone when you could expect the owner of a $40,000 car to go through the rigmarole of unclipping, manual manoeuvring and securing in place. So, at some considerable expense, a 'Z-fold' hood configuration was devised and built into a module, weighing only

30kg, which was delivered complete and bolted into the car at a single workstation, using just eight bolts. Once the electric actuators had been added, the roof would close in 12 seconds, and close attention to detail ensured freedom from leaks and draughts.

If one counts the beginning of the Boxster development programme from the freezing of the specification after the Boxster concept appeared at the beginning of 1993, it took only three and a half years to develop the definitive production car and exhibit it at the 1996 Paris Salon d'Auto. This short development period underlined how much time had been saved by carrying across work already completed for the 996/911. In effect, two-thirds of the foundation – the whole front end, and the engine – had already been engineered and needed only detail attention. The majority of the effort had gone into perfecting the mid-engine installation, and developing the chassis to match the needs of the different layout.

The Boxster body heralded a number of innovations (or breaks with tradition, depending on your attitude) which helped Porsche achieve volume production at reasonable internal cost. The design included a number of pre-assembled modules which

Left: Structural development work was largely shared between the 996 and the Boxster. The design made use of high-strength (yellow) and ultra high-strength (red) steels to achieve high stiffness in the cabriolet body, together with good crash-test performance including occupant protection in the roll-over case, hence the hoops located behind the seats.

Below: An "empty" nose is not necessarily a disadvantage in designing to resist frontal impact. There is no need to allow for the interference of engine mass and stiffness, and the structure itself can be optimised. The result, as seen here in an impacted Boxster, is deformation of the nose, but perfect maintenance of the windscreen and door surrounds, in turn indicating good occupant protection.

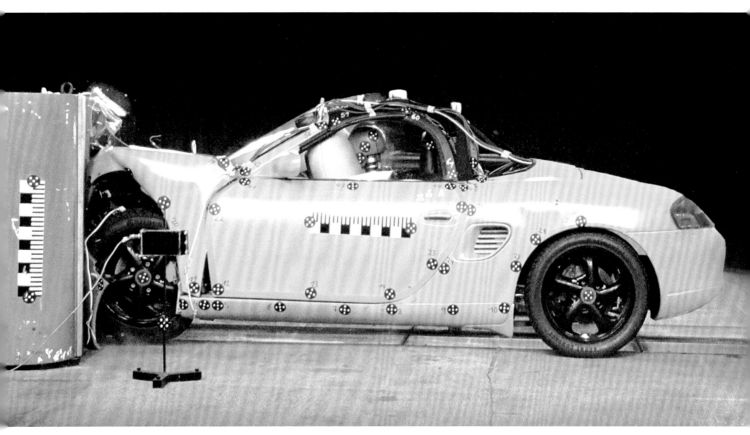

reduced the on-line assembly time, and also meant the basic body was identical for both left and right-hand drive; right-hand drive remained important for the UK market and for Japan. Most of the body panels were pressed in the BMW factory in Eisenach, in the former East Germany. Given the dies, Eisenach had sufficient capacity in its huge modern press shop to supply Porsche with all it needed – and had the technology to deal with the high-strength materials and forming techniques involved.

In an even bolder move, forced on Porsche by burgeoning demand as soon as the Boxster had been launched, assembly was transferred from Zuffenhausen to the Valmet works at Uusikaupunki in Finland. To put it mildly, Zuffenhausen would have been pushed to meet the demand, even working flat-out in three shifts. Apart from anything else, the 911 was being built in record and still-increasing numbers, and had to take priority. Valmet, with a large, modern and flexible facility which was already assembling Saab 900 Convertibles and Opel/Vauxhall Calibras, had the necessary capacity, the skills and the right attitude towards quality control. It took Valmet well under a year to roll out its first production car, in September 1997.

More punch

From the outset, demand for the Boxster had been very strong, tending towards the insatiable – which was precisely why the move to Finnish assembly had to take place.

For two years, product development was confined to such features as an advanced side impact protection system, using 30-litre side airbags. At the back of everyone's mind, however, was the potential ease with which the 2.5-litre engine could be stretched in capacity to provide more output. The most obvious move was to lengthen the stroke from 72mm to the 911's 78mm, yielding a capacity of 2,687cc. The result was a comprehensively updated Boxster, launched in 1999 for the 2000 model year. Porsche pointed out at the time that 'Production of the 2.5-litre Boxster will be ending with the market launch of the two new models. But without doubt the original Boxster ranks high in the chronicle of Porsche sports cars, having exceeded all sales targets in a production run of more than 50,000 units, making this one of the best sellers in the Porsche family.' Beyond dispute, the Boxster was already delivering what the 924 and its series successors had failed to do – and had done it with a degree of commonality with the 911 which delivered production economies, and higher profitability as a result.

The enlarged 2.7-litre engine delivered 162kW (an additional 12kW) at 6,400rpm, and 260Nm of torque (another 15Nm) at 4,750rpm. Another significant change was the adoption of 'drive-by-wire', replacing the mechanical throttle linkage with an electrical one. Drive-by-wire had already just been introduced in the Carrera 4 but was still very new where Porsche was concerned. So worried had its engineers been about the danger of a single failure that they duplicated both the accelerator pedal sensors, the throttle actuators and the drive-by-wire computers, complete with a reversion mode which allowed a limp home in the event even of a double failure. The complication was worth it, because drive-by-wire made the task of controlling the engine within ever-tightening emission limits easier, while also being more readily compatible with systems like PSM (Porsche Stability Management) and cruise control.

To comply with the latest, and upcoming emission legislation in the USA and in Europe, all Boxsters also now featured new-technology trimetallic catalytic converters, using metallic substrate. Compared with previous converters, the precious metal loading was more than doubled. Secondary air injection was another emission-taming feature.

Alongside this up-gunned standard Boxster, there emerged the Boxster S. In this case a larger cylinder bore, 93mm (an extra 7.5mm, but still not all the way to the Carrera's 96mm) was combined with the 78mm stroke to yield a capacity of 3,179cc. With the supporting services recalibrated to match – the 2.7 and 3.2 engines used the same drive-by-wire compatible Motronic ME7.2 management system as the Carrera 4 – the larger unit produced 185kW (252PS) at 6,250rpm, and 305Nm of torque peaking at 4,500rpm. Both were very useful increases on the 2.7, let alone the 2.5, and were duly reflected in the performance. With the assistance of a new 6-speed manual gearbox, the Boxster S was claimed to reach 100km/h in 5.9sec, and proceed to a maximum speed of 260km/h (161mph). Such figures made the 2.7 Boxster look almost pedestrian. Still using the 5-speed manual transmission, it took 6.6 seconds to reach 100km/h, and its maximum speed was a mere 250km/h (155mph). In both engines, compression ratio was a high 11:1, requiring the use of 98RON petrol.

Alongside its new 6-speed manual gearbox, the Boxster S offered the equally new 5-speed Tiptronic S automatic, as an option. Apart from the features so long appreciated, the new unit allowed the driver to override the transmission, even with D selected at the lever, by operating thumb pads set into the steering wheel, reflecting a growing trend among high-performance cars.

While the Boxster 2.7 inherited the entirely satisfactory chassis setup of its predecessor, the Boxster S was another matter. It was capable of usefully higher speeds and was capable of reaching them more quickly. Thus, to the engineers, it needed attention to the chassis and above all perhaps to the brakes, to absorb the extra energy that could be thrown at them. The chassis moves were mostly simple: uprated springs and stiffened dampers were accompanied by the fitting, as standard, of 17in wheels with 7in rims at the front and 8.5in at the rear, shod with 205/50 and 255/40 section tyres. Buyers could opt instead for even bigger wheels, 18in with an extra half-inch rim width, tyre sizes then being 225/40-18 and 265/35-18. More subtly, the rear hubs and arms were revised to reduce changes in wheel alignment with vertical wheel movement, while bigger wheel bearings reduced any danger of camber change due to deformation. The bigger wheels, tyres and brakes, plus the 6-speed gearbox and other features, imposed a weight penalty of 35kg on the Boxster S – 1,295kg versus 1,260kg at the kerb.

The bigger wheels made space for larger-diameter ventilated brake discs, now also cross-drilled for the sake, said Porsche, not only of better cooling but also of more effective water-film dispersal in wet conditions. The disc diameters became 318mm (12.5in) at the front and 299mm (11.8in) at the back, all equipped with four-pot fixed calipers.

One important new feature in all Boxsters was the fitting of the POSIP (Porsche Side Impact Protection) safety system as standard. The 30-litre side airbags with their carefully developed deployment geometry, ensured efficient protection at head and chest level even with the roof open and the side windows down.

Especially for the Boxster S, subtle external recognition cues were important, at least from the marketing point of view. Hence, as Porsche summed it up, 'Titanium-coloured air scoops at the front and the titanium-coloured Boxster S designation on the rear luggage compartment lid identify Porsche's new roadster at very first sight. Further signs of distinction recognisable right from the start are the standard 17-inch wheels in special design for the Boxster S, brake callipers painted red, and the twin exhaust tailpipe.' In fact, all new-series Boxsters featured red-painted brake calipers – a neat cosmetic touch.

And the next move is …

With the launch of the revised Boxster series for the 2000 model year, a new guessing-game began within the motoring press, and Porsche enthusiasts in general. The Boxster was strictly a two-seat cabriolet. When would Porsche turn it into a hardtop coupé, with or without two extra semi-seats squeezed into the back? The frustration of the happy cabriolet owner who eventually begets children is always a marketing consideration. We had to wait awhile to see what would transpire, but in the meantime a few touches still had to be put to the Boxster itself.

For the 2001 model year, any changes were minor, and affected only the car interior, which gained new instruments and cabin lighting. Then nothing much happened for two years, but for the 2003 model year the Boxsters emerged with a redesigned hood, incorporating a fourth hoop which enabled the roofline to be extended aft and then dropped more steeply, allowing a heated glass rear window to be fitted in place of the previous plastic one. Power-operated roof opening and closing time, using electro-hydraulic actuation, was only 12 seconds.

The other major news for the 2003 Boxster was the arrival of a completely new VarioCam system. The previous system, involving movement of the timing chain, had always been of limited authority and difficult to make fully variable, which was becoming increasingly desirable. Now Porsche moved to something more closely resembling a conventional hydraulically-operated camshaft variator, allowing infinitely variable adjustment of camshaft angle through a range of 40 (crankshaft) degrees, compared with 15 degrees with the previous system. This in turn allowed the use of more extreme valve timing to the benefit of peak power, while retaining good low-end torque and driveability. The 2.7-litre's output rose to 168kW (228PS) at 6,300rpm, and the 3.2-litre unit's to 191kW (260bhp) at 6,200rpm. They were not huge improvements, but they were useful, especially when taken together with a further small improvement in fuel economy.

The new VarioCam system called for an uprated engine management system, Motronic 7.8, first seen in the 911 Turbo and able to provide the control output necessary for fully variable timing adjustment. As a further small refinement in the engine department, the return line to the fuel tank, from which fuel had formerly been taken on an 'on demand' basis, was deleted. The new fuel system, comprising not only the pump, but also the filter and the pressure regulator in the tank, ensured that no more fuel was supplied than was needed, eliminating the wasteful (and fuel-heating) process of return-to-reservoir.

Facelift

For the 2005 model year, still with no sign of a dedicated coupé, the Boxsters were given a facelift – no more than that, but a package of useful improvements to go with the revised appearance. Most obviously, this included new headlamp clusters with separate headlamps, and integral foglamps. The rear air intakes were enlarged, and more subtly, all external surfaces, including the door panels, were made slightly concave. Also, for the sharp-eyed, the wheel sizes had increased, yet again. The standard car was now on 17in wheels and the Boxster S on 18in wheels as standard with 19in as an option. Close attention to detail had managed to reduce drag coefficient to 0.29 for the Boxster and 0.30 for the S. Lift forces front and rear had also been reduced.

Mechanically, the engines were unchanged, but significant alterations to the inlet and exhaust manifolds improved gas flow and, on the inlet side, ram effect. The result was a useful rather than a remarkable increase in output, the 2.7 now delivering 176kW (240PS) at 6,400rpm and 270Nm of torque between 4,700rpm and 6,000rpm, and the 3.2S 206kW (280PS) at 6,200rpm and 320Nm, again between 4,700rpm and 6,000rpm. It was interesting to see how Porsche's engineers had learned to exploit the combination of VarioCam and variable inlet manifold geometry to achieve the kind of torque spread more often associated with a Turbo, although generally at higher speeds.

The power and torque increases – power up by 8kW in the 2.7 and 15kW in the 3.2 – naturally led to

Porsche wanted to present the Cayman as a distinct model, rather than simply as a "Boxster with a roof". Every effort was made to exploit the advantages of the enclosed bodywork, especially in terms of stiffness and of luggage space and access. Front-end styling touches made a difference too, although there were limits as to how far the process could be taken.

a further performance improvement, the Boxster S now returning a 5.5sec time to 100km/h and a maximum speed of 268km/h (166mph). To help with sprinting, the base Boxster gained a revised 5-speed manual gearbox with shorter lever travel; the same went for the Boxster S, but for its 6-speed gearbox.

Although the front and rear tracks were increased slightly, by 24mm and 35mm respectively, significant chassis changes were few, larger and wider wheels excepted, but they were present. PASM (Porsche Active Suspension Management) became an option, combining variable ride height with selectable damper stiffness. Adding to the electronic complexity (as a result of which Porsche moved to a more advanced databus system), PSM (Porsche Stability Management) was made standard, in order, as Porsche said, 'to enhance active safety to an even higher level when applying the brakes, or accelerating, and in bends.' Beautifully balanced and grippy though the Boxster might be, its low polar moment probably still made it a handful for the unwary, and PSM was the answer. Drivers were surely also helped by a move which Porsche had hesitated to make for many years: variable-ratio steering.

Few changes were made to the standard brakes, but faith was implied in the future of ceramic brakes with their offering as an option for the Boxster S. Despite being even larger in diameter (350mm/13.8in), the ceramic discs were lighter.

Unseen beneath the surface, the body had gained substantially in strength and stiffness, through the use of new high-strength metals and more advanced manufacturing techniques. Torsional stiffness was up by 9 per cent, and stiffness in bending by no less than 14 per cent. As a result, body weight increased by 18kg, and the engineers looked for ways of clawing some of this back. The front and rear luggage compartment lids were switched from steel to aluminium, saving 6kg at the front and 3kg at the rear. Further weight was saved with a cast magnesium frame for the new folding roof, aluminium being retained for the corner brackets only. But the biggest saving, of around 10kg, was achieved by deleting the spare wheel.

Ghosted picture of the Cayman betrays the essential similarity to the Boxster, but also shows the revised and stiffer body, the cabin still a strict 2-seater.

As Porsche insisted: 'With the number of severe tyre defects on the road constantly decreasing, with growing demand for extra space in the front passenger department, and with the option to reduce weight by 10 kilos, the need for a spare wheel has become an increasingly significant issue. So Porsche has taken a clear decision, completely dropping the emergency wheel and car jack on the new Boxster, which are replaced instead by a tyre sealant and an electrical compressor.' Drivers these days, Porsche also suggested, were often not up to the task of replacing a wheel at the roadside. To what extent this was attributable to the ever-increasing size of wheels and tyres was not discussed.

Cayman

And so up to date: for the 2006 model year, Porsche formally announced (more or less) what everyone had been expecting, a proper coupé derivative of the Boxster. Two things immediately stood out. First, it was called Cayman – strictly speaking, Cayman S, there being no 'base' version. Second, rather than offering the Boxster powertrains, it recreated the engine dimensions of the 996/911 at launch: bore 96mm, stroke 78mm, for a familiar-looking capacity of 3,387cc (or 3,386cc if you took the Porsche press release at face value: but the dimensions actually give just over 3,387). The cylinder heads – and the crankshaft with its main bearings 3mm bigger than those in the Boxster – were a direct carry-over from the 911 Carrera, so it was indeed very close to the old 911 powertrain, although minor modifications and the need to meet later, more severe emissions legislation had taken off the slightest of edges: the Cayman meeting Euro 4 and US LEVII standards. Thus we had 217kW (295PS) at 6,250rpm, where the 996 was launched with 221kW (300PS) at 6,800rpm. There was a slight peak-torque deficit too, 340Nm compared with 350: but with the aid of the latest VarioCam, making its first appearance outside the 911 range, and of variable intake manifold geometry, maximum torque spreads all the way from 4,400rpm to 6,000rpm. Why a larger engine than in the Boxster S? The Porsche sales pitch was that the Cayman was a distinct model, halfway between the Boxster and the Carrera. Therefore it had to be given a performance edge, and what could have been easier?

Understandably, body apart, most features of the Cayman looked familiar, although Porsche's engineers,

ever the perfectionists, had tweaked where necessary. Hence for example first and second gears in the 6-speed manual gearbox had been lowered slightly. The 5-speed Tiptronic was once again an option.

Together with the unexpectedly bigger engine, however, the closed coupé body was the focus of interest. The design aim was clearly spelt out by Porsche at the Cayman's announcement: 'The new Cayman S stands out as a genuine Porsche at very first sight, boasting classic design features reminiscent in part of the Porsche 550 Coupé introduced back in 1953 and the Porsche 904 Carrera GTS Coupé, a legend to this day. At the same time the new Sports Coupé stands out significantly in its design and proportions from both the Boxster and the 911 … The front end of the car with its separate foglamps is just as characteristic as the side-line with air intakes

Slanting Cayman tailgate opens high for easy access to the rear luggage compartment. Not evident in this view is the high compartment floor resulting from the need to house the engine and transmission beneath. In the Cayman, further thought had to be given to the question of day-to-day maintenance checking.

ahead of the rear wheels, the strongly curved roof, and the rear section slowly tapering down to the bumper. The rear end, in turn, is dominated by the large tailgate perfectly accentuated and rounded off by the sweeping lines of the rear wings and the dual tailpipe extending out right in the middle.' Not present in the Boxster, for obvious reasons, was the Cayman's 1,160 x 900mm tailgate. In the coupé, luggage space was deemed more important and every means was tried to add to it wherever possible. The eventual total was 410 litres, of which 260 were accessed via the tailgate, above the transmission. The remaining 150 litres were in the nose.

From an engineering point of view, the basic Cayman S body structure was naturally based on that of the Boxster, although the latter had originally been designed to achieve satisfactory stiffness purely as a cabriolet. Adding the fixed coupé roof made the Cayman shell exceptionally stiff in torsion and strong in bending. In bending mode, the Cayman values more than doubled those of the Boxster. Its torsional stiffness, quoted by Porsche at 31,500 Newton metres per degree, was almost the same as on the 911 Coupé. The engineers pointed out that this figure meant it

Above: Cars are too often seen from ground level, when an overhead shot would give a better impression of overall shape and aerodynamic efficiency. Here, the smooth blending of the Cayman "hull" and "greenhouse" is seen, together with some impression of the car's smooth shape in plan as well as elevation.

Right: The Cayman powertrain looks like a simple repeat of the Boxsters. However, having shrunk the flat-6 engine down to 2.5-litre (later 2.7-litre) capacity, Porsche engineers then reverted to the original 3.4-litre capacity for the Cayman which, in effect, thus used the 996 engine with some adaptation.

would take the maximum torque of some 92 Cayman engines to bend the car's body by 1 degree. The drag coefficient, matching that of the basic Boxster, was 0.29. Aerodynamic tweaks reduced the overall lift force towards maximum speed by 56kg; at the rear of the car, a new retractable wing rose as soon as the speed exceeded 120km/h (75mph). Porsche suggested that this wing, as a completely separate aerofoil, generated less drag than the faired-in spoiler seen on the Boxster. The Cayman was also notable for the near-complete fairing of its underside, reducing drag and calling for dedicated intakes to help cool the engine and transmission bays.

The added stiffness of the body brought benefits in terms both of handling and roadholding – fewer and smaller 'parasitic' changes to chassis geometry as a result of body flexing – and in safety. The Cayman exploited its stiffness to achieve excellent results in all the standard passive safety tests, and was naturally equipped with a full range of passive safety features including the Porsche Side Impact Protection System (POSIP), already seen in the Boxster.

Given its stronger powertrain, it was inevitable that the Cayman would claim better performance figures than the Boxster S. The specific claims – and bearing in mind that Porsche's performance claims generally err on the side of caution – were 5.4sec to 100km/h, and a maximum speed of 275km/h (183mph). Fuel economy, in the official test cycles, differed little from that of the Boxster S.

The higher performance set the engineers wondering how much needed to be done to the already excellent Boxster chassis. Their answer was simply to stiffen it: updated springs and dampers, larger-diame-ter anti-roll bars. Nothing else was needed, although the trajectory-correcting PSM was made standard, as on the facelifted Boxster. The PASM system was included in the options list. The Boxster S brakes were deemed up to their task and were barely changed and as in the Boxster S, ceramic brake discs were also optional.

That, then, was and is the Cayman, sitting in the gap – as Porsche would have it – between the Boxster and the 911. As in most Porsche models and variants, it is possible to load the car with expensive options if you have a mind to: park assistant, rear-view mirrors with an automatic anti-dazzle function, PCM (Porsche Communication Management) including DVD navigation, and that is without choosing from the available seating and trim choices. But did it have those two additional small seats in the back? No, it didn't, and that must have been a deliberate market-ing decision. Unless, of course, then engineers felt it would be cruel to sit anyone directly above the engine. But at least in the Cayman, unlike most mid-engined coupés, you can at least throw things onto the plat-form behind the seats, and reach back for them.

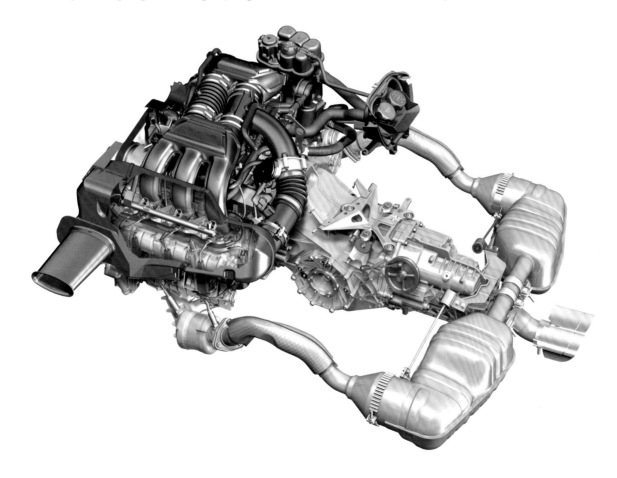

CHAPTER 15

The later Turbos; 993 and beyond

As observed in Chapter 6, the Turbo, long regarded as a separate model from the basic 911, had a tendency to disappear and reappear from time to time. Rarely did a new Turbo series appear simultaneously with a new-series 911, and things were not about to change. The new Type 993, last in the line of air-cooled 911s, made its debut in 1994, but the 993-based Turbo appeared only in 1995.

There are two real technical divides between the early-series Turbos (Chapter 7) and the later ones, covered in this chapter. First, the early cars used a single turbocharger, while the later ones are equipped with two smaller turbos, one each side, making for a much tidier layout and – because each turbocharger rotor is lighter, with less inertia – much better response also, with greatly reduced 'turbo lag'. Second, the 993 Turbo marked the end of rear-drive, except for a handful of special derivatives intended for competition, or at least for sale to the competition-minded, otherwise, 4WD became standard. Announcing the 993 Turbo at the 1995 Geneva Show, Wendelin Wiedeking said that to avoid the problems of stability and control which might arise from putting huge amounts of power through one end of a car, any Porsche with more than 400PS would now be equipped with 4WD as a matter of course.

993 Turbo

Just as the 993 was the last of the air-cooled 911 series, so its turbo equivalent was the last air-cooled Turbo. Surprisingly little needed to be done to the naturally aspirated engine to suit it for turbocharging, at least in the mechanical sense. The pistons were dished to lower the compression ratio to 8:1 (compared with 7.5:1 for previous Turbos) but the strengthened crankshaft and connecting rods served the engine well. So did the generous provision of cooling oil spray into the undersides of the pistons, and the measures taken to control oil temperature. The only specific measures undertaken for the sake of integrity was some minor redesign of the bottom ends of the cylinders, for more positive location and clamping within the crankcase.

The twin turbochargers, KKK K16, were installed on either side of the engine, each accepting exhaust gas from the three cylinders on its side and pumping air towards the very large intercooler mounted above the engine, partly within the fairing formed by the

rear spoiler. To avoid tight U-bends in the pipework, each exhaust was then led around the front of the engine, then rearwards through a catalytic converter (with thermally 'tough' metallic substrates) and so to an exhaust pipe on each side. Although the exhaust pipes ran close to one another, no balancer pipe was fitted – perfect side-to-side matching of performance was the function of the engine management unit. The incoming air, compressed at up to 0.8 bar and emerging from the intercooler, was then channelled into an inlet manifold carried over from the 993.

The new Bosch Motronic 5.2 engine management system fulfilled many new functions. It accepted signals from, among others, knock sensors in each head, from a new inlet air mass-flow sensor, and from four lambda sensors, upstream and downstream of each catalytic converter. Apart from basic management of fuel injection and ignition timing, the system could also react to incipient knocking either by retarding the ignition or by varying the wastegate setting on each side. It also served the new OBD II on-board diagnosis system, the twin lambda sensors per side allowing it to monitor the state of the catalytic converters. Although complex, the entire turbocharging system was neat and near-symmetrical, something which usually appeals to engineers. The outcome of all this was an output

Ghosted view of 993 Turbo, from overhead rear shows little of the engine beyond the giveaway air cooling fan, but shows the 993 "hips" to advantage, and emphasises the common feature of all second-generation Turbos, the 4WD transmission which Porsche insisted should become standard on any car offering more than 400PS.

of exactly 300kW (408PS) at only 5,750rpm, with massive torque; not only a peak of 540Nm at 4,500rpm, but also – thanks to the efficient control exercised by the engine management unit – a high, near-flat torque curve of the kind we have now become used to in turbo engines, with 450Nm already available at 2,500rpm. The car's performance fully reflected these figures and for the first time in a standard road-going Porsche, we were talking less than 4.5sec to 100km/h. The maximum speed increased to 293km/h (181mph).

The 6-speed manual transmission was reworked to accept the very high torque input, but also to provide the forward output, via a viscous coupling, to the Carrera 4 type front differential. The internal gear ratios were amended to take account of the even higher performance. One important change here was

the provision of a hydraulic servo mechanism, taking pressure from the power steering circuit, to reduce the clutch load and travel, which the high clamping loads (needed to transmit the torque via a single-plate clutch) would otherwise have made excessive. Altogether, the 993 Turbo weighed 82kg more than the naturally aspirated car, and the 4WD transmission would have accounted for around 55kg of this.

Just as the basic engine proved well able to accept the extra loads, so did the chassis, for the most part. The standard (stiffened and lowered) 993 Sport settings were retained, but there were two important changes. First, because of the further increase in performance, stopping became even more of a challenge. The answer was obvious: a further increase in the size of the ventilated discs, which went out to 12.7in diameter. To keep braking loads within reason without fitting a huge vacuum servo, hydraulic assistance was adopted. The second move was to adopt an advanced form of alloy wheel construction (friction welding) which enabled the spokes to be hollow, thus retaining more than adequate strength without carrying material where it would do no good. The result

Above: From the front quarter, the short-lived 993 Turbo looks like a "beefier" version of the naturally aspirated version, but with enlarged air intakes at the front. Just visible is the enlarged, fixed rear spoiler installed above the high-capacity intercooler. Wheels were wider and brakes larger, to match the output now available.

Right: One of a kind – an air-cooled twin-turbo engine as installed in the 993 Turbo. High output was achieved with considerable boost pressure and clever engine management, despite having only two valves per cylinder – with pressure charging, gas flow area is slightly less important. Oil cooling of many hotter parts, on the other hand, was vital.

was a saving of 2–3kg per wheel, which must have made a useful contribution to ride comfort and road-holding. Making room for the bigger brakes, the wheels were now 18in as standard, with front 225/40 and rear 285/30 tyres respectively, carried on 8in and 10in rims.

From the design point of view, the 993 Turbo could be distinguished by its new and more dramatic front end with larger air scoops (for oil and brake cooling) as

well as the large fixed spoiler beneath which lurked the intercooler. The spoiler itself used the latest plastics technology to save 40 per cent in weight without sacrificing stiffness.

Beyond the standard 993 Turbo came the specialised rear-driven road-racers of which one, the GT2, merits mention because it was built in numbers large enough (25 units per year) to be suitably homologated for motorsport purposes, and was certainly driven on the road by many enthusiasts. Engine tuning, predominantly a matter of fitting larger turbochargers (KKK K21 instead of the standard K16s) and turning up the boost pressure, produced 316kW (430PS).

Perhaps inevitably, the 993 Turbo was greeted with huge enthusiasm by the motoring press, who trotted out the superlatives. Customers must have agreed, because in a relatively short production run the car reached a total of 6,314 units, a great deal for such an expensive and formidably fast machine. But as the road testers pointed out, this was also a car which could behave in a totally docile manner when driven gently, and it was sufficiently comfortable and durable

to encourage thoughts of long, demanding drives in adverse conditions, which would have had the owners of some rivals shuffling their feet and looking for excuses. Yet despite all the praise, this version would not last long, because its horizon could only extend to the introduction of the water-cooled, 24-valve Type 996. At that point, once again there would be a hiatus during which the enthusiasts would ask themselves whether there would be a successor model, and how good it would be. With the Turbo more than any other product, Porsche seemed to have developed the ability to pose the question: if this one is this good, what scope can there possibly be for serious improvement?

2000: 996 Turbo

Of necessity, the 993 Turbo died when the naturally aspirated car ceased production. Yet again, the Turbo derivative of the new car was not immediately available. In fact, there was a wait of around two years before we saw what could be achieved with a water-cooled 24-valve engine. As with the naturally aspi-

Left: Side-on drawings of the three later generations of 911 Turbo show the evolution of body shape during the late 1990s and into the 21st century. The 993 Turbo (top) represents the last of the "old" shapes and platforms. The 996 (centre) is visibly bigger, sitting on a longer wheelbase, with a higher-volume body and revised "glasshouse", while the 997 Turbo (below) is very much a further extension of the theme, aerodynamically refined both above and below the waist.

rated 996, there was a problem: the new engine's capacity was only 3.3-litres, yet there was an undisputed requirement that the new Turbo should be more powerful, in order to be quicker, than its predecessor. Porsche could not have customers wondering whether they had waited two years for a car that was no faster. There was also the problem that in the meantime, exhaust emission requirements around the world were tightening. In Europe, Euro 4 limits were being made ready to take over from Euro 3. In the USA, ULEV standards were being called for at least in a proportion of new production cars. The engineering challenge was considerable.

The most interesting thing was that they did not use the 996 engine as their basis. Instead, they retained the dimensions of the old 993 engine, 100mm by 76.4mm; exactly 3,600cc, but it was water-cooled. Using technology originally developed for racing – and developed for not very much money – the 996 Turbo retained the original 993 crankcase; but squeezed between the crankcase and the new 4-valve cylinder heads were water jackets, occupying the same volume as the original deeply finned, air-cooled cylinder triplets, and separate 'wet' alloy liners with Nikasil bores. The logic of this approach had originally been to create an engine compatible with a midships installation, so that 911 'lookalikes' could be raced with the engine and transmission reversed from their hallowed and original places, in turn allowing desirable things like a downforce-inducing venturi aft of the back wheels, and a lower polar moment of inertia for better handling and response.

Right: The 996 Turbo engine was something of a hybrid, not simply a "blown" version of the 3.3-litre, 24-valve 996 unit, but built around the inner structure of the 3.6-litre 993 but with 12-valve 996 heads, and water jackets around the cylinders, derived from racing experience. VarioCam Plus was standard and the compression ratio was 9.4:1 for "unblown" efficiency, the management system ensuring freedom from high-output detonation.

The trouble was, mid-mounted engines couldn't be air-cooled. There was simply no way of getting enough air in there. Hence the apparently stop-gap evolution of the water-cooled derivative, which worked remarkably well in competition. Now, Ludvigsen suggests, the chance came to amortise its development costs over a much longer run of engines, for a production 996 Turbo. Weighing against that, it would mean the naturally aspirated and Turbo versions of the 996 would have fundamentally different engines. On the other hand, it also meant the 996 Turbo could enter the fray with a capacity of 3.6 rather than 3.3 litres, and that seems to have decided the matter.

Once the decision had been taken, work proceeded much according to the process established with the 993 Turbo. Twin KKK K17 turbos were fitted, one for each cylinder bank. Their exhausts flowed through a completely revised system now incorporating two catalytic converters – a fast-warming 'precatalyst' and

THE LATER TURBOS; 993 AND BEYOND

a main unit – at each side, before entering the massive and complex transverse silencer arrangement at the rear, still with its exhaust pipe at each end.

The maximum boost pressure was 0.8 bar as before and the intercooler was still huge, but the engine's compression ratio was quite remarkably higher at 9.4:1. This was a tribute to the controlling influence of the engine management system, now up to Motronic 7.8. If the system, controlling all the engine's operating parameters according to its mapped memory plus signals from the knock sensors, can ensure there is no danger of detonation, why not take advantage and, by using a higher basic compression ratio, make the engine more thermally efficient in light-load conditions where the turbochargers are barely taking an interest? This was one of the engineering moves which helped to make the 996 Turbo more economical, more efficient and more responsive across most of its operating rev range. Fuel consumption figures achieved during the European and US emission test cycles indicated improvements of up to 18 per cent. Rather meanly in some eyes, Porsche responded by reducing the size of the front-mounted fuel tank to a distinctly modest 64 litres (14.1 imperial gallons) which, better economy or not, wasn't going to last long for an enthusiastic driver making the most of the performance.

Two other new features played a significant role. The 996 Turbo was actually the first car in the range to use the VarioCam Plus system, altering the inlet valve timing and switching the valve lift between low and high load. With the cam covers lifted, the cylinder heads took on a somewhat misleadingly new appearance for this reason. In fact, the valve geometry was as in preceding 4-valve heads, with a fairly narrow angle between the valves, the only important difference other than the cam profiles themselves being the use of double rather than single valve springs. The Turbo was also equipped with what Porsche called 'E-gas', otherwise an electric 'drive-by-wire' throttle linkage. The VarioCam Plus in particular ensured that the engine's torque, although not greatly superior to that of its predecessor, was deployed in a virtually flat plateau all the way from 2,700rpm to 4,600rpm. The

principle, running from the hot to the cold side. An oil/coolant heat exchanger was fitted, as in the 996 Carrera, but with 10 per cent more capacity. The coolant radiators themselves were no less than 50 per cent bigger than in the naturally aspirated car, accompanied by matching reprofiling of the front-end air intakes and cooling ducts.

Following the lead of the 993 Turbo, the transmission was of course 4WD as standard, its parameters chosen to allow up to 40 per cent of the drive torque to reach the front wheels. The system was in effect as in the 996 Carrera 4, but with an altered propeller shaft length. A twin-mass flywheel was used to guard against cyclic vibration transferring to the driveline. The 6-speed manual gearbox was carried over, but an important addition to the options list was the Tiptronic flick-shift automatic transmission, for the first time in a Turbo, and with five forward speeds. The new unit was equipped with what Porsche called Electronic Transmission Management (ETM), using a 'fuzzy logic' technology to achieve infinitely variable adaptation to driving style and road topography, rather than switching between five predetermined programs in the manner of previous Tiptronics ever since 1990.

The offer of Tiptronic meant that two sets of performance figures had to be quoted, instead of just one. The manual car was beyond doubt the faster, claiming 0–100km/h in 4.2sec (Tiptronic, 4.9sec) and a maximum speed of 305km/h (190mph) with the Tiptronic achieving 'only' 298km/h (185mph). Yet again, the brakes were enlarged, to a full 13in diameter within the confines of the standard 18in wheels. Like all 996s, the Turbo returned to a conventional vacuum servo, rather than the hydraulic brake assistance of the 993. Careful attention was paid to conducting heat away from critical areas of the calipers, but of much more technical interest was Porsche's offering of ceramic (carbon fibre reinforced silicon carbide) brake discs, albeit as a very expensive option. The ceramic discs were claimed to offer even better performance and to last six times as long, but in service some problems emerged, not with hard-driven 911 Turbos but with gently driven ones, in which the discs never fully warmed, or suffered unusual thermal gradients, and consequently suffered cracking. So long as a driver warmed up his brakes progressively, racing-style, and then kept them hot, there was no problem.

The 996 chassis, attached to the new and formidably still body shell, needed little in the way of change. The rear wheels and tyres were made wider still, 295/30-18 on 11in rims, the extra rear arch flare

Above: Flank intakes are hidden when the 996 Turbo is seen from the rear quarter, but the additional air extractors in the corners of the larger rear bumper are evident, as is the carefully shaped rear "wing" spoiler incorporating the rear brake light. From this angle, the overall effect is very clean.

Left: The 996 Turbo was offered in Cabriolet form, underlining the confidence the engineers felt in the stiffness of the basic 996 platform – with suitable strengthening of course. Below the waist, the Cabriolet was aerodynamically identical to the standard coupé.

actual peak value was 560Nm, just 10Nm up on the 993, while the peak power was quoted as 309kW (420PS) at 6,000rpm.

The question of cooling was taken very seriously indeed. 'As on the standard engine of the 911' according to the Porsche press release, ignoring the fact that this was a significantly different unit, the cooling flow through the cylinders and heads used the crossflow

THE LATER TURBOS; 993 AND BEYOND

needed for proper clearance increasing the car's overall width by 65mm. The sports-specification suspension was lowered by 10mm compared with the Carrera. Just as important, perhaps, was the new offering of PSM which, through the ABS, could intervene with 'dabs' of individual wheel braking, or by easing back the power via the drive-by-wire throttle, to correct any deviation from the driver's intended course, as deduced by the system's computer.

Seen from outside, the first impression of the 996 Turbo was of a car which swallowed a huge amount of air. The sheer area of the three front intakes made an impression. So did the new-style headlamps, among the earliest to use the then-new gas-discharge (Litronic) technology to enhance output and colour value. At the rear, meanwhile, the wing design was again new, and the fresh-air intakes to feed the intercooler – which needed almost as much air as the radiator – were a new and evident feature. The drag coefficient for the revised shape was quoted as 0.32, but one has also to bear in mind that the frontal area had increased, so total drag remained much the same.

As always, the 996 Turbo was amenable to 'tuning' by the apparently simple expedient of increasing turbocharger boost pressure. This policy resulted, in 2001, in the GT2, in which the extra boost (with other engineering changes to match) delivered 355kW (483PS) at 5,700rpm, and 640Nm of torque between 3,500rpm and 4,500rpm. However, the GT2 was really a club racer, showing a weight saving of 100kg by virtue of everything that had been stripped out of it. This included, in the manner of previous semi-competition Club Sport derivatives, most of the internal sound insulation material, as well as other items like the back seats. To ensure the additional output reached the road surface, the rear tyres were 315/30ZR18 on 12in rims; at the front, the 235/40ZR18s looked almost puny by comparison. Performance claims included the ability to reach 100km/h in exactly 4sec, and a maximum speed of 319km/h (198mph). This, in other words, was edging

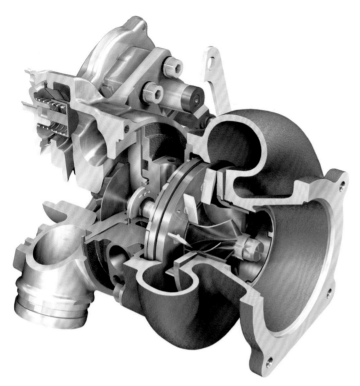

Left: To withstand the higher exhaust gas temperatures of a petrol engine, the guide vanes of the variable-geometry turbocharger had to be manufactured from special alloys "borrowed" from aerospace gas turbines. But the VG characteristics provided the advantage that it was possible to use only two turbos whereas two pairs per side, and complex plumbing, would otherwise have been needed – if they had fitted.

Below left: No "hybrid" this: the 24-valve, 3.6-litre 997 Turbo engine was developed from the outset to deliver its 480PS (355kW) smoothly and reliably. Engine management limits torque output to "only" 620Nm to allow the transmission to survive, with the result that the "peak" extends from under 2,000rpm all the way to 5,000rpm. The entire exhaust system is remarkably neat and compact – it needs to be, in order to fit.

down towards Carrera GT territory, although without the positive aerodynamic downforce. The GT2 was scarcely a practical road car, but it showed the direction in which the engineering might be taken.

997 Turbo

In practice, however, the Porsche engineers at Weissach were looking at some more startling options. They knew that in creating a new 911 Turbo based on the 997 (see Chapter 18), they would have to offer their most enthusiastic (and richest) customers a considerable advance on the 996 Turbo. And so they did.

The 997 Turbo was officially unveiled at the 2006 Geneva Motor Show, and a few weeks later, with snow still on the ground at Weissach and rivulets of melt water flowing across its test track, Porsche held a

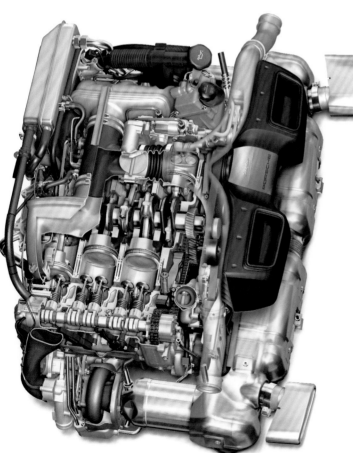

Above right: This Porsche drawing shows the complex arrangement of airflow through both ends of the car, to keep both the engine and the brakes cool, and to supply the massive airflow needed by the engine itself when developing full power. Consequently, the rear flank intakes were supplemented by invisible NACA-type intakes moulded into the otherwise flat underbody fairing.

Right: Not least in order to keep weight in bounds while creating the stiffest-ever 911 body shell, Porsche engineers had recourse to a variety of advanced materials. In this diagram, yellow is high-strength steel, green is ultra-high strength steel (note the frontal impact load distributor around the lower bulkhead) and blue is weight-saving aluminium alloy, used extensively in the doors.

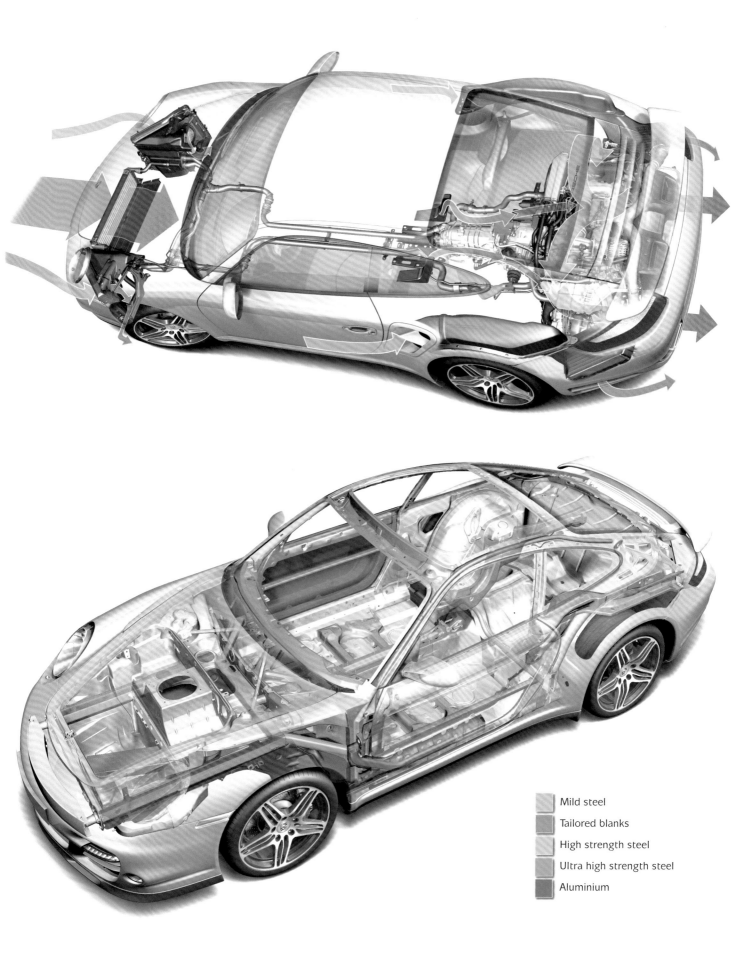

Mild steel

Tailored blanks

High strength steel

Ultra high strength steel

Aluminium

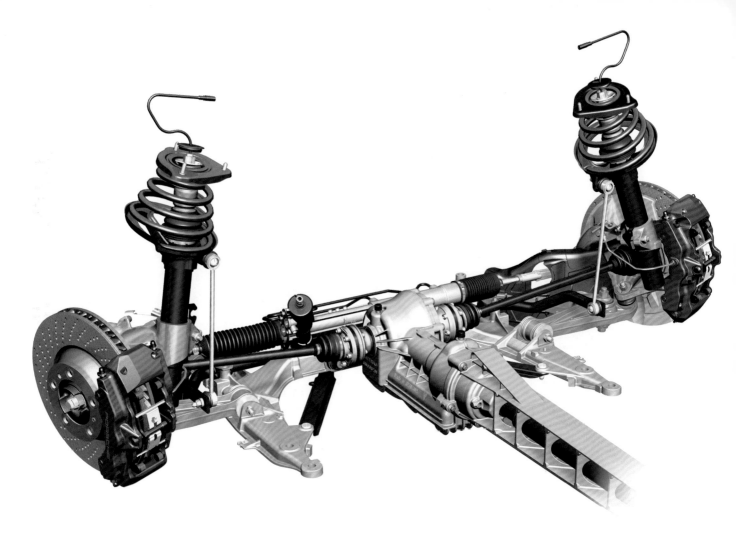

seminar at which it presented the major aspects of 997 Turbo technology. The engine was the first focus of attention: although still a 3.6-litre unit, the output was up to 355kW (480PS), with 620Nm of torque spreading in a huge plateau all the way from 1,950rpm to 5,000rpm.

The key to this startling increase was a switch to variable-geometry turbochargers, using controlled-angle inlet guide vanes, still one each side. There is nothing new about variable-geometry turbochargers, but they had only ever previously been seen on diesel engines. This is because diesel exhaust gas is around 200°C cooler than petrol exhaust gas. Variable inlet guide vanes can survive in a diesel exhaust, while they melt when attached to a petrol engine. At least they did, until Porsche, working with its suppliers, resorted to very special materials from the aerospace industry, and found ways of making small but very accurate components.

A theoretical alternative would have been to use two fixed-geometry turbochargers in a series-parallel arrangement: a small turbo for low-end boost, a larger one for higher speeds, but the 997 back end, pulled

Above: Heavily revised for the 997 Turbo, the front driveline remains faithful to the principle of an extremely compact front differential with output shafts passing the suspension struts to reach the front wheel hub assemblies. The most important new feature of the standard 4WD transmission system was Porsche Traction Management, PTM.

Right: At the heart of the 4WD transmission, the PTM uses sophisticated electronic control and a fast-acting multi-plate clutch to vary the front-to-rear torque split – not only to optimise traction, but to balance the car's handing by ensuring that excessive oversteer is countered by feeding more output to the front wheels, and vice versa.

tightly around the powertrain, simply did not provide the space for the plumbing such a system would have needed. Thus, variable geometry it had to be, and the results were duly impressive.

To complement the 997 Turbo engine, the 4WD transmission had been heavily revised. A new controllable torque-transmission multiplate clutch was used, with high-gain electromagnetic servo operation giving very quick, and extremely efficient response, able to

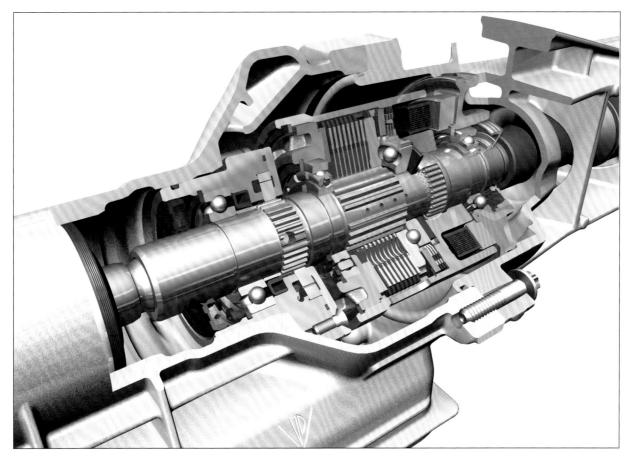

control the distribution of torque (by regulating the proportion being fed to the front) all the way – in theory – to 100 per cent to one end or the other, in response to various computer control signals. It was no longer a matter of whether one or more wheels were spinning.

The 997 Turbo was equipped with Porsche Traction Management (PTM) which had proved its worth in the Cayenne, and had been adapted as a handling-trimmer for the Turbo. Now, if excessive understeer was detected, the PTM would transfer drive aft, to counter the problem, and vice versa. To prove the point, demonstrations were made on the problematic surface of the Weissach track; and indeed, the effect could easily be felt when the 997 Turbo was thrown into an adverse-camber downhill bend, of the kind which would have proved a severe test for any previous 911. In conjunction with newly developed tyres on the standard 19in wheels, said Porsche, the 997 Turbo was capable of lapping the formidable and revered old *Nordschleife* of the Nürburgring below 7min 50sec, enough to challenge for pole position in a 1960s Grand Prix.

There were other aspects of the 997 Turbo, including the work that had gone into developing weight-saving aluminium closures, as a result of which the new car weighed fractionally less than its predecessor. It was also made clear just how much work had been done in the wind tunnel. Flows were optimised every-where, and no more so than out of sight, across the flat and all-enveloping undertray, now with NACA intakes to channel cooling air to the rear brakes and the engine compartment. There was a new double-surface rear wing, too.

That presentation brought the Turbo story up to date, although clearly not to a conclusion. At some point, further improvements will emerge. Pressed on the point, Porsche engineers express an eagerness to be able precisely and continuously control the load on each individual wheel, in order to optimise cornering grip and performance, transient handling and stability. They will also, no doubt, be seeking even more power in future cars – but one should not ignore their new-found eagerness to save weight. It may well be that any new-generation Turbo will be smaller and lighter, as well as dynamically superior even to the 997.

CHAPTER 16

2002: Cayenne

Porsche had always been capable of building an SUV. In its archives lay the history of the specially adapted wartime Volkswagen, and of the military projects on which it had worked, with so little ultimate reward, during the 1950s. From a later era came the files on a project from the first half of the 1970s, when Ferry Porsche had recognised the merit of the Range Rover concept and wanted to do something similar, yet at the same time radically different, building what would much later have been called an SUV on the 911 chassis. This would have variable ride height enabling it to be optimised for both on-road and, with greater ground clearance, off-road operation. Later still there was all the engineering that had gone into the 4WD 911s, and the 959, in their epic rallying exploits, especially in the Paris–Dakar event.

All Porsche had ever lacked was the money and the additional engineering resources to carry through any such project while continuing with the rest of its programme. By the mid-1990s, however, two things had changed. Wiedeking had nursed the once-troubled company into consistent profitability and the money was there, or at least theoretically available. Second, there were signs that the SUV market was beginning to grow apparently exponentially. The most influential aspect of this trend was that SUVs were moving up-market, becoming not only socially acceptable but socially obligatory among certain customer groups, and that some of those customers might soon be deciding between a new 911 and an up-market SUV. Apart from all the long-established suspects, including the Range Rover which Ferry Porsche had admired, it came to be known that both Mercedes, with the M-class, and BMW with the X5 were planning to enter the fray. It was no longer a question of whether and how Porsche could buy itself a place at this table, but whether it could possibly decline the invitation to the feast.

The initial plan foresaw a collaboration with Mercedes, which could have done with a partner as part of a plan not to create the M-class, but to replace the venerable G-wagen. But the discussions with the people just up the road at Stuttgart-Unterturkheim came to nothing, according to Ludvigsen, because Mercedes wanted to seal the deal with the one thing that wasn't on offer – a minority interest in Porsche. Accordingly, and very logically, Porsche sought an alternative agreement with the Volkswagen. After all Ferdinand Piëch, chairman and CEO of Volkswagen, was also a member of the extended Porsche family

and sat on its supervisory board. Also, up to that point, Volkswagen, like Porsche, had been missing out on the growing SUV market.

By June 1998, the two companies were ready to announce their joint venture, without at that stage being specific as to its form. What would soon be decided was that they would share a common platform but that each would undertake its own styling and chassis development, and supply its own engines.

Two other questions remained to be answered. One was where and how the new Porsche would be developed, since Weissach, larger though it had grown, could not accommodate a whole extra model development team alongside its existing commitments. The other was where it would be built, since this was to be an addition to the range and Zuffenhausen was full of 911s – apart from which, it would have been necessary almost to gut and re-equip the factory to accommodate what was clearly going to be a much larger vehicle.

That it would be a much larger vehicle was decided early on. The joint Porsche-VW planning team settled on a wheelbase of 2,855mm (112.4in), placing it very firmly in the same category as the Range Rover, the Mercedes M and the BMW X5. This would be no competitor for the Toyota RAV-4, and that, surely, suited Porsche rather more than Volkswagen. In any event, to overcome the problem of overcrowding at Weissach, Porsche created a new design and development office at Hemmlingen, between Weissach and Stuttgart. One of its first tasks was to identify how much of the vehicle would constitute the 'platform' – the structure and sub-assemblies common to both Porsche and Volkswagen. Anything not thus included would be down to each participant to develop and fit individually.

A different kind of 4WD: the Cayenne development team could look back to projects throughout the lifetime of the company, but it took a joint venture with Volkswagen to achieve production, and a new product line for Porsche. Engine and external body cladding was all-Porsche, but the underpinnings were shared.

Reverting in a sense to its familiar consultant role, Porsche undertook the bulk of this development, Volkswagen contributing its share of the cost. The shared structure consisted of not only the main floor and inner-body pressed panels, but all the box-sections which built up to form the complete body frame, right up to roof level. Even without the external panels which would differ between what would become the Porsche Cayenne and the Volkswagen

Touareg, the structure was formidably stiff and strong. The Porsche team made significant use of its recently acquired expertise in high-strength steels and laser-welded tailored blanks, and in critical areas extra strength was achieved through the use of seam-welding rather than conventional spot-welding. Because this was a time when a certain amount of panic had set in, notably in the USA, about the problem of SUVs 'toppling' when cornering fast on the road, special attention was paid to keeping the upperworks light, so as to lower the centre of gravity.

As design progressed, so did the search for a factory. Porsche felt it should be in Germany rather than farther east , which is what Volkswagen had in mind. In a kind of compromise, Porsche chose a site near Leipzig, in the former East Germany. In its official announcement, in September 1999, Porsche said it would invest over DM 100 million in the site, its buildings and machinery. By some standards this was a modest amount for an all-new plant, but it was planned for a production volume of 20,000 units per year, a relatively modest volume (Volkswagen planned

Above: Design sketches for the Cayenne, released at the time of the model's introduction, give some indication of the way in which a Porsche identity was sought, notably with a "front face" bearing some 996 design cues though necessarily on a larger canvas. The aim was to create the look of a "civilised" SUV rather than a workhorse.

Above right: The basic Cayenne structure, shared with the Volkswagen Touareg, was an extremely stiff frame in which high-strength and lightweight materials were combined to create a body which, while SUV-tall, retained a relatively low centre of gravity to guard against the risk of toppling in high-performance road driving.

Right: An all-new factory was created at Leipzig to assemble the Cayenne, remote from the Volkswagen Touareg facility further east, in Bratislava. Having its own plant enabled Porsche to apply its in-house standards in every respect. Leipzig also undertook the necessary low-volume production of the Carrera GT (Chapter 17).

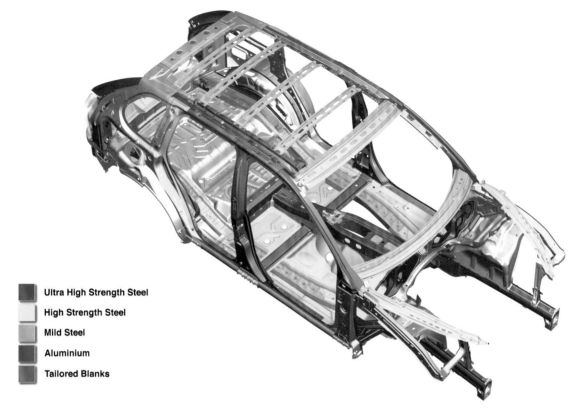

Ultra High Strength Steel

High Strength Steel

Mild Steel

Aluminium

Tailored Blanks

to build four times as many Touaregs) and would employ only 300 people. Porsche pointed to the success of Valmet's production of the Boxster as an example of what could be achieved in a factory remote from Stuttgart. The 1999 statement also made it clear that Leipzig would be part of an integrated network with Volkswagen's Wolfsburg and Bratislava (Czech Republic) plants, the latter supplying most of the pressings and assembling the Touareg, and Zuffenhausen which would supply the Porsche engine.

That announcement having been made, everything went quiet so far as the outside world was concerned, and the guessing-game began, encouraged by the usual trickle of unauthorised spy-photographs. Eventually, in March 2002, some months ahead of the launch

The 4.5-litre V8 was a state-of-the-art 32-valve 90-degree engine notable for the care taken to ensure it would run properly at the most extreme off-road angles of pitch and tilt. Naturally aspirated, it delivered 340PS; with twin turbochargers this rose to 450PS with a torque "plateau" of 620Nm from 2,250rpm to 4,750rpm.

proper, Porsche released a handful of official product pictures and an outline description. It could well afford to do so, because the Cayenne was not going to take sales from the existing range, only from the opposition. The name Cayenne itself was officially announced in June 2000, and towards the end of 2001 Porsche issued a historical overview which reminded the market of Porsche's existing 4WD pedigree, going back as far as the Lohner-Porsche of 1901 and running all the way through to the 959 and the Carrera 4. None of which really meant very much, because the Cayenne would be an altogether different kind of vehicle.

Just how different was revealed in a background briefing ahead of the official launch, in May 2002. The Cayenne was to have an all-new 4.5-litre V8 engine, a 4WD system making use of Porsche Traction Management (PTM), and air-sprung suspension with variable ride height, self-levelling and Porsche Active Suspension Management (PASM) which would provide continuously varying computer control of damper setting according to road condition. Outline technical specifications were attached, making it clear that all Cayennes would have the V8 engine, but that there would be a choice between naturally aspirated and turbocharged versions. Only for the 2004 model year did a "base" version appear, powered by a 3.2-litre, 250PS derivative of VW's 24-valve VR6 engine.

The definitive car was first seen in public when the Leipzig factory was officially inaugurated in August 2002, and the vehicle went on to be shown first at the Paris Salon of that year, and then at the British Motor Show in Birmingham.

Considerable effort had been put into incorporating Porsche styling cues into the Cayenne body, but given the size and height of the vehicle, it wasn't easy. One might almost argue that the styling was in any case misleading. This was not a visually tough machine looking for off-road action: it was, rather like its BMW and Mercedes rivals and the Range Rover, a big SUV you could take anywhere without feeling embarrassed. That said, the chassis beneath was as capable of traversing demanding country, if the owner wasn't worried about marking the expensive bodywork.

That Cayenne might not have been an 'ultimate' off-roader, because its suspension was all-independent, and the most serious off-road machines tend still to have live axles at least at the rear, for the sake of constant ground clearance. Against that the Cayenne could offer its variable ride height, courtesy of its air-sprung suspension, and that meant there was

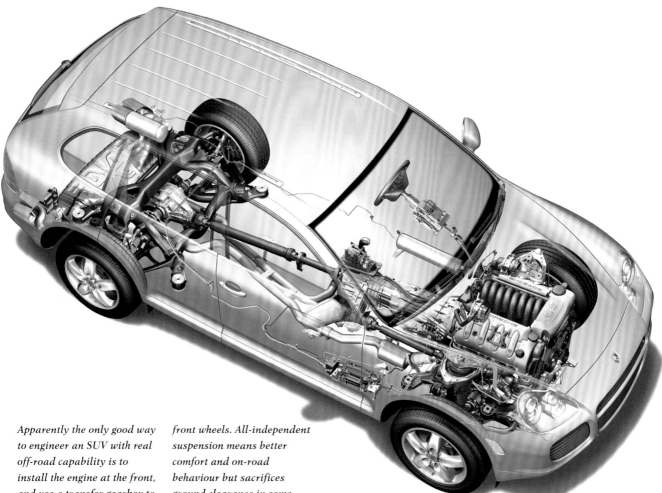

Apparently the only good way to engineer an SUV with real off-road capability is to install the engine at the front, and use a transfer gearbox to split the drive, running a propeller shaft forward and alongside the engine to the front wheels. All-independent suspension means better comfort and on-road behaviour but sacrifices ground clearance in some demanding situations. Cutaway drawing shows Porsche's solutions.

generally enough ground clearance anyway, while behaviour on the road was that much better.

Specifically, the Cayenne used a double-wishbone arrangement at the front, with the fat air-spring struts reaching down from the upper mounting points to pick up on the lower wishbones. As was becoming widespread practice, the wheel hub extended upwards in a 'swan neck' so that the upper wishbone could be above wheel level, making for improved geometry with small camber and castor changes, even during large vertical wheel movements. The lower wishbone, plus the substantial anti-roll bar and the front final drive, were all mounted to a strongly built sub-frame made not of cast alloy, as it would have been in a sports car, but fabricated from pressed steel sheet. Total vertical wheel travel was 220mm (8.7in) at the front and 249mm (9.8in) at the rear, with the air springs. Rear wheel travel was slightly reduced with the steel coil springs.

At the rear, another subframe, fabricated from a mixture of welded pressings and heavy-gauge steel

tube, provided mountings for the rear suspension and the rear final drive. The suspension, reflecting Porsche practice in the most recent 911s, consisted of five independent arms roughly equivalent to double wishbones, plus a track control arm – although the reality was more subtle than that. Again, the air spring and damper units, this time inclined steeply inwards, passed between the arms of the upper 'wishbone' to pick up on the wheel hub. Both front and rear subframes mounted to the body at four points, via bushes intended to eliminate parasitic horizontal movement, while retaining good isolation of vertical vibration fed from the road surface. The rear subframe bushes were hydraulically damped.

The air suspension, developed in association with the chassis division of tyre manufacturer Continental, was not standard across the range: it cost too much. Instead it was standard on the Turbo and optional on the Cayenne S, which in standard form used conically wound coil springs (allowing longer wheel movement without coil binding) with their axes offset from that of the dampers, to reduce the danger of stiction. The variable ride height, available only with the air suspension, could be set by the driver as high as 273mm

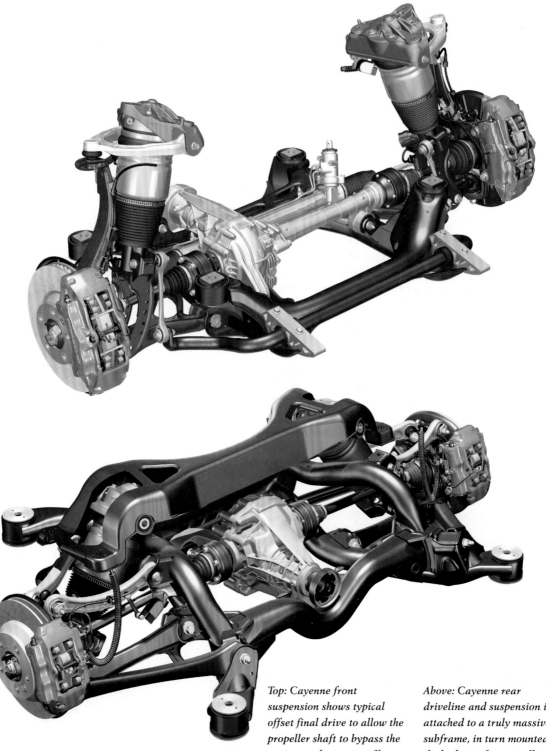

(10.75in) ground clearance for off-road operation. Porsche pointed out that the increase in ride height also increased the arrival and departure angles, making it possible to tackle steeper slopes.

One illustration of the care and thought which went into exploiting the potential of the air suspension is to tabulate the six ride heights (ground clearances) possible in the Cayenne S:

Top: Cayenne front suspension shows typical offset final drive to allow the propeller shaft to bypass the engine, and strong, stiff subframe. Double wishbones are widely separated with typical "swan-neck" upward extensions from the wheel hubs, and have to provide clearance for the fat air spring and damper units which also vary ride height.

Above: Cayenne rear driveline and suspension is attached to a truly massive subframe, in turn mounted to the body via four equally massive hydraulically-damped bushes. In this case the suspension geometry is "modified" double-wishbone, with an extra link ensuring that the proper wheel alignment is retained in the most adverse conditions.

Position	Height	Driver/Auto	Note
Load	157mm/6.18in	Driver	Resets to Standard on moving off
Very low	179mm/7.05in	Auto	Above 210km/h (130mph)
Low	190mm/7.48in	Auto	Above 125km/h (75mph)
Standard	217mm/8.54in	Driver or Auto	(Default)
High	243mm/9.57in	Driver	Max 80km/h (50mph), then resets to Standard
Offroad	273mm/10.75in	Driver	Max 30km/h (20mph), then resets to High

At high speeds on the road, therefore, the Cayenne automatically lowered itself in two stages, each time gaining in stability and reducing its effective frontal area. At the same time, speed limits were imposed on the higher settings to reduce the roll-over moment should the driver switch from off-road progress to high-speed cornering on the road. The lowest ride height of all was provided purely to lower the sill for

Drawing shows how the various Cayenne chassis elements fit together within the body frame. Though they look massive when viewed in isolation, in this context they seem compact, leaving plenty of free space. Note the amount of free space in the nose forward of the engine.

easier loading, the vehicle automatically rising as soon as it moved off. At its highest suspension setting, the Cayenne was said to be capable to fording water up to 555mm (21.85in) deep.

Dynamic self-levelling of the body was another feature easily engineered with the air suspension, ensuring that the headlamps remained level at all times and that the aerodynamics were optimised, with a Cd of 0.39; the Cd can vary markedly, and always for the worse, in a vehicle where a heavy load makes it run pitched nose-up.

There were big wheels and fat tyres for a big vehicle, naturally. Both models come as standard with 8J x 18 wheels running on 255/55 R18 tyres and were

these not hefty enough, 9J x 19 or 9J x 20 wheels were offered, with tyre sections 275/45 and 275/40 respectively. Such large, low-profile tyres were by no means a good choice for serious off-road conditions in which sidewall strength (as well as self-cleaning tread patterns) can become an issue, and special wheel and tyre developments were needed before the Cayenne could be considered a reliable 'safari transport'. On the road, however, where Porsche expected the majority of its customers would spend most of their time, the quality of the chassis and all the choices that went into it were soon evident.

Since the vehicle was also heavy – the eventual homologated kerb weight was 2,245kg, plus an extra 110kg for the Turbo – and capable of high performance, it was also equipped with massive brakes. These used ventilated discs all round, those at the front being 350mm (13.8in) diameter running in six-pot calipers, with 330mm (13in) discs at the rear, and four-pot calipers. Cross-drilling of the discs for additional cooling and dust dispersal was overruled when it was found that the drillings could also trap small stones, which could then wreak havoc on the disc surfaces.

The power-assisted steering was a 'first' for Porsche, using variable ratio. For a long time Porsche had stuck to fixed-ratio steering in the belief that consistent feedback contributed to delicacy of control, but the Cayenne was a different matter. Delicacy would be less of an issue in this relative monster than manoeuvrability. To provide reasonably geared steering without making it unduly 'quick' around the straight ahead, a variable ratio was highly desirable. Having made the decision, Porsche well and truly implemented it, giving the Cayenne steering with a reasonable 16.7:1 ratio in mid-travel, yet with only 2.65 turns of the steering wheel between locks – distinctly 'quick' by most standards. What is more, the experience proved so successful that Porsche adopted variable-ratio steering for the coming 911 generation.

Equally new was the combination of three electronic-based systems available on the Cayenne, and standard on the Turbo. The first was PASM, already alluded to, but also providing the driver with the ability to select between degrees of ride comfort quality. The second was PSM, standard in all Cayennes and working in the now familiar manner of trajectory-correction or stability enhancing (ESP-type) systems, working mainly by applying momentary stabs of braking on individual wheels, with the

ability also to ease back on engine torque delivery if necessary.

The third, and entirely novel system was Porsche Traction Management (PTM), again standard across the range and, in effect, a refinement of its 4WD control. The function of PTM was to vary the front-to-rear torque split (38:62) according to need. It was able to direct the transmission to transmit up to 100 per cent of the available torque to either end of the vehicle as required. The torque split at any given moment was dependent not only on traction as determined by wheel speed sensors, but also by sensors measuring vehicle speed and lateral acceleration, steering angle and accelerator pedal position. Thus the system not only provided optimum grip on off-road conditions, but also behaved as a handling modifier in high-speed road driving, shifting the torque split forward to reduce oversteer, or vice versa. Integrated into the PTM system, for use in off-road conditions, was the transmission low-range selector and a rear differential lock. In road use, the strategy adopted was to use PTM as the main handling 'trimmer', with PSM intervening, as Porsche put it, only when the vehicle was driven 'to the extreme limit'.

Newly developed 6-speed Tiptronic S

What, then, of the transmission itself? In the first instance, the Cayenne came only with a new interpretation of the Tiptronic S transmission, with six forward speeds, developed in collaboration with the Japanese specialist Aisin. This would be the standard transmission for the Cayenne Turbo, and in theory an option for the base version, although in practice the 6-speed manual gearbox for the latter would only become available, from ZF, for the 2004 model year.

The original Porsche press information pack for the Cayenne was remarkably light on references to the heart of its 4WD transmission, the transfer box which contained, running rearwards from the main gearbox with which it was integral, first the neat 2-speed 2.7:1 epicyclic range-change (hence 'shift-on-the-fly' – no need to stop to change ranges), then the sprocket for the multiple chain drive transferring torque sideways to the front-wheel drive, then the electrically actuated, computer-controlled multi-plate clutch controlling the front-to-rear torque split. The drive to the front wheels passed to the right of the engine sump

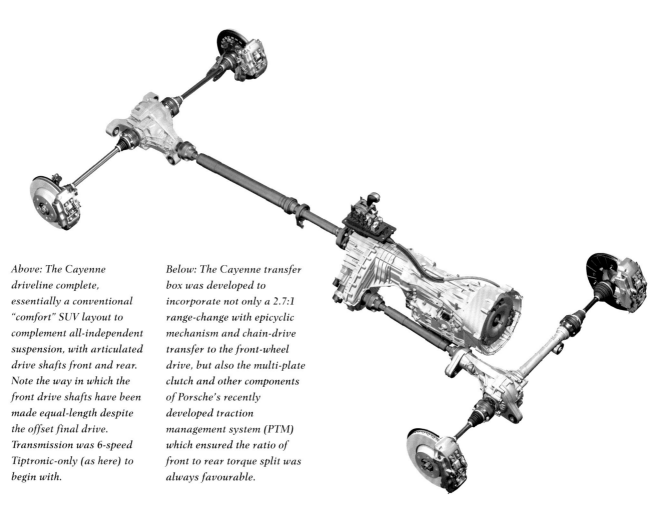

Above: The Cayenne driveline complete, essentially a conventional "comfort" SUV layout to complement all-independent suspension, with articulated drive shafts front and rear. Note the way in which the front drive shafts have been made equal-length despite the offset final drive. Transmission was 6-speed Tiptronic-only (as here) to begin with.

Below: The Cayenne transfer box was developed to incorporate not only a 2.7:1 range-change with epicyclic mechanism and chain-drive transfer to the front-wheel drive, but also the multi-plate clutch and other components of Porsche's recently developed traction management system (PTM) which ensured the ratio of front to rear torque split was always favourable.

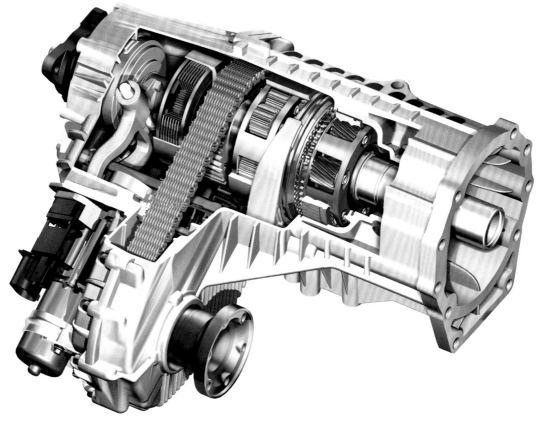

from the driver's point of view, the front differential being well offset, with a cross-shaft taking drive across the subframe before being articulated to drive the left front wheel.

One very neat feature of the Cayenne 4WD system was the provision of a single integrated control, in the form of a 'paddle' on the centre console, enabling the driver in one move to prepare the transmission and suspension for off-road operation. Selecting the off-road configuration sets the PTM to low ratio and activates a special off-road control map for the differential locks, PSM to activate the traction-orientated off-road ABS and ABD systems, and causes the air suspension (where applicable) to rise to the basic off-road ride height.

New engine

At the heart of the Cayenne, one might well say, was an all-new 90 degree V8 4-cam, 32-valve 4.5-litre all-alloy engine. Ideally the vehicle needed a range of engines: its companion model the Volkswagen Touareg was very quickly made available with a range of power units ranging from an in-line 5-cylinder diesel and a petrol V6, to a massive V10 diesel and a petrol W12. Porsche didn't need to cater for the lower end of the big-SUV market. As its planned production volume revealed, its aspirations lay elsewhere. Its only viable strategy was to develop a base engine which would give the Cayenne more than adequate performance, and then turbocharge it to extend the range upwards.

There is no evidence that Porsche's engineers ever considered anything but a V8 configuration for this engine. Their basic power requirement automatically led to a naturally aspirated capacity of around 4.5 litres, which meant that eight cylinders was the minimum: with six, each individual cylinder would have been too big, recalling the 'big-banger syndrome' from which the 3-litre, 4-cylinder 968 engine suffered. A suitably dimensioned 90 degree (for optimum balance) V8 would be effectively a 'power cube', and very easy to install in a vehicle of the Cayenne's size.

The basic parameters were quickly laid down. Within an alloy block with cylinder bore centres spaced at 108mm, the engine would be 93 x 83mm, oddly (but insignificantly) also the dimensions of the 2.7-litre Boxster S. With twice as many cylinders, the Cayenne engine would displace 4,511cc. The block would be cast from high-silicon aluminium alloy,

Above: From the rear quarter, the Cayenne is less obviously a Porsche, more typical of the many vehicles which emerged in the late 1990s to compete in the booming luxury SUV class. A closer look reveals the attention paid to aerodynamics and to detailing beneath the car, which had the benefit of variable ground clearance.

Right: Cayenne yielded nothing in terms of safety design. Not only was its structural impact resistance extremely high, but it provided its occupants with a comprehensive suite of protective restraint systems including front, side and "curtain" airbags, all shown inflated in this illustration.

requiring no liners. After careful consideration and departing from other recent Porsche practice, the block casting would feature a 'closed deck' – continuous upper surfaces, rather than free-standing cylinders. This, it was felt, would better support the gaskets in containing the higher compression and combustion pressures which would be created within the turbocharged version.

There was no harking-back to the 928's V8 which, after all, had ceased production in 1995; engine technology had moved on a lot since then. Not only had once-exotic features become commonplace and any

21st century powertrain designer faced with the need to comply with the latest exhaust emissions legislation, and looking at an engine designed in the 1970s like that of the 928, would surely observe that he wouldn't start from there. Thus for example, the Cayenne engine was given a straightforward dual chain drive to its four camshafts, rather than the strange cross-over secondary chain arrangement in the 4-cam 928. The crankshaft, a conventional counter-balanced design, ran in five main bearings supported, as in most modern all-alloy engines, by a substantial lower ladder-frame. Cast alloy pistons were shaped to give a compression ratio of 11.5:1 in the naturally aspirated engine, and forged pistons to give 9.5:1 in the Turbo. The combustion chambers were optimised for low emissions, the four valves per cylinder symmetrical, with just under 30 degrees between them, and operated directly via bucket tappets with single valve springs and hydraulic lash adjustment.

The sparking plugs were central, and vertical, in the best possible place. The inlet camshafts incorporated VarioCam variators to alter the inlet valve timing within a 25-degree range – but there was no valve lift-changing VarioCam Plus. A metal-substrate precatalyst and main catalytic converter, the type favoured by Porsche, was installed on either side of the engine, which met Euro 4 and American LEV standards. Engine management was down to the latest Motronic 7.1.1 control system, responsible for the now well-tried OBD2 facility, and the throttle valve was drive-by-wire, any concerns Porsche might have had about this technology having vanished with in-service experience.

To this extent, the engine seemed much like several other recently introduced 32-valve V8s. What made it more typically Porsche, in several ways, was the care which went into the induction arrangement of the naturally aspirated engine, and the special concern which was evident that the engine should happily withstand operation at the sometimes extreme angles of pitch and tilt which can be encountered in severe off-road use. This was a challenge which Land Rover, for example, had encountered when adapting BMW's diesel engines for use in the Range Rover. Porsche therefore determined that their V8 should be able to operate continuously at angles of up to 45 degrees in pitch or tilt or combinations of the two. This involved ensuring that sufficient oil could run directly into the sump at all times. The oil pump pickup was therefore arranged so that it could not suffer starvation within these limits, and that the crankcase venting system was protected against

splash oil ingestion, which would have allowed oil to enter the engine air intake.

On the intake side, careful design of the manifold enabled the engine to exploit the oscillating pipe charge principle, in which pressure oscillations generated during the intake stroke improve the cylinder charge if the length and diameter of each cylinder duct is properly chosen. This, together with the VarioCam, contributed not so much to the peak torque of the naturally aspirated engine, but to the way its torque curve spread so usefully, especially into the lower speed range.

The result of all this was that the basic Cayenne engine delivered a power output of 250kW (340PS) at 6,000rpm, with its peak torque of 420Nm extending plateau-like, all the way from 2,500rpm to 5,500rpm, an ideal (and somewhat diesel-like) characteristic especially for off-road operation. Large and heavy though the vehicle was, the output was sufficient to propel it to 100km/h in 7.2sec, and on to a maximum speed of 242km/h (150mph). And then there was the Turbo.

This was one area in which Porsche engineers could lean heavily on their experience with the recent 911 Turbos. Naturally enough, the V8 was a twin-turbo design, although the units came from the Japanese supplier IHI rather than Porsche's long-serving supplier KKK. Each turbocharger served one bank of cylinders via its own individual intercooler, forward of the wheel arch on that side, and a differently arranged inlet manifold with larger duct diameters. Maximum boost pressure was a modest 0.6 bar (8.5psi), dropping under Motronic control of the bypass valves to 0.5 bar (7psi) at peak power. Apart from its reduced compression ratio, the Turbo version also had cylinder heads cast from an alloy with significantly better thermal strength, and the undersides of the pistons were cooled (as in all 911 Turbos) by an intense oil spray. The exhaust valves were given double springs. The improvement in performance was substantial: a power output of 331kW (450PS), still at 6,000rpm, and a torque 'plateau' of no less than 620Nm running from 2,250rpm to 4,750rpm. As a result, the Cayenne Turbo could reach 100km/h in only 5.6sec, and maximum speed was put at 266km/h (165mph). Equally impressive, though in a different way, was the mixed-cycle fuel consumption, which emerged as 15.7 litres/100km (18.0mpg).

Most press reaction to the Cayenne was favourable, although voices were heard protesting that this was not the kind of vehicle Porsche should ever have built, no matter how capable. There was general agreement that in spirited driving, the Turbo's official 18mpg was considerably optimistic. On the whole, customers seemed to take the positive view – and each Cayenne sale was incremental so far as Porsche was concerned. If anything, the demand from the top (and most profitable) end of the market was for even more performance, and once the Cayenne was properly played-in and any initial in-service problems overcome, Porsche's engineers set out to provide it.

Turbo S

The result, launched for the 2006 model year, was the Cayenne Turbo S, billed as the second most powerful Porsche model homologated for road use, after the recently released Carrera GT. 'Tuning' a turbocharged engine can amount to little more than raising the boost pressure, having first made sure that all the affected components can withstand the additional loads. Thus an increase of 0.2 bar, accompanied by an expansion of the VarioCam operating range from 25 to

For the 2007 model year, Porsche introduced a substantial package of improvements for the Cayenne, including a larger-capacity (3.6-litre, 290PS) V6 engine. Externally, the main styling changes were to the 'front face' of the vehicle.

40 degrees, slightly larger intercoolers with improved through-flow, and suitably recalibrated engine management, the Turbo S delivered 383kW (521PS) at 5,500rpm, and a torque plateau of 720Nm running from 2,750rpm to 3,750rpm – a slightly narrower 'table' than in the standard Turbo, but a higher one.

Despite this formidable output, few chassis changes were called for. One which would have been more or less demanded by customers was the provision of even bigger wheels and tyres as standard, the selected size being 275/40R20, with a Y speed rating, and a tyre pressure monitoring system (an option on lesser Cayennes) installed as standard. Four exhaust pipes were another giveaway. The larger standard wheels created the space for even bigger brakes, the front and rear ventilated discs extending to 380mm (15in) and 358mm (14in) respectively. Thus there could be no argument that brake system capacity had expanded to match the further improved performance, with the Cayenne Turbo S able to reach 100km/h in 5.2sec, and achieve a maximum speed of 270km/h (167mph).

Where does the Cayenne go from here? It will be interesting to see, with public and social opinion seemingly turning against very large and heavy SUVs, however capable. No doubt Porsche has learned a great deal in the years that have already passed since its introduction, and other ideas are being explored on the computer screen in Weissach.

CHAPTER 17

2003: Carrera GT and beyond

214

It seemed, as the 21st century dawned, that Porsche faced an acute challenge. The 911 series had been developed to the Nth degree and there were further improvements still in the pipeline, but was that enough to enable the company legitimately to claim a place at the top 'supercar' table, the cutting edge of modern technology? And the answer was no.

Porsche had already built a concept car with the potential to fulfil that purpose. In fact, it was not so much a concept car as a competition car whose purpose had been cut short – in fact, stillborn – by management decision. Towards the end of the 1990s Porsche had decided, because of the existing regulation, to switch its competition effort from turbocharged to naturally aspirated engines. To that end, a new engine and car were designed. The engine was a V10, in effect a scaled-up version of the V10 which had been prepared for, but not raced in F1. The new engine, installed in a hastily prepared car which carried over a lot of previous-era components, ran successful tests at the very end of 1999, but the project was then canned at the insistence of Wendelin Wiedeking. This was on the grounds that it would divert too much engineering capacity from production car development programmes, most of all – at that moment – the Cayenne.

That did not mean the work would be wasted. Instead, the engine, the basic structure and the mid-engined chassis would be clothed in an exciting one-off body and turned into a show-stopping concept car which would express and emphasise Porsche's continuing ability to build leading-edge sports cars. Any decision as to whether to build the car, or something like it, in series could wait until public reaction had been judged. Consequently, the car appeared, as a smoothly futuristic cabriolet with plenty of Porsche styling cues, at the Paris Salon in September 2000, and duly created its sensation. The car was presented as the Carrera GT, harking back to the mid-1950s and the competition versions of the 4-cam 356 Carrera. In keeping with Porsche tradition and inclination, the two cars built were both 'runners', although not especially easy to drive since one transmission item carried-over from the racing programme was a small-diameter racing clutch.

The question now was whether to build the car in series. Much of 2001 was taken up with studies of how big the demand might be, and how much it would be necessary to charge in order to sell a reasonable number at a profit. Porsche, and especially Wiedeking, had no intention of repeating the 959 experience in which a large amount of money

vanished through the door every time a car was delivered. To that extent, although it would be technically advanced, any production Carrera GT would be state-of-the-art, rather than well in advance of it. Also, far more attention would be paid to its styling and image. As for any production, rather than create a distraction in the overcrowded Zuffenhausen works, a better solution by far would be to assemble it in the more relaxed but ultra-modern environment of the factory already nearing completion in Leipzig, which was tasked with assembling the Cayenne.

Very early in 2002, the decision was handed down at the Detroit Motor Show. The accompanying press release was headed 'Porsche Executive Board reaches decision to build the Carrera GT.' The aim would be to build 'around 1,000' units, with a commercial launch in the second half of 2003. The car, said the release, would be based on cutting-edge racing car technology. This would apply to the aerodynamic bodywork and the chassis as well as to the V10 engine and 6-speed gearbox. The 5.5-litre engine would deliver 410kW (558PS) and 600Nm of torque. Its maximum speed was guaranteed to be over 330km/h (205mph). That was the bones of it, and it whetted the appetites of enthusiasts for the next two years.

The thing was, having made the promise, it must be adhered to. Thus the task of developing the production Carrera GT

From the front, there was something about the Carrera GT which said "Porsche" despite the tendency of so many mid-engined supercars to look remarkably similar. The car was intended as an image-builder for the company in overall terms, not simply a technology demonstrator in the manner of the 959, nearly 20 years earlier.

followed on closely from the successful conclusion of the Cayenne programme. Even if this was not going to be a full production model coming off the lines in thousands a year, the target figure of 1,000 units was still large if seen from a batch point of view. Not only would the engineering need to be thorough, which at Porsche one could take as read, but a certain amount of tooling and a very careful back-up organisation would be called for. The rich enthusiasts who bought this car would expect proper support, just as they would expect a proper product, and no excuses.

From an engineering point of view, the heart of this car would be its V10 engine. A few years earlier, a V10 would have been an oddity, but the pragmatists of Formula 1 had changed that. We were in an era where eight cylinders were too few (too little piston area, too much limitation on maximum engine speed)

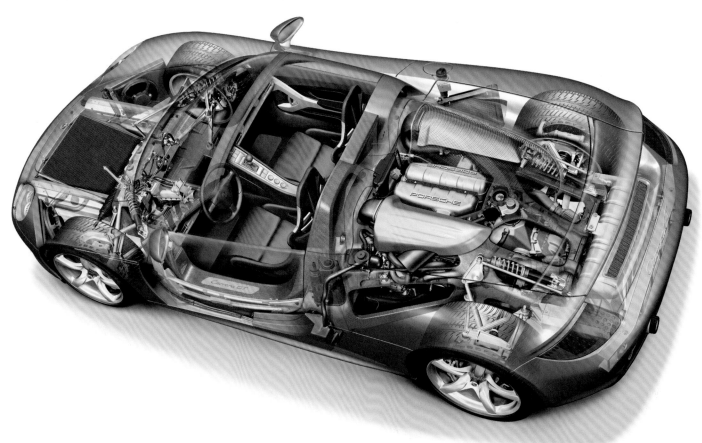

but 12 cylinders were too many (too many contacting surfaces, too many frictional losses, reduced efficiency). It followed that a V10 was just right, and so it proved, for the top F1 teams. Thus the idea that one of the world's most advanced sports cars would also have a V10 no longer raised eyebrows.

Left: In near-overhead view, other external body details of the Carrera GT become apparent, including the distinctive rear-deck bulges over the cam covers of the deliberately part-exposed engine, and the blended-in and highly effective rear spoiler.

Below left: "See-through" drawing of Carrera GT reveals general layout, with the big V10 engine attached to the rear of the cockpit "tub", the tight seating for two, the carefully contrived front and

rear suspension and even the rather nominal front luggage compartment, smaller in volume than the fuel tank.

Below: Leaning heavily on stillborn Formula 1 technology, the 5.7-litre naturally aspirated V10 engine delivered a reliable 612PS at no less than 8,000rpm. Note the simple induction trumpets beneath those bulged covers, but the extremely complex fabricated exhaust system. Radiators were mounted in the front wings, as in the 996.

One of the crucial decisions in the design of any vee-configured engine is the angle between the cylinder banks. In a V10, ideally this should be 72 degrees (one fifth of the 360 degrees of a complete circle) to achieve even firing intervals. But the V10 is not perfectly mechanically balanced anyway, unlike a V12, and a few degrees of variation for the sake of optimum packaging make little difference. Whatever it was that caused that earlier Porsche F1 engine design team to settle on 68 degrees, the angle was retained for the sake of exploiting the work that had already been done. The narrow angle meant there was too little room within the vee for any substantial manifolding, so the inlet ducts were downdraught, running straight through from a plenum chamber above each bank, while the exhausts were racing-practice, equal-length fabricated 'bunch of bananas' outboard.

The parameters were quickly frozen. One concern was that given the promised maximum speed of 330km/h, the mooted 410kW power output was not going to be enough for the production car. In order to increase the power to 450kW (612PS) without compromising durability, the team elected to bore-out the engine slightly from its original 96 x 76mm (5,501cc) to 98 x 76mm (5,733cc), retaining the orig-

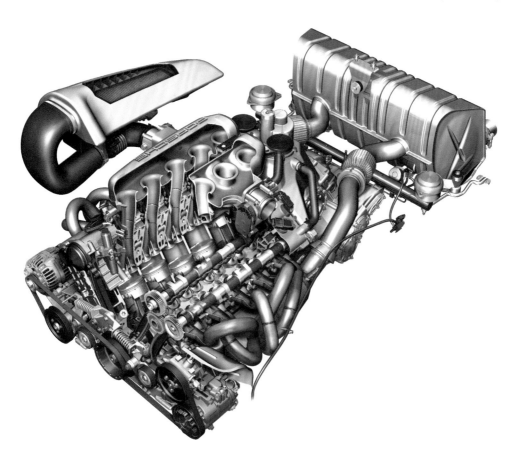

inal crankshaft unchanged, together with the short stroke which would enable the engine to rev to very high speeds for a big road-going unit. In other respects, the V10 was remarkably conventional. The cylinder block was a closed-deck casting in Nikasil, the silicon-aluminium combination with which Porsche was already so familiar. The short-throw, and very stiff six-bearing crankshaft was forged steel, the connecting rods titanium. The forged alloy pistons provided the high compression ratio of 12:1. The four valves per cylinder were operated directly from two overhead camshafts per cylinder bank, above the cylinder heads cast from high thermal-strength light alloy, as in the Cayenne Turbo.

Two features which would not have been found in a racing engine (and were thus the result of changes and additions) were the duplex chain drive to the camshafts where any competition engine would have used a noisier intermeshing gear train, and the VarioCam variators on the inlet camshafts. These allowed 40 degrees of valve timing adjustment and helped to turn the engine from a rather sudden and violent racing unit into a powertrain which could be

driven quietly on the road, while still providing the top-end power. Also out of place on a racing engine, and another reason why the capacity had to be slightly enlarged, was the full-house emission control system, a precatalyst and a main catalytic converter for each cylinder bank, enabling the unit to comply with the Euro 4 regulations coming into force in 2005.

As in other Porsche models, lambda sensors were installed both upstream and downstream of the catalytic converters, feeding information to the OBD2 diagnostic system. Overall engine management was the responsibility of a Motronic 7.1.1 system, the same type fitted in the Cayenne except that for the Carrera GT there were two such units, each responsible for controlling one cylinder bank as though it were an in-line 5-cylinder engine. This was not in itself a new idea, since the BMW and Mercedes V12s had been designed on this basis for a decade. The throttle valves, again one per cylinder bank, reporting back to the Motronic so to speak, were drive-by-wire.

In its definitive form the 5.7-litre V10 reliably delivered 450kW (612PS) at 8,000rpm, and 590Nm of torque – slightly down on that original 2001 under-

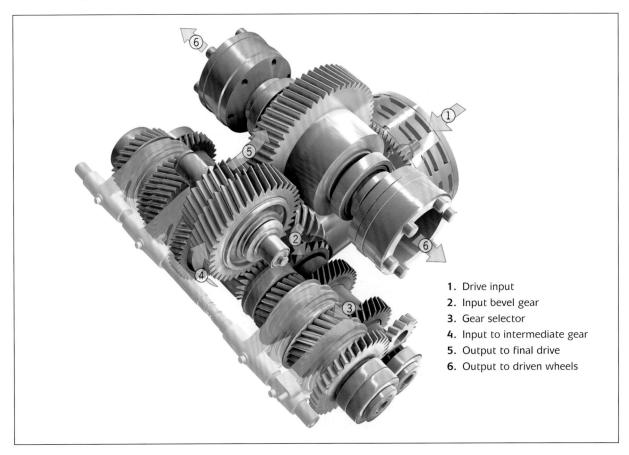

1. Drive input
2. Input bevel gear
3. Gear selector
4. Input to intermediate gear
5. Output to final drive
6. Output to driven wheels

Left: Layout of the 6-speed gearbox, installed transversely aft of the engine in the manner of modern Formula 1 cars, deserves close study. Its object was at least partly to achieve a compact installation lengthwise, leaving the extreme rear of the car free for the exhaust system.

Above: Layout of the Carrera GT transmission is easier to understand from this diagram, in conjunction with the preceding illustration. The transmission itself, shown in red, includes the compact and effective – but expensive – twin-plate ceramic clutch. The complete unit extends no farther aft than the rear wheel rim, yet accepted up to 590Nm of torque.

taking – at 5,750rpm. The maximum governed speed was 8,400rpm. The output was sufficient to deliver the 330km/h maximum speed, together with the ability to reach 100km/h from rest in 3.9sec.

If, barring its odd number of cylinders, there was little about the Carrera GT engine that was truly original, the same could not be said of its transmission. Because the engine was set so low in the chassis, there was no clearance for a full-diameter clutch. The concept cars had simply used a small-diameter, heavily sprung competition clutch, but the production Carrera GT was equipped with new technology in the form of a carbon-ceramic composite clutch, capable of

transmitting the necessary torque through a smaller-diameter unit without calling either for massive and tireless thigh muscles or a complex servo mechanism.

Behind the clutch unit, the 6-speed gearbox was set transversely, in a manner far more familiar to F1 enthusiasts. The input from the clutch was turned through 90 degrees via bevel gearing, into a mainshaft with gears on either side of the car's centre-line, mating with gears on a parallel layshaft. From the centre of this shaft, a helical spur output led to the differential and so to the drive shafts. Although unusual-looking, the arrangement had by then been well proven in competition and helped to make the overall transmission layout extremely compact.

The Carrera GT body was a semi-monocoque constructed largely from carbon fibre composite, a method yielding very low weight, but also well suited to the small production volume foreseen. Even the sub-frame to which the engine and rear suspension were mounted was of the same material. Yet this was no strong but spartan racer; this was a fully equipped car meeting all safety requirements, its specification including a full suite of airbags. The luggage compartment at the front was not large, but it was there. However, the fuel tank capacity, at 92 litres (20.2 gallons), was larger than the luggage capacity, which was 76 litres when measured to VDA guidelines. The car's nose also carried not only the headlamps, remi-

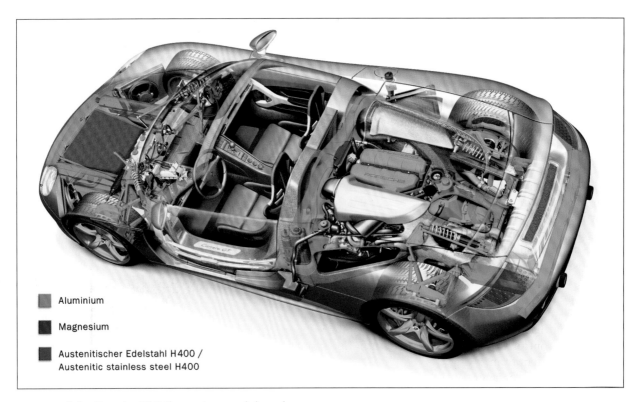

Aluminium

Magnesium

Austenitischer Edelstahl H400 /
Austenitic stainless steel H400

niscent of the Porsche 917 (but using much later lamp technology), but also three separate radiators, the flanking two ducting their exhaust into the front wheel arches. Nestling in the tail was a rear wing which was raised to its fully effective height as soon as the speed exceeded 125km/h (75mph), lowering again below 80km/h (50mph).

Above: Porsche's structure-and-materials drawing shows lots of weight-saving aluminium and magnesium, and some very high-grade stainless steel, but fails to make it clear that the "core" of the Carrera GT was a composite "tub", another technology carry-over from competition practice.

Below: The Carrera GT "tub" itself was both light and extremely stiff, as such composite structures always are, provided just-adequate room for two, and incorporated fore and aft extensions to provide the impact resistance required of a road-going car. It is interesting to consider just how the V10 engine and transmission unit was inserted.

Perhaps the most surprising thing about this sleek-looking body shell, at a first reading of the specification sheet, was a drag coefficient of 0.39, which looked distinctly mediocre. One had to look deeper, however. The entire underside of the car was shaped to provide aerodynamic downforce, using the diffuser effect. Porsche calculated that at maximum speed, the total downforce was some 4,000 Newtons, split 30:70 between front and rear. One does not, sadly, generate this kind of downforce, with the benefits of added stability and maximum cornering speed, without paying the price in drag. A flat-bottomed Carrera GT might have returned a Cd of 0.32, but then it would have paid the price in its high-speed dynamics.

The suspension did not compromise. Here were double wishbones at both ends, fabricated out of high-strength tube, with bell-cranks connecting them to remote spring/damper units picking up on convenient structural strong points to feed their loads into the body. This, it has to be said, was an arrangement for precision of control, and for lightness, not for refinement and freedom from road noise.

Also for the sake of lightness, the Carrera GT wheels were made of forged (rather than cast) magnesium, saving 25 per cent weight when compared with equivalent aluminium alloy wheels. The wheels, 19in front and 20in rear, were attached using competition-style single central bolts. Tyre sizes, specially developed for the car, were 265/35 ZR19 front and 335/30 ZR 20 rear. The tyres were among the earliest to feature tread zones with rubber of different hardness, the outer sections softer than the inners, providing better cornering grip without unduly compromising straight-running durability. A standard feature, as in the Cayenne Turbo, was a tyre pressure monitoring system.

Electronic chassis aids in the Carrera GT included four-channel anti-spin control (ASC) which reduced engine torque output if it sensed the driven wheels beginning to spin. Within ASC, a new function, EDC (Engine Drag Control) performed in the opposite matter, automatically applying extra torque if a sudden lift-off created the danger of the rear wheels locking, with the threat of loss of control. The Carrera GT being what it was, however, the driver could inhibit these functions via a dashboard-mounted pushbutton.

The final ingredient of this formidable but compact chassis was the brakes. Since the clutch used the new carbon ceramic composite material, it would have been illogical for the brakes not to have followed suit, so they did. In fact the Carrera GT was equipped with 380mm (15in) ceramic ventilated discs, which

To say the least, the Carrera GT front suspension was unusual for a road car, tightly fitted around the nose of the composite tub, with a bell-crank arrangement to feed loads into the high-mounted spring/damper units, themselves anchored to strongpoints close to the A-pillars. Size of brake discs and calipers is worth noting.

Porsche pointed out was 30mm more than the similar discs first fitted to the 911 GT2. The discs were 50 per cent lighter than equivalent cast-iron discs, adding further to the unsprung weight saving already achieved with the magnesium wheels. Six-pot alloy calipers were fitted front and rear.

As to the pricing of the Carrera GT, towards the end of 2003 Porsche GB announced that the first cars would be delivered to UK customers in 2004, priced at 461,058 Euros – around £320,000 depending on the precise rate of exchange. One certainly hopes Porsche cleared their profit at that level. But what, thereafter, became of the Carrera GT? Did the promised 1,000 units see the light of day? It has to be said that in its comprehensive press release for the 2006 model year, the company simply repeated what it had been saying about the car ever since the 2004 model year. Signs of evolution came there none; and in the meantime, the 911, and especially the 911 Turbo, had moved on to the point where the Carrera GT's performance no longer seemed quite so exceptional.

CHAPTER 18

2004: Type 997

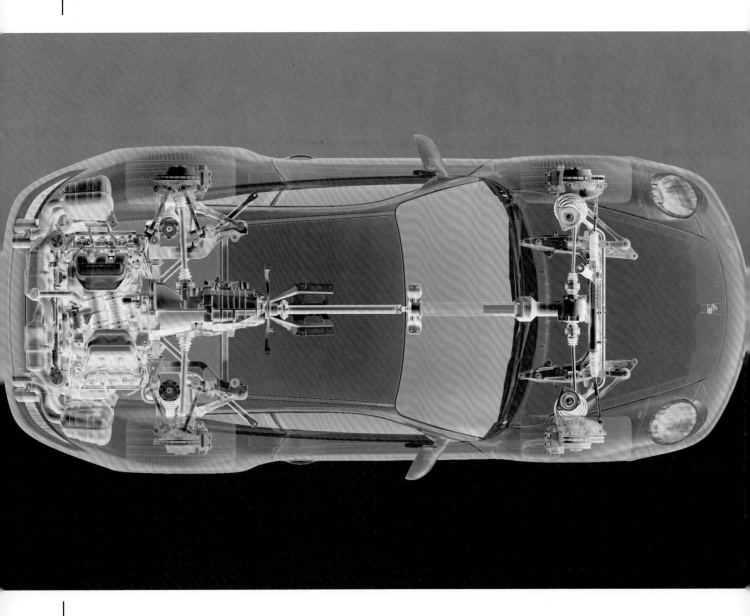

Although the Type 996 had been well received, Porsche's engineers kept working away at improvements. A pattern was being established: a package of improvements would be gathered together, and every few years they would be incorporated in an updated 911 series distinguished by a gentle restyling, never enough to break the obvious family resemblance. Thus it was that in 2004, seven years after the 996 had first been seen in public in Paris, that the 997 was revealed.

The most immediately obvious headline to launch the 997 was that for the first time since 1977 – as Porsche reminded its audience – the 911 Carrera came in two versions with engines of different sizes. The 911 Carrera carried over the existing 3.6-litre engine with minor improvements, while its sister the 911 Carrera S, was powered by an engine bored-out to 3.8-litre capacity, for a distinctly higher output of 261kW (355PS). There were, of course, many other changes.

The exterior design changes were subtle, certainly more so than those marking the transition from 993 to 996. The new body had to cover a wider front and rear track, leading to what Porsche described as a 'slimmer, more accentuated waistline'. There were visible changes to the headlamps, now with clear glass covers and high-tech lamps, the wings and wheel arches. New door mirrors were now mounted on twin arms, and the rear spoiler had been aerodynamically optimised. So too, out of sight, had the car's underside, now more or less completely faired-in, with access panels and cut-outs to allow air to enter where it was needed. Apart from their effect on the car's appearance, taken together these changes reduced the drag coefficient to an impressive 0.28. In fact, time spent in the wind tunnel had exerted a subtle effect on the entire shape of the front end, with radii and curvatures altered to minimise drag.

Within the body structure, changes to manufacturing processes had yielded improvements. In particular, the stronger bonding of the sill members to the rest of the structure had increased torsional stiffness by 15 per cent, and bending stiffness by a remarkable 40 per cent. Such can be the benefits of a careful study of spot-welds and where to place them. New safety features included upper-side airbags housed in the door sills, rather than in the roof cantrail.

Another visually evident change was larger-diameter tyres. For years, the Porsche 911 had been gaining in wheel size while reducing tyre aspect ratio, the two factors balancing out to maintain a near-constant tyre circumference, in turn allowing the shape of the wheel arches to remain the same without the danger of tyre fouling at full bump wheel travel. But in the 996, tyre aspect ratios were already so low that another inch of wheel size – to accommodate bigger brake discs and also, frankly, because both the stylists and top-range customers were clamouring for huge wheels – could only be introduced if the outer circumference of the tyre was allowed to increase. This was the reason for the 997's enlarged arches.

The increase in circumference was not large, 2.5 per cent at the front and 5 per cent at the rear, but it made the difference. Porsche said it resulted in 'significantly better transmission of power through the reduction of specific tyre loads, a reduction in tyre pressure at least under certain conditions, and an even higher standard of performance'. What it meant in practice was that the standard 3.6-litre 911 Carrera came on 18in wheels with 8in rims at the front and 10in rims at the back, with respective tyre sections 235/40 and 265/40. The corresponding figures for the Carrera S were 19in wheels, 8in front rims and 11in rear, the tyre sections 235/35 front and 295/30 rear.

Engines

For the basic version, the 3.6-litre engine was carried over with few changes, although two are worth a mention. Work on the inlet side, especially the air filter arrangement, yielded a small gain, while the installation of a dedicated vane-type vacuum pump, integral with the oil pump on the right-hand cylinder bank, meant the supply for the brake servo no longer had to be tapped from the manifold. As a result, the new figures for the 3.6-litre's output were 239kW (325PS) at 6,800rpm, with peak torque of 370Nm at 4,250rpm. Alongside this small gain, the engineers had also found small ways to trim a total 2kg from the unit's weight, an indication of the seriousness with which Porsche was beginning to regard weight growth in its products. Both engines continued their use of VarioCam Plus.

The 3.8-litre was another matter. The potential had always existed, within the 118mm bore centre spacing, to open out the cylinder bores from their

The 997 in "ghosted" plan view – in this case, a Carrera 4. Further increases in track, at the front but more so the rear, have led to a reappearance, in less obvious form, of the "hips" characteristic of the 993. Headlamp treatment has also been changed, and there are many more under-the-skin refinements including variable-ratio steering, which Porsche so long resisted.

existing 96mm. Now it was done, the new bore diameter of 99mm combining with the existing 82.8mm stroke to yield a swept volume of 3,824cc. Carefully retuning the inlet manifold for optimum results, and raising the compression ratio from the standard 11.3:1 to 11.8:1, the engine team extracted 261kW (355PS) at 6,600rpm, and maximum torque of exactly 400Nm at 4,600rpm. These figures were sufficient to see the Carrera S accelerate to 100km/h in 4.8sec, and on to a maximum speed of 293km/h (182mph).

To go with these new engines, especially the 3.8-litre with its higher torque output, there came a new 6-speed manual gearbox, with higher torque capacity than before thanks to thicker shafts and wider gears, yet also lighter, and with reduced gear lever travel. It provided yet another example of Porsche's new determination to save weight wherever possible. The overall gearing was reduced by 5 per cent, to counteract the effect of the increased tyre size, and ensure that maximum speed continued to be achieved very close to maximum engine power in top gear. Improvements to the alternative 5-speed Tiptronic resulted in even better shift quality.

Chassis

One of the most basic moves in creating the 997 was to widen its front and rear track by 21mm and 34mm respectively, thus increasing roll stiffness irrespective of any other move. The track change was achieved by redesigning the front and rear subframes to locate the lower arm mounting points further outboard. As part of the process, the subframes were made stiffer yet lighter, and the front subframe was optimised from an

Left: Standard-product Carrera emphasises the visual distinction of the new front-end treatment – the simpler-looking headlamps and separate sidelamp clusters, the front air intakes with their aerodynamic splitters. Yet again the wheels and tyres are larger-diameter, although this is less obvious short of side-by-side comparison.

Below left: Few external clues to the difference between the standard Carrera and this 3.8-litre Carrera S, without looking at the badges, although in fact the standard

wheels are 19-inch compared with the Carrera's 18-inch rims. Even from this angle the smooth undertray cannot be seen, but the door mirrors on their twin arms are another 997 feature.

Below: Carrera 4S seen from overhead rear. This is a view which shows the new rear hips swelling over the big wheels and the 34mm wider track. The shape looks and is extremely clean, although many of the secrets of the excellent 0.28 drag coefficient are hidden beneath the car or in the detailing.

Left: Detail of the Carrera 4S rear spoiler in its lifted position, bringing the benefits of reduced rear lift and improved internal airflow.

Below left: Bored-out from 96mm to 99mm to increase capacity to 3.8 litres, the 997

"S" engine delivers 355PS even in naturally aspirated form, with the aid of VarioCam Plus. Scrupulous as always in their development, Porsche engineers actually found ways to pare 2kg from the engine's weight.

impact safety point of view. At the rear, new sand-cast light alloy wheel hubs were 10 per cent lighter, usefully reducing the unsprung weight. Other than this, there were no fundamental changes to the satisfactory arrangements introduced with the 996.

Two fundamental changes were made, however – fundamental, at least as far as the 911 was concerned, although resulting from satisfactory experience in that big beast the Cayenne. The first was variable-ratio power assisted steering, and the second, PASM. Porsche had always retained constant-ratio steering in the 911, taking the view that consistency of feel and reaction was everything, long after most manufacturers had switched to variable-ratio – slower to react around the straight-ahead, to avoid the 'sneeze factor', but quicker towards extremes of travel, in situations where delicacy of control might not matter as much as speed of reaction. Paradoxically, it was a choice which might have been forced on Porsche rather sooner, but for the adoption of power-assisted steering which meant that drivers could cope with what might otherwise have been the heavy loads associated with increasing wheel and tyre size, even in the 911 with most of its weight on the back end. However, variable ratio was really the only way to give the Cayenne reasonable steering, and the response was so positive that it was duly introduced on the 997, reducing the number of turns of the wheel between locks to just over 2.6. At the same time, the steering wheel was made adjustable for both reach and height, to the relief of some drivers who had left the slim suppleness of youth behind them.

PASM had been another Cayenne innovation, a computer-controlled damping system which reacted intelligently to a series of parameters corresponding to different manoeuvres, and whose basic setting could also be selected by a driver who wanted a normal or a harder, more sporting ride. PASM was standard on the Carrera S and optional on the basic Carrera. As a bonus, there was a cunning interface of PASM with the Tiptronic S transmission, ensuring that both

Above: Ghosted drawing, for a change, of the 997 Cabriolet, showing not only the general layout of the latest-series 911 but also the way in which the hood is fitted within the body profile, still leaving space for two vestigial back seats. Body stiffness in the 997, including the Cabriolet, was further improved.

Below: One could not, these days, sell a cabriolet in the 997 class without a power-operated hood. This multi-image shot shows the way in which the Cabriolet hood retracts to sit beneath its smooth fairing, a combination of mechanical ingenuity and electronic sensing and control.

systems were in compatible modes for particular styles of driving.

Almost as a matter of principle, and despite the basic Carrera's performance being so closely matched to that of the 996, Porsche up-rated the 997 brakes. The ventilated discs in the Carrera now measured 318mm (12.5in) diameter at the front and 299mm (11.8in) at the rear, while the Carrera S discs went up to 330mm (13in) all round. In all cases new, stiffer 4-pot calipers were standard, and the PCCB ceramic brake disc option continued to be offered.

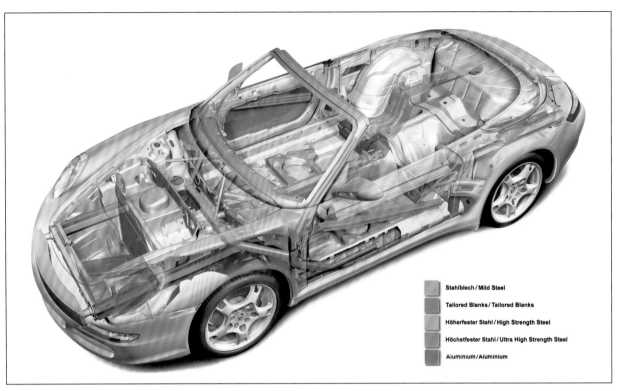

Stahlblech / Mild Steel

Tailored Blanks / Tailored Blanks

Höherfester Stahl / High Strength Steel

Höchstfester Stahl / Ultra High Strength Steel

Aluminium / Aluminium

Expanding the range

The 997 was introduced, as Porsche GB's 2004 press release explained: 'only as a two-wheel drive Carrera model. The current line-up of wide-bodied all-wheel drive models (Carrera 4S, 911 Turbo) plus the GT2, GT3 and GT3 RS, will continue in production.' Yes, of course they would – for a while. Thus the product

Above: Continuing the Cabriolet theme, Porsche's now familiar structure-and-materials drawing demonstrates the use of advanced materials, in particular around the windscreen arch and front bulkhead in order to meet the requirements of roll-over crash protection, while front and rear impact are also taken care of.

Left: One of the Carrera 4 improvements, hidden away under the surface, was the multi-plate viscous coupling located between the front and rear sections of the transmission. For the 997 Turbo, and described in Chapter 15, the changes to the 4WD transmission system – standard for all Turbos since the 993 – were more far-reaching.

listing for the 2005 model year included just the two 997 newcomers, but no less than nine 996 derivatives (including four Turbo derivatives) still on offer. They would all within the following two years, shift to the 997 as their base. Mid-2005 brought news that the Carrera 4 and 4S had moved over, followed later that summer by their Cabriolet versions. The 997 had become the new standard – and somewhere in Weissach, engineers were assembling the next package of improvements, and the stylists would once again be subtly changing the appearance of a replacement series which, the calendar suggests, should appear around 2011.

Index